THE
RADIO AMAT

CW00917152

QUESTION & ANSWER

REFERENCE MANUAL

FIFTH EDITION

R.E.G.PETRI. G0OAT

Introductory text for each topic

Progressive multiple choice Q & A

Short explanatory answers

Using the scientific calculator

Circuit recognition

This book, although prepared especially for students of the City & Guilds 'Radio Amateurs' Examination' contains material suitable for C & G 'Electronics Servicing' and BTEC 'Radio N' and 'Electrical and Electronic Principles N.'
This book contains over 1240 multiple choice questions, a section on circuit recognition, and examples worked through on the scientific calculator. A number of useful charts have been included in appendix A.

Published by R.E.G.Petri.
'Tarnwood', Denesway,
Meopham, Kent. DA13 0EA.

First Edition March 1984.
Reprinted May and September 1984.
Second Edition March 1985 (with revisions)
Third Edition October 1986 (with revisions)
Fourth Edition January 1990 (with major revisions and changes)
Fifth Edition August 1995 (enlarged edition with major revisions and additions)

ISBN 0 9509335 4 6

Printed in Great Britain by
Whitstable Litho Printers Ltd
Whitstable, Kent

Contents

Chapter   **Page**

Foreword   vi

Introduction   vii

1   **D.C.Calculations**   1-1
     Ohm's Law — Resistors in series — Resistors in parallel —
     Power in the d.c. circuit.
     Q & A.   1-4
     Key and Answers.   1-14

2   **Alternating Current and Wavelength**   2-1
     Frequency — Period — Peak and Peak-to-Peak values —
     RMS values — Average values — Frequency and
     wavelength.
     Q & A.   2-4
     Key and Answers.   2-9

3   **Capacitance**   3-1
     Capacitors in parallel -- Capacitors in series —
     R & C in series — Time-Constant.
     Q & A.   3-4
     Key and Answers.   3-11

4   **Inductance**   4-1
     Inductors in series — Inductors in parallel Time-Constant.
     Q & A.   4-4
     Key and Answers.   4-10

5   **Capacitive Reactance**   5-1
     Q & A.   5-2
     Key and Answers.   5-6

6   **Inductive Reactance**   6-1
     Q & A.   6-2
     Key and Answers.   6-6

7   **Impedance**   7-1
     R & L in series -—The impedance triangle — R & C in series.
     Q & A.   7-3
     Key and Answers.   7-8

Contents

8   **Resonance**   8-1
The series resonant circuit — The parallel resonant circuit —
Selectivity, Bandwidth and Q — Q Factor.
Q & A.   8-5
Key and Answers.   8-15

9   **Transformers and Power Supplies**   9-1
The transformer — Turns and voltage ratio — Impedance matching —
Power supplies — Half-wave and full-wave rectification —
The filter circuit — The stabilised supply.
Q & A.   9-5
Key and Answers.   9-13

10   **Solid State Devices**   10-1
The semiconductor material — the junction diode — The forward
and reverse biased diode — The bipolar transistor — the practical
common emitter amplifier — The Field Effect Transistor —
The common source JFET amplifier — classes of operation —
digital and linear integrated circuits.
Q & A.   10-7
Key and Answers.   10-21

11   **Radio Receivers**   11-1
The superheterodyne receiver — Adjacent channel and image
channel rejection — Choice of IF — The double superheterodyne
receiver.
Q & A.   11-4
Key and Answers.   11-19

12   **Radio Transmitters**   12-1
Types of transmission and classes of emission — Amplifier class
of operation — The simple transmitter — The CW, AM transmitter —
The FM transmitter — The SSB transmitter.
Q & A.   12-5
Key and Answers.   12-19

13   **Antennas and Feeders**   13-1
The transmission line — Twin transmission line — Coaxial cable
Velocity factor — Characteristic impedance — The half-wave dipole —
The vertical antenna — The yagi antenna — The trap dipole —
The long wire antenna — standing wave ratio — Field strength.
Q & A.   13-6
Key and Answers.   13-23

14   **Propagation**   14-1
Propagation in the HF band 3 - 30MHz —
Propagation above 30MHz.
Q & A.   14-4
Key and Answers.   14-13

Contents

15   **Measurement**   **15-1**
Test instruments — The moving coil meter movement —
A.C., D.C. and R.F. measuring instruments — The oscilloscope —
The VSWR meter — The decibel — Power (dBW).
Q & A.   15-6
Key and Answers.   15-16

16   **Transmitter Interference**   **16-1**
Transmitter interference — Interference precautions.
Q & A.   16-3
Key and Answers.   16-11

17   **Electromagnetic Compatibility**   **17-1**
Electromagnetic compatibility — Sources of interference and their
effect on TV and Radio — Strong signal and overload effects —
Intermodulation — Blocking — cross modulation —
Devices susceptible to strong electromagnetic fields.
Q & A.   17-6
Key and Answers.   17-19

18   **Operating Practices and Procedures**   **18-1**
List of Q codes and their meaning — The phonetic alphabet —
Signal reports (RST code) — Establishing a call (CW and telephony)
The station log — Repeaters — Satellites — Safety precautions.
Q & A.   18-4
Key and Answers.   18-13

19   **Licensing Conditions**   **19-1**
A selection of questions based on the current licensing
conditions issued by the Radio Amateur Licensing Unit.
Key. *(There are no written answers to this section.)*   19-13

20   **Circuit Recognition**   **20-1**
A number of individual circuits are given in this section for
identification practice and discussion.
Key. *(There are no written answers to this section.)*   20-6

21   **Using the Scientific Calculator**   **21-1**
This section contains worked answers to a selection
of the questions in this book.

       Appendix A. Useful Charts
A1 Frequency/Wavelength conversion.
A2 Power/dBW conversion.
A3 Feeder Loss/Power in Load.
A4 Antenna Gain/Antenna Input Power/ERP.
A5 VSWR Chart.
A6 Decibel Table.

       Appendix B. City and Guilds Syllabus

Foreword

The Radio Amateur Examination and the Novice Radio Amateur Examination are the keys to acquiring the Radio Amateur or Novice licences which are the passports to the fascinating multi-faceted world of amateur radio.

Good study material is essential in preparing for both examinations. The author has devoted two years of dedicated work to writing this book. The material and style reflect his theoretical and practical experience as a student, radio station engineer, radio investigation officer, radio laboratory manager, and radio system development and installation manager in the field of VHF, UHF and cellular radio.

His teaching experience currently includes the RAE and computing at a local adult education centre.

I recommend this publication to you as part of your systematic preparation for the Radio Amateur Examination. Some of the material contained will also be suitable for the Novice Radio Amateur Examination. A sound knowledge of basic principles relevant to radio will stand you in good stead throughout your life.

Ingemar Lundegard   G3GJW
RSGB Executive Vice President 1995

Introduction

This book has been written to provide supplementary core material for the Radio Amateurs' Examination (RAE) candidate. It will also provide some useful background and practice material for other radio communication and electronics courses, including the City and Guilds of London Institute (C & G) Electronics Servicing and certain unit topics included in the Business and Technician Education Council (BTEC) Radio and Television and the Electrical and Electronic Principles syllabus.

It is hoped that this book will prove to be a useful guide to the RAE lecturer who may be unfamiliar with the syllabus. The chapters can be taken in any order, each one being complete in itself. However, it is recommended that chapters 1 to 10 are taken in that order. This book will also provide a useful source of questions for an employer when interviewing potential technicians for certain branches of the radio and electronic service industries.

This fifth edition has undergone major changes in size, content and structure. It contains 21 chapters, most of which are now divided into three sections.

The first section of each chapter is an introduction to the topic, containing background information to supplement a typical lecture. Where it is considered beneficial, some chapters contain a list of 'Points to note.'

The second (middle) section of each chapter is the multiple choice question and answer section, this is a revised version of the fourth edition. Many of the questions are, by design, intended to be progressive as they work through a topic, and informative by their choice. In this respect they differ from the examination format of random questioning on a topic. There is only one answer to any question. The questions contained in this book are not attributable to the City & Guilds of London Institute.

The third section is the key, followed by a written short form answer to each question, including worked mathematical examples where necessary. If the question is not covered, either in the introduction, or by the lecturer, the reader will not be left without some form of explanation. For ease of identification, the edges of the answer pages are shaded. It is expected that course lecturers will be advising on the amount of coverage that they consider necessary for each topic.

Although not called for specifically in the syllabus, items such as circuit recognition, and using the scientific calculator, are in my opinion of sufficient importance to be included in course work and in this book. This book contains the guidelines for a typical RAE course of one session per week for 25 - 30 weeks. The majority of sections may be covered in one session or less, with the exception that sections 1, 10, 11, 12, and 13 may require at least two sessions.

Students should be aware that the RAE is a serious examination, and that in the majority of cases at least an extra 2 - 6 hours study per week, in the form of reading, experimenting, and simply talking to other amateurs will be of benefit.

There seems to be a common belief that passing a multiple choice examination is easy, and that even with no prior knowledge every student must have a 25% chance of passing, statistically this is far from the truth, and any potential student who believes this would probably fare better by placing the course and examination fees on the National Lottery. The multiple choice examination thoroughly explores every nook and cranny of a candidates knowledge. It tests the whole syllabus and avoids the old 'essay' type answers of the past, and being computer marked, it removes any inconsistency between examiners.

I am constantly reminded that many students have difficulty in obtaining practical experience, I would therefore suggest that there is no substitute, particularly in the early days of the hobby, for joining a good radio club or society. The use of citizens band (CB) radio could be considered as one way of inexpensively getting on the air before obtaining an amateur radio licence. CB will provide experience of setting up a simple station, measuring output power and standing wave ratio, and also adjusting and setting up simple antennas. However; the operating practices and disciplines frequently encountered on CB radio are in no way typical of those encountered on the amateur bands.

I must now record my thanks to the people and organisations who have given their valued opinion and assisted in the production of this fifth edition. Firstly Cellnet, who greatly assisted in the final stages of production of this edition. John Black, John Crump G7CGG, Shaun Petri G0NMX and Daniel Petri. The Radio Society of Great Britain for constructive comment. The City and Guilds of London Institute for permission to include the current syllabus. The Radio Agency for discussing current licensing conditions. Chartwell, H.W.Peel and Company for supplying the background chart for the front cover.

Be aware that the circuit diagrams etc. in this book are not intended for constructional purposes or practical application. There are many good books available on constructional projects and techniques. All information is based on that available at the time of publication. Future editions will be updated as necessary.

It is recommended that every student and instructor obtains a copy of the current licensing conditions 'Amateur Radio Licence (A) or (B) Terms, Provisions and Limitations Booklet' BR68 from The Library, Radiocommunications Agency, South Quay Three, 189 Marsh Wall, Docklands, London E14 9SX. And also the current examination syllabus from The City and Guilds of London Institute, 1 Giltspur street, London, EC1A 9DD.

This fifth edition contains many additions and changes to style and layout, therefore, any suggestions for improvement will be gratefully received and considered for future editions.

R.E.G.Petri. G0OAT

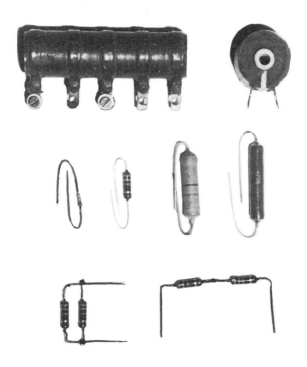

Top left to right, High-power, wirewound tapped resistor.
High-power, wirewound dropper section.
Middle left to right, 1/8W, 1/2W and 2W carbon composition resistors.
13W wirewound vitreous resistor.
Bottom left, 1/2W resistors connected in parallel.
Bottom right, 1/2W resistors connected in series.

1. D.C. Calculations

In this section we will -
1. solve problems using Ohm's Law.
2. calculate effective resistance, voltage, and current in series and parallel circuits.
3. calculate power in the d.c. circuit.

Ohm's Law
Current (I) amperes, Potential difference - p.d, (V) volts, and Resistance (R) ohms, are related by Ohm's Law. Ohm's Law is a basic tool for working electrical problems.

Ohm's Law states :-
1. *The current flowing in a circuit is directly proportional to the applied e.m.f. or voltage:-*
  $I \propto V$ Doubling V will double I. Halving V will halve I. (R to remain unchanged.)

2. *The current flowing in a circuit is inversely proportional to the resistance:-*
  $I \propto \dfrac{1}{R}$ Doubling R will halve I. Halving R will double I. (P.d. to remain unchanged.)

From the above statements we get the following three Ohm's Law formulae:-

$$I = \frac{V}{R} \qquad V = I \times R \qquad R = \frac{V}{I}$$

Where :-
R = Resistance in ohms. Symbol Ω.
I = Current in amperes. Symbol I.
V = Potential difference in volts. Symbol V.

The three forms are easily remembered by using the Ohm's Law triangle of fig.1. Simply cover the unit required with one finger and the formula remains. E.g. If V is unknown, cover V, and IR, meaning I times R remains. If I is unknown, cover I, and V/R (V over R) remains. If R is unknown, cover R, and V/I (V over I) remains. From Ohm's Law the VOLT may be defined as that e.m.f. or p.d. which when applied across a resistance of 1 ohm causes a current of 1 amp to flow.

Fig.1 The Ohm's Law triangle.

Resistors In Series
The two resistors shown in fig.2 are said to be connected in series. There is only one path in which the current can flow. The total or effective resistance R_T of a series circuit is simply the sum of the individual resistances in the circuit :-

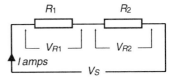

$$R_T = R_1 + R_2 + R_3 + \cdots\cdots + R_N$$

(Where R_N is the Nth series resistor).

Fig.2 The series circuit. The current I is the same in each resistor. The p.d. across each resistor may not be the same.

Points to note. (Series circuit)
1. The total resistance is the sum of the individual resistances in the circuit.
2. Adding series resistance increases the total resistance R_T.
3. R_T will always be higher than the highest single resistance in the circuit.
4. The same current flows in each resistor and in every part of the circuit.
5. An ammeter inserted at any point in the circuit will read the same current.
6. The p.d. across the individual resistors may not be the same.
7. The sum of the p.d.s across the individual resistances in the circuit, equals the supply voltage. $V_S = V_{R_1} + V_{R_2} + V_{R_3} + \cdots + V_{R_N}$
8. The p.d. across any resistor in the circuit is given by *the current in that resistor in amperes, times the value of that resistor in ohms*.
9. Ohm's Law formulae apply.
10. A practical circuit will include the resistance of all the connecting wires etc:

Resistors in Parallel
The three resistors shown in fig.3 are said to be connected in parallel.
The applied p.d. is the same across each resistor, but the individual branch currents can be different. Any number of resistors can be added in parallel, resulting in a decrease in effective resistance and an increase in supply current I_T.

The effective or total resistance R_T of a parallel circuit containing *any number of resistors* is given by :-

$$\frac{1}{R_T} = \frac{1}{R_1} + \frac{1}{R_2} + \frac{1}{R_3} + \cdots + \frac{1}{R_N}$$

(Where R_N is the Nth parallel resistor.)

When there are *only two resistors* connected in parallel the following formula can be used to calculate the total resistance :-

$$R_T = \frac{R_1 \times R_2}{R_1 + R_2}$$ ⟸ | This formula must only be used for two resistors in parallel. |

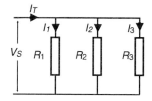

Fig.3 A parallel circuit containing 3 resistors. The applied p.d. is the same across each, but the individual branch currents can be different.

The total current I_T in the parallel circuit is given by :-
$$I_T = I_1 + I_2 + I_3 + \cdots + I_N$$

Points to note. (Parallel circuit)
1. The applied p.d. is the same across all the parallel branches.
2. A voltmeter connected across any branch will read the supply voltage.
3. The supply current I_T splits among the parallel branches.
4. The current is not necessarily the same in all the branches .
5. Adding extra parallel paths reduces the effective resistance of the circuit.
6. Any number of resistors or branches can be connected in parallel.

7. Adding extra parallel paths causes an increase in supply current.
8. The effective resistance of a parallel circuit is always lower than the lowest value of parallel connected resistor.

Power

Power (P) is the rate of using or expending energy. Power is measured in watts (W).
In a resistor or heating element electrical energy is converted into heat. It is normally the physical size and construction that determines the power rating, i.e. how many watts it will dissipate - in heat - into the surrounding atmosphere. In a lamp, electrical energy is converted to light. An electric motor converts electrical energy into mechanical rotation. The power amplifier stage of a transmitter converts DC input power into RF output power.

In power engineering the common units are the *kilowatt, kW* (10^3W) and the *megawatt MW* (10^6W). In communication engineering the power levels are commonly *milliwatts mW* (10^{-3}W), and *microwatts* μW (10^{-6}W). However, in radio engineering, power levels can vary from 100kW or more for powerful t.v. and radio transmitters, down to very low power - maybe in the order of *picowatts pW* (10^{-12}W) in the antenna circuit of a sensitive receiver.

Electrical power in the d.c. circuit is given by the formula :-

1) $W = VI$ *or* $V \times I$

Now from Ohm's Law $I = \dfrac{V}{R}$, by substituting $\dfrac{V}{R}$ in 1) for the current I : -

2) $W = V \times \dfrac{V}{R} = \dfrac{V \times V}{R} = \dfrac{V^2}{R}$ (Note. $V \times V = V^2$)

And since $V = I \times R$, by similar substitution in 1) above we get :-

3) $W = I \times R \times I = I^2 \times R$ *or* $I^2 R$

The above three power formulae and their transpositions are :-

$W = VI$ $\Rightarrow$ $V = \dfrac{W}{I}$ $\Rightarrow$ $I = \dfrac{W}{V}$

$W = \dfrac{V^2}{R}$ $\Rightarrow$ $V = \sqrt{WR}$ $\Rightarrow$ $R = \dfrac{V^2}{W}$

$W = I^2 R$ $\Rightarrow$ $I = \sqrt{\dfrac{W}{R}}$ $\Rightarrow$ $R = \dfrac{W}{I^2}$

The percentage efficiency of a stage is given by $\dfrac{Useful\ power\ output}{Power\ input} \times 100\%$

Note. When formulae are written, a P is often used in place of W, *and* E is often used in place of V.

D.C.Calculations

1. **The unit of electrical pressure is the -**
    a) Ohm   b) Volt   c) Amp   d) Watt

2. **A current flow of one coulomb per second is referred to as the -**
    a) Ohm   b) Volt   c) Amp   d) Watt

3. **The unit of opposition to the flow of current is the-**
    a) Ohm   b) Volt   c) Amp   d) Watt

4. **Which of the following sets of materials are all electrical insulators?**

a) Ceramic	b) Copper	c) Silver	d) Glass
Brass	Glass	Gold	Mica
Iron	Mica	Copper	Ceramic

5. **Which of the above sets of materials are all electrical conductors?**

6. **Which one of the following statements is true?**
    a) Only some materials have the property of electrical resistance.
    b) Only dry insulators have the property of electrical resistance.
    c) Only good conductors have the property of electrical resistance.
    d) All materials have the property of electrical resistance.

7. **When an electric current flows in a resistor -**
    a) volts will flow in the external circuit.
    b) the resistance value will increase.
    c) the electron flow ceases.
    d) energy is dissipated in the form of heat.

8. **The unit of electrical power is the -**
    a) Ohm   b) Volt   c) Amp   d) Watt

9. **Ohms law calculations may be performed by using one of the following sets of formulae -**

a) $I = V/R$	b) $I = V/R$	c) $I = R/V$	d) $I = R/V$
$V = IR$	$V = IR$	$V = R/I$	$V = I/R$
$R = I/V$	$R = V/I$	$R = V/I$	$R = V/I$

10. **The power in watts, dissipated by a resistor, may be calculated from one of the following sets of formulae -**

a) $W = V^2/R$	b) $W = V/R$	c) $W = V^2 I$	d) $W = R^2/I$
$W = I^2 R$	$W = IR$	$W = I^2 V$	$W = I/R$
$W = VI$	$W = V^2/I$	$W = IR$	$W = RV$

11. When the resistance of a circuit is increased, the current will -
   a) decrease.
   b) rise slightly and then returns to its previous value.
   c) do nothing.
   d) increase.

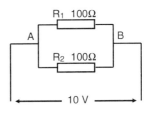

Fig.4

12. The resistors shown in fig.4 form a -
   a) series circuit.
   b) star circuit.
   c) parallel circuit.
   d) delta circuit.

13. The effective resistance of the circuit shown in fig.4 is given by -
   a) $\dfrac{R_1}{R_2}$
   b) $\dfrac{R_2}{R_1}$
   c) $\dfrac{R_1 \times R_2}{R_1 + R_2}$
   d) $R_1 + R_2$

14. What is the effective resistance of the circuit shown in fig.4?
   a) 2Ω
   b) 10Ω
   c) 50Ω
   d) 100Ω

15. If a 10 volt supply is connected across points A and B in fig.4, the total supply current will be-
   a) 10A
   b) 50mA
   c) 200mA
   d) 1mA

16. What is the current flowing in R_1 fig.4?
   a) 20A
   b) 1000mA
   c) 100mA
   d) 0.5mA

17. What is the current flowing in R_2 fig.4?
   a) 5A
   b) 400mA
   c) 250mA
   d) 100mA

18. The resistors shown in fig.5 are -
   a) connected in series.
   b) connected in parallel.
   c) forming a delta circuit.
   d) forming a star circuit.

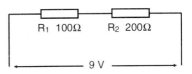

Fig.5

19. The effective resistance of the circuit shown in fig.5 is given by the formula-
   a) $\dfrac{R_1}{R_2}$
   b) $\dfrac{R_2}{R_1}$
   c) $\dfrac{R_1 \times R_2}{R_1 + R_2}$
   d) $R_1 + R_2$

20. The effective resistance of the circuit shown in fig.5 is-
   a) 2Ω
   b) 300Ω
   c) 66.6Ω
   d) 7.07Ω

21. What is the total current flowing in the circuit shown in fig.5?
    a) 3A   b) 300mA   c) 30mA   d) 3mA

22. What is the current flowing in R_2 fig.5?
    a) 300mA   b) 30mA   c) 3mA   d) 300A

23. What is the current flowing in R_1 fig.5?
    a) 100mA   b) 30mA
    c) 1.5mA   d) 600A

24. What is the power dissipated in R fig.6?
    a) 12W   b) 144W
    c) 24W   d) 1W

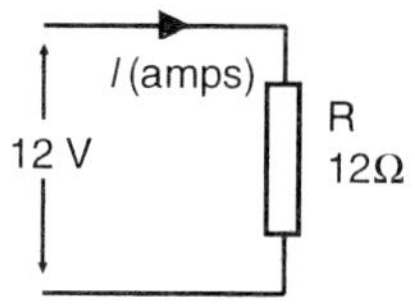

25. What is a suitable power rating for R in fig.6?
    a) 1.5W   b) 18W
    c) 30W   d) 100W

Fig.6

26. The voltage developed across the 12Ω resistor in fig.6 is-
    a) 12V   b) 24V   c) 144V   d) 1V

27. The current flowing in the 12Ω resistor shown in fig.6 is-
    a) 144A   b) 24A   c) 12A   d) 1A

28. What is the effective resistance of the
    circuit shown in fig.7?
    a) 66.6Ω b) 6.66Ω
    c) 50Ω d) 3.33Ω

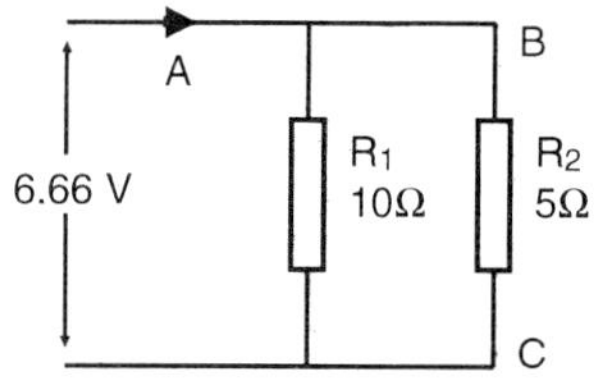

29. What is the current flowing in R_1 fig.7?
    a) 66.6A   b) 6.66A
    c) 0.66A   d) 1.33A

Fig.7

30. What is the current flowing in R_2 fig.7?
    a) 33.3A   b) 0.75A
    c) 0.66A   d) 1.33A

31. An ammeter inserted at point 'A' fig.7 will indicate a current of :-
    a) 1A   b) 2A   c) 5A   d) 10A

32. What voltage would you expect to measure across points B and C in fig.7?
    a) 1.33V   b) 2.66V   c) 3.33V   d) 6.66V

33. What is the total resistance of the circuit shown in fig.8?
    a) 3.33Ω   b) 15Ω
    c) 50Ω   d) 66.6Ω

34. What is the total current flowing
    in the circuit shown in fig.8?
    a) 1A   b) 15A
    c) 50A   d) 66.6A

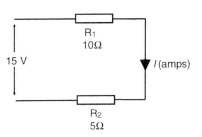

Fig.8

35. What is the current flowing in R$_2$ fig.8?
    a) 1A   b) 15A
    c) 50A   d) 33.3A

36. The p.d. across R2 fig.8 is-
    a) 5V   b) 15V
    c) 50V   d) 66.6V

37. The p.d. across R1 fig.8 is-
    a) 5V   b) 10V
    c) 25V   d) 50V

38. The power dissipated in R2 fig.8 is-
    a) 5W   b) 10W
    c) 15W   d) 50W

39. The total power dissipated in the circuit shown in fig.8 is-
    a) 5W   b) 10W
    c) 15W   d) 50W

40. What is the effective resistance
    of the circuit shown in fig.9?
    a) 2000Ω   b) 1000Ω
    c) 500Ω   d) 100Ω

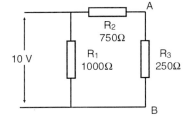

Fig.9

41. What is the current flowing in R$_1$ fig.9?
    a) 1mA   b) 10mA
    c) 100mA   d) 1000mA

42. What is the current flowing in R$_2$ fig.9?
    a) 1mA   b) 10mA
    c) 100mA   d) 1000mA

43. Referring to fig.9. What is the p.d. between points A and B?
a) 0.25V b) 0.75V
c) 2.5V d) 7.5V

44. Referring to fig.10. What is the p.d. between points A and B?
a) 33.3V b) 66.6V
c) 10V d) 100V

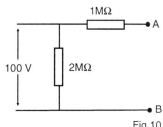

Fig.10

45. Referring to fig.10. What is the current flowing in the 1MΩ resistor?
a) 200A b) 100A
c) 1A d) Zero

46. Referring to fig.11. What is the current flowing in the 2Ω load?
a) 1A b) 2A
c) 4A d) 12A

47. The battery shown in fig.11 has an internal resistance 'r' of 1Ω. What is its terminal voltage when a 2Ω load is connected?
a) 3V b) 4V
c) 8V d) 12V

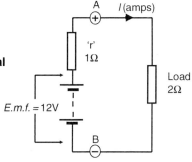

Fig.11

48. A cursory glance at the circuit shown in fig.12 should enable you to estimate that the effective resistance is-
a) about 500Ω
b) greater than 3000Ω
c) greater than 2.1Ω
d) less than 2.1Ω

49. A fairly accurate estimate of the resistance of the circuit shown in fig.13 would be-
a) about 2MΩ b) less than 2MΩ
c) less than 2.2Ω d) greater than 7.1Ω

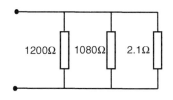

Fig.12

50. A voltage of 1000 volts is applied across terminals A and B fig.13.
What current will flow in the circuit?
a) 500µA b) 1000µA
c) 2.1µA d) 2007µA

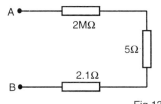

Fig.13

51. Referring to fig.14. The effective resistance
    measured between A - B is approximately -
    a) 120kΩ   b) 121kΩ
    c) 128kΩ   d) 8 Ω

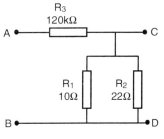

52. Referring to fig.14. The effective resistance
    between points C and D is-
    a) 121kΩ   b) 6.87Ω
    c) 32Ω   d) 22Ω

Fig.14

53. Referring to fig.14. A 120 volt supply is connected across points C and D.
    What is the p.d. across points A and B?
    a) 120mV   b) 22V   c) 120V   d) Zero

54. Referring to fig.14. When a supply of 120 volts is connected across terminals
    C and D, what current will flow in the 120kΩ resistor?
    a) 1mA   b) 120A   c) 12A   d) Zero

55. Referring to fig.14. A voltmeter having a sensitivity of 1000Ω/V, is switched
    to the 100 volt range and connected across points A and B. What will the
    meter read when a 100 volt supply is connected across points C and D?
    a) 100V   b) 54.54V   c) 45.45V   d) Zero

56. What is the effective resistance of the
    circuit shown in fig.15?
    a) 6.66kΩ
    b) 21kΩ
    c) 30kΩ
    d) 66kΩ

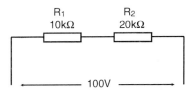

Fig.15

57. What is the p.d. developed across R₂ fig.15?
    a) 66.6V   b) 33.3V
    c) 50V   d) 100V

58. A multi-range voltmeter with a sensitivity of 200Ω/V is switched to the 100
    volt range in order to check the p.d. across R₂ fig.15.
    What will the meter indicate?
    a) 66.6V   b) 33.3V
    c) 50V   d) 100V

59. If the meter reading is different in question 58, from the calculated value in question 57, this will be due to-
  a) the stray magnetic field of the meter.
  b) temperature rise in the meter coil.
  c) ageing of the resistors.
  d) the resistance of the meter connected across R_2.

60. From the answers to questions 57 and 58, any differences between the calculated value and the measured value may be reduced by-
  a) fitting heat sinks on the meter coil.
  b) increasing the sensitivity of the meter.
  c) reducing the sensitivity of the meter.
  d) shunting the meter with a diode.

61. Referring to Q 58. The most accurate indication of the p.d. would be given by-
  a) a thermocouple meter.
  b) an electronic voltmeter with a resistance of $100M\Omega$.
  c) a multi-range meter with a resistance of $100k\Omega$.
  d) a spark gap voltmeter.

62. Referring to fig.16. What is the power dissipated in resistor R2?
  a) 2.5W   b) 5W
  c) 250W   d) 500W

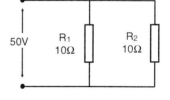

63. What is the total power dissipated by the circuit shown in fig.16?
  a) 2.5W   b) 5W
  c) 250W   d) 500W

Fig.16

64. Referring to fig.16. Power is dissipated in the form of-
  a) heat.
  b) magnetic radiation.
  c) current flow.
  d) U.V. light.

65. If the resistor R_2 in fig.16 is disconnected, the power dissipated in R_1 will-
  a) not change.
  b) double.
  c) halve.
  d) increase four times.

D.C.Calculations

66. Referring to fig.17. What is the current flowing in the 47kΩ resistor?
    a) 376mA   b) 470mA
    c) 17mA   d) 58.4mA

67. Referring to fig.17 what is the power
    dissipated by the 47kΩ resistor?
    a) 746W   b) 37.6W
    c) 13.6W   d) 3.76W

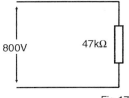

Fig.17

68. Using a high resistance voltmeter,
    what voltage would you expect to
    measure across R_1 fig.18?
    a) 100V   b) 50V
    c) 20V   d) 10V

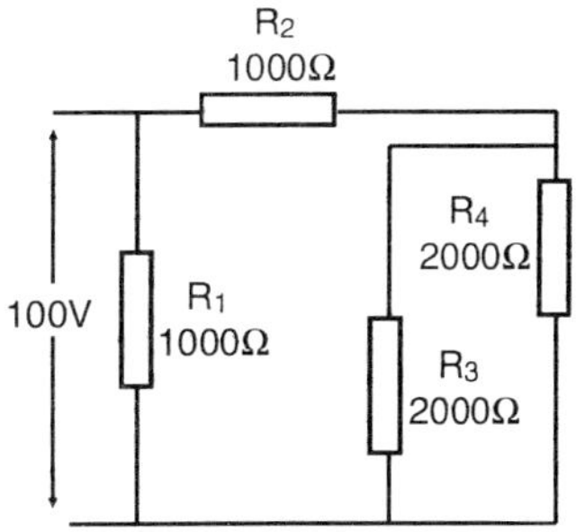

69. What p.d. is developed across R_2 fig.18?
    a) 100V   b) 50V
    c) 20V   d) 10V

70. What is the current flowing in R_1 fig.18?
    a) 100mA   b) 50mA
    c) 25mA   d) 2.5mA

Fig.18

71. What is the current flowing in R_3 fig.18?
    a) 0.1A   b) 50mA
    c) 25mA   d) 2.5mA

72. Referring to fig.19. The power dissipated by the non-inductive load 'R' is
    150 watts. What current will be indicated on the ammeter 'A'?
    a) 0.3A
    b) 1A
    c) 150A
    d) 500A

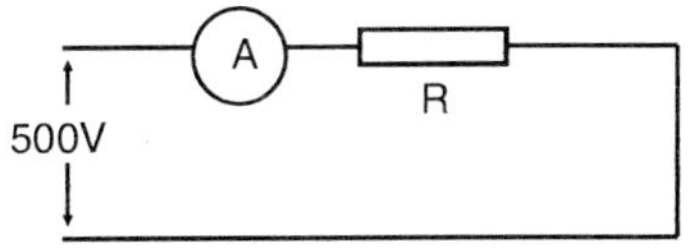

Fig.19

73. Referring to fig.20, the current in the load is 187mA.
    What is the power dissipated in the load?
    a) 18.7W
    b) 80W
    c) 150W
    d) 187W

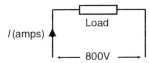

Fig.20

74. Referring to fig.20. If the applied voltage is reduced to 400 volts, what power will be dissipated in the load?
    a) 4.3W   b) 8.9W
    c) 12.25W   d) 37.4W

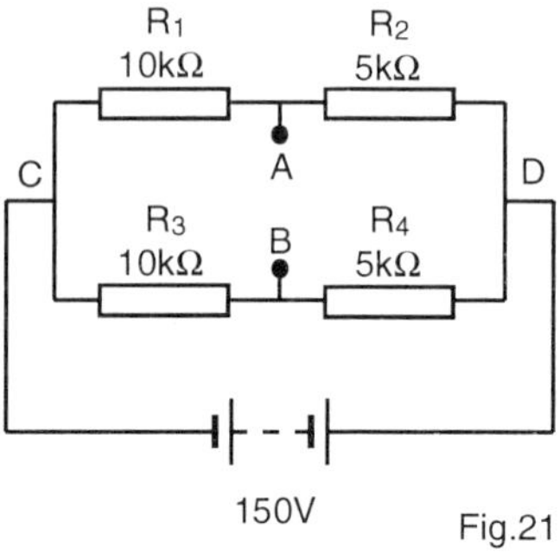

75. What is the p.d. between A - B in fig.21?
    a) 150V   b) Zero
    c) 50mA   d) 25mA

76. What is the p.d. between C - D fig.21?
    a) 150V   b) 100V
    c) 50V   d) Zero

Fig.21

77. Referring to fig.21. What is the current flowing in the upper branch of the circuit?
    a) Zero   b) 10mA
    c) 15mA   d) 150mA

78. The direction of conventional current flow in fig.21 is from-
    a) C to D   b) A to B   c) B to A   d) D to C

79. The direction of electron flow in the circuit shown in fig.21 is from-
    a) C to D   b) A to B   c) B to A   d) D to C

80. What power is dissipated in each of the 5kΩ resistors shown in fig.21?
    a) 0.5W   b) 1W   c) 1.5W   d) 3W

81. Referring to fig.21. What is the total power dissipated in the circuit?
    a) 1.5W   b) 3W   c) 4.5W   d) 6W

82. Referring to fig.21. If points A and B were soldered together, what would be the effective resistance of the circuit between points C and D?
    a) 50kΩ b) 25kΩ c) 12.5kΩ d) 7.5kΩ

83. The power dissipated in each of the 10kΩ resistors in fig.21 is-
    a) 1W   b) 1.2W   c) 1.5W   d) 5W

84. The actual value of a 1kΩ 5% tolerance resistor will be between-
    a) 995 - 1005Ω b) 999 - 1001Ω
    c) 950 - 1050Ω d) 997 - 1003Ω

D.C.Calculations

85. The graph shows the voltage/current relationship in a d.c. circuit.
    What is the resistance of the circuit?
    a) 72Ω
    b) 2Ω
    c) 0.5Ω
    d) 0.12Ω

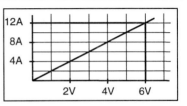

Fig.22

86. Referring to fig.23. All resistors have the same value.
    What is the total current flowing in the circuit?
    a) 10mA
    b) 20mA
    c) 40mA
    d) 80mA

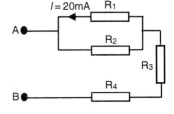

87. In fig.23, the p.d. across R_3 is 10 volts.
    What voltage is applied at A and B?
    a) 10V
    b) 15V
    c) 20V
    d) 25V

Fig.23

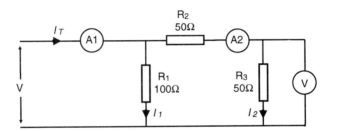

Fig.24

88. Referring to Fig.24. The voltmeter V has a very high resistance and therefore its effect on the circuit being measured may be ignored. The voltmeter V indicates 50 volts across R_3. What is the supply voltage V, and the current measured on ammeter A1?
    a) 1000V/5A
    b) 500V/2.5A
    c) 100V/2A
    d) 50V/1A

89. Referring to Q 88 and fig.24. What power is dissipated by resistor R_2?
    a) 5W
    b) 25W
    c) 50W
    d) 250W

90. Referring to Q 88 and fig.24. What power is dissipated by resistor R_3?
    a) 10W
    b) 25W
    c) 50W
    d) 100W

91. Referring to Q 88-90 and fig.24. What is the total power dissipated by the circuit and what current is recorded by ammeter A2?
a) 50W/1A   b) 100W/1A
c) 200W/1A   d) 400W/4A

92. Refer to Q 88 and fig.24. If resistor R_3 is disconnected what is the total power dissipated by the circuit, and what current is indicated by ammeter A2?
a) 50W/1A   b) 100W/0A
c) 150W/0A   d) 200W/0.9A

93. Referring to Q 88 and fig.24. If resistor R_3 is disconnected what voltage will voltmeter V record?
a) 100V   b) 75V
c) 50V   d) 10V

94. Referring to fig.24. If resistor R_1 is disconnected, the total power dissipated by the circuit will-
a) increase   b) decrease
c) drop to 50W d) remain the same

Answers - D.C. Calculations

1	b	21	c	41	b	61	b	81	b
2	c	22	b	42	b	62	c	82	d
3	a	23	b	43	c	63	d	83	a
4	d	24	a	44	d	64	a	84	c
5	c	25	b	45	d	65	a	85	c
6	d	26	a	46	c	66	c	86	c
7	d	27	d	47	c	67	c	87	d
8	d	28	d	48	d	68	a	88	c
9	b	29	c	49	a	69	b	89	c
10	a	30	d	50	a	70	a	90	c
11	a	31	b	51	a	71	c	91	c
12	c	32	d	52	b	72	a	92	b
13	c	33	b	53	c	73	c	93	a
14	c	34	a	54	d	74	d	94	b
15	c	35	a	55	c	75	b		
16	c	36	a	56	c	76	a		
17	d	37	b	57	a	77	b		
18	a	38	a	58	c	78	d		
19	d	39	c	59	d	79	a		
20	b	40	c	60	b	80	a		

Answers - D.C. Calculations

1. The volt, symbol V, is the unit of electrical pressure. A Pressure of 1 volt will cause a current of 1 amp to flow in a resistance of 1 ohm.

2. If one coulomb of electricity passes a given point in 1 second we can say that a current of 1 ampere (abbreviated 'amp' or 'A') is flowing. Similarly 5 coulombs passing a given point in 1 second equals 5 amps.

3. The unit of electrical resistance is the ohm, symbol Ω. A resistance of 1 ohm will pass a current of 1 amp when the applied p.d. = 1 volt.

4. Glass, mica and ceramic are all insulators. They offer a very high resistance to the flow of electrical current. For practical purposes they do not conduct electricity.

5. Silver, gold and copper are all electrical conductors. They offer very little resistance to the flow of current. The resistance of a particular conductor is affected by its cross-sectional-area, length, and ambient temperature.

6. All materials possess electrical resistance. Conductors have a very low resistance, whilst insulators have a very high resistance (in the order of many megohms $M\Omega$).

7. The flow of current in a resistor will cause power to be dissipated in the form of heat.

8. The unit of electrical power is the watt, symbol W.

9. The three basic formulae to remember are :-

$$I = \frac{V}{R} \qquad V = IR \qquad R = \frac{V}{I}$$

10. The three basic formulae for calculating power (watts) are :-

$$W = VI \qquad W = I^2 R \qquad W = \frac{V^2}{R}$$

11. Assuming the applied voltage remains the same, increasing the resistance of the circuit will decrease the current. The current in a circuit is inversely proportional to the resistance.

12. The resistors are connected in parallel.

13. The total or effective resistance of *2 resistors only* in parallel is :-

$$R_T = \frac{R_1 \times R_2}{R_1 + R_2}$$

The general formula, for any number of resistors in parallel is :-

$$\frac{1}{R_T} = \frac{1}{R_1} + \frac{1}{R_2} + \frac{1}{R_3} \ldots \ldots + \frac{1}{R_N}$$

Where R_T is the total or effective resistance, and R_N is the value of the Nth parallel resistor.

14. Use the formula for 2 resistors in parallel.

$$R_T = \frac{R_1 \times R_2}{R_1 + R_2} = \frac{100 \times 100}{100 + 100} = \frac{10,000}{200} = 50\Omega .$$

However, since both resistors are the same value we can say that :-

$$R_T = \frac{Value\ of\ one\ resistor}{Number\ of\ resistors} = \frac{100}{2} = 50\Omega.$$

15. The R_T has been calculated in A14, 50Ω. The applied voltage is 10V.

By Ohm's Law - $I = \dfrac{V}{R} = \dfrac{10}{50} = 0.2A\ or\ 200mA.$

16. Since both resistors are the same value, the total current of 0.2A will divide equally between R_1 and R_2, so that 0.1A (100mA) will flow in each.

Alternatively - by Ohm's Law :- $I_{R1} = \dfrac{V}{R_1} = \dfrac{10}{100} = 0.1A\ or\ 100mA.$

17. Refer to A16 above.

18. The resistors are connected in series.

19. The total or effective resistance, R_T, of the series circuit is the sum of the individual resistors in the circuit. $R_T = R_1 + R_2 + R_3 \ldots . + R_N$
Where R_N is the value of the Nth series resistor.

20. Total resistance of fig.5. $R_T = R_1 + R_2 = 100 + 200 = 300\Omega.$

21. By Ohm's Law. $I = \dfrac{V}{R} = \dfrac{9}{300} = 0.03A\ or\ 30mA$

22. Since this is a series circuit there is only one path for current to flow. Therefore, 30mA will flow in each resistor.

23. See A22 above.

24. Use the formula $P\ (watts) = \dfrac{V^2}{R} = \dfrac{12^2}{12} = \dfrac{144}{12} = 12W.$

25. In practice a components power rating is chosen to be higher than the calculated maximum power. In this case 18W is the best option because 1.5W would be too low and burn out. The 30W and 100W resistors would operate satisfactorily but are likely to be larger and more expensive.

26. 12 volts will be measured across the resistor.

27. Using Ohm's Law. $I = \dfrac{V}{R} = \dfrac{12}{12} = 1A\ or\ 1000mA.$

28. $R_T = \dfrac{R_1 \times R_2}{R_1 + R_2} = \dfrac{10 \times 5}{10 + 5} = \dfrac{50}{15} = 3.33\Omega$.

29. $I_1 = \dfrac{V}{R_1} = \dfrac{6.66}{10} = 0.666A \;\; or \;\; 666mA.$

30. $I_2 = \dfrac{V}{R_2} = \dfrac{6.66}{5} = 1.33A.$

31. The total current I_T is the sum of the individual branch currents.
From A29 and A30 - $I_T = 0.66 + 1.33 = 1.99A$ or 2A (Rounded up).

32. The resistors are in parallel, therefore we will measure the applied p.d. across each, in this example 6.66 volts.

33. $R_T = R_1 + R_2 = 10 + 5 = 15\Omega.$

34. $I = \dfrac{V}{R_T} = \dfrac{15}{15} = 1A.$

35. In the series circuit there is only one current path. 1 amp will flow in R_1 and R_2.

36. The voltage or p.d across R_2. $V_{R2} = I R_2 = 1 \times 5 = 5V.$

37. The voltage or p.d across R_1. $V_{R1} = I R_1 = 1 \times 10 = 10V.$

38. The facts :- $R_2 = 5\Omega$, $I = 1A$, $V_{R2} = 5V$. $P(watts) = VI = 5 \times 1 = 5W.$

39. Total power in circuit. $P(watts) = VI = 15 \times 1 = 15W.$

40. R_2 and R_3 are in series, the pair being connected in parallel with R_1.
$R_T = \dfrac{R_1 \times (R_2 + R_3)}{R_1 + (R_2 + R_3)} = \dfrac{1000 \times (750 + 250)}{1000 + (750 + 250)} = \dfrac{1,000,000}{2000} = 500\Omega.$

41. $I_{R1} = \dfrac{V}{R_1} = \dfrac{10}{1000} = 0.01A \;\; or \;\; 10mA.$

42. The R_T of R_2,R_3 in series is 1000Ω. The applied p.d. 10V. The current flowing in this path will be the same as R_1 since R_1 is also 1000Ω.
$I_{R2,R3} = \dfrac{V}{R_2 + R_3} = \dfrac{10}{750 + 250} = \dfrac{10}{1000} = 0.01A \;\; or \;\; 10mA.$

43. P.d. across A - B. $V_{R3} = I_{R3} R_3 = 0.01 \times 250 = 2.5V.$

44. With A - B open no current will flow in the 1MΩ resistor, hence no voltage drop across it, therefore the p.d. between points A - B will be 100V.

45. With A - B open no current will flow in the 1MΩ resistor.

46. The current in the 2Ω load is the total circuit current.

$$I = \frac{E}{r+R} = \frac{12}{1+2} = \frac{12}{3} = 4A.$$

47. The terminal voltage of the battery and the p.d. across the load will be the same. $V_{Load} = I \, R_{Load} = I \times R_{Load} = 4 \times 2 = 8V$. Due to the internal resistance of the battery 4 volts are *'lost'* in it.

48. When resistors are connected in parallel, the effective resistance of the combination is always less than the value of the lowest individual resistor.

49. Here three resistors are connected in series, the effective resistance will therefore be greater than the highest value resistor in the circuit (2MΩ).

50. The current is limited by the additive effect of all three resistors in series. Total resistance $R_T = R_1 + R_2 + R_3$. Now since the 5Ω and 2.1Ω resistors have very low value compared with the 2MΩ (2,000,000 ohms) resistor they can be ignored for approximation. In this case the approximate current will be :-

$$I = \frac{V}{R} = \frac{1000}{2,000,000} = 0.0005A \;\; or \;\; 0.5 \; mA \;\; or \;\; 500\mu A.$$

51. Referring to the two previous answers it should be fairly obvious that 120kΩ is the approximate value required. (Note. No current will flow between C-D.)

52. Now the situation changes. Looking in at point C - D (Points A - B open, therefore no current can flow in the 120kΩ resistor) we see the 10Ω and 22Ω resistors only in parallel, having an effective resistance of :-

$$\frac{R_1 \times R_2}{R_1 + R_2} = \frac{10 \times 22}{10 + 22} = \frac{220}{32} = 6.87\Omega.$$

53. With a 120V supply across C - D the p.d. across A - B will also be 120V. Since no current is flowing in the 120kΩ resistor - no voltage can be dropped across it.

54. When path A - B is open no current will flow in the 120kΩ resistor.

55. A voltmeter having a sensitivity of 1000Ω/V, will, on the 100V range, have an effective resistance, 'R_M' of $1000 \times 100 = 100k\Omega$. Hence 100kΩ will be connected across A - B. We then have a series path for current, consisting the 100kΩ voltmeter in series with the 120kΩ resistor R_3 already in the circuit. We can now use the voltage division formula to find the potential difference, V_{RM}, across R_M :-

$$V_{RM} = \frac{R_M}{R_M + R_3} \times V = \frac{100,000}{100,000 + 120,000} \times 100 = 45.45 \; volts.$$

56. The total or effective resistance of the series circuit is simply the sum of the individual resistances, i.e. $R_T = R_1 + R_2 = 10,000 + 20,000 = 30,000\Omega$.

57. The voltage across R_2 (20,000Ω) may be found as in A55 by using the voltage division formula :-

$$V_{R_2} = \frac{R_2}{R_1 + R_2} \times V = \frac{20,000}{10,000 + 20,000} \times 100 = 66.66 \ volts.$$

58. The resistance of the 200Ω/V meter on the 100V range is 20,000Ω.
I.e. $200 \times 100 = 20,000\Omega$. It is connected across the 20,000Ω resistor R_2.
The effective resistance of the meter and R_2 in parallel is 10,000Ω, this is in series with R_1, also 10,000Ω. The voltage divides between R_1, and the combination of R_2 and the meter. Since both R_1 and the combination are each 10,000Ω, the voltage divides equally and the meter will read 50V.

59. The resistance of the voltmeter has a loading effect on the circuit being measured. You can see from the above example, A58, that the effective resistance of part of the circuit consisting R_2 changed when the meter was connected.

60. Use a meter with high sensitivity (High Ω/V). A meter of 10,000 Ω/V has less loading effect, hence it is better for electronic measurement, than one of 100 Ω/V.

61. From the above comments it may be assumed that the electronic voltmeter will be the best choice. This is correct, but such instruments are not always readily available and you will probably resort to the multi-range meter, if you do, make allowances for its resistance and choose one with a high Ω/V figure.

62. Calculate the power in R_2 :- $P = \dfrac{V^2}{R_2} = \dfrac{50^2}{10} = \dfrac{2500}{10} = 250W.$

63. The total power in the circuit is the sum of the power in each resistor. Since R_1 and R_2 are equal, both have 50V across them, the power in each is the same, see above answer. The total power, $P_{TOTAL} = P_{R1} + P_{R2} = 250 + 250 = 500$ watts.

64. Power is dissipated in the form of heat. A resistor must be able to get rid of the excess heat or component failure may result. Heat may be dispersed by radiation, convection or conduction. Metal heat sinks and cooling fans are frequently used to reduce component temperature.

65. Providing that the supply voltage remains at 50V the power in R_1 will remain 250 watts. The total power supplied by the source will be 250 watts.

66. The current in the 47kΩ resistor $I = \dfrac{V}{R} = \dfrac{800}{47,000} = 0.017A \ or \ 17mA.$

67. The power dissipated by the 47KΩ resistor is $P = \dfrac{V^2}{R} = \dfrac{800^2}{47,000} = 13.6 \ watts.$

68. Inspection of fig.18 shows that the supply source is directly connected across R_1. We should measure 100V across R_1.

69. Here life becomes a little more complicated. First rearrange the circuit to show R_3 and R_4 in parallel and connected in series with R_2. Since R_3 and R_4 are both 2000Ω, their effective resistance is 1000Ω, this is in series with R_2 - 1000Ω. The voltage will divide across R_2 and the R_3/R_4 combination. $V_{R2} = 50V$, also $V_{R3,4} = 50V$.

70. The current in R_1. $\quad I_{R_1} = \dfrac{V}{R_1} = \dfrac{100}{1,000} = 0.1A \ \ or \ 100mA.$

71. The current in R_3. In A69 we calculated 50 volts across R_3. Therefore :-

$$I_{R_3} = \frac{V_{R_3}}{R_3} = \frac{50}{2000} = 0.025A \ \ or \ 25mA.$$

72. The power dissipated in R is 150 watts. The supply is 500V.

Rearrange the formula $P = V I$ to give $\ I = \dfrac{P}{V} = \dfrac{150}{500} = 0.3A \ \ or \ 300mA.$

73. An 800V source is supplying a current of 187mA ($187 \times 10^{-3}A$) to a load. The power dissipated by the load, in watts, is given by :-

$P = V I = 800 \times 187 \times 10^{-3} = 149.6W \ \ or \ 150W$ (Rounded up).

74. Perhaps the easiest solution here is to use Ohm's Law to first calculate the resistance of the load from the data given in Q73:-

$$R = \frac{V}{I} = \frac{800}{187 \times 10^{-3}} = 4,278Ω \ \ \text{(Load resistance)}$$

The power dissipated with a supply voltage of 400V :-

$$Power \ in \ watts = \frac{V^2}{R} = \frac{400^2}{4,278} = 37.4W.$$

75. This circuit can be regarded as a bridge circuit, the points A and B, due to the balancing of resistors, are at equal potential and there is no potential difference between them, therefore, no current will flow between A and B.
A meter inserted across A and B will read zero.

76. The potential difference between C and D is simply the supply voltage 150V.

77. The current in the upper branch of the circuit can be found using Ohm's Law :-

$$I = \frac{V}{R_1 + R_2} = \frac{150}{(10,000 + 5,000)} = \frac{150}{15,000} = 0.01A \ \ or \ 10mA.$$

78. By convention current flow is from positive to negative (D - C).

79. Electron flow is from negative to positive (C - D).

80. Since both upper and lower path of fig.21 have the same resistance, the same current will flow in each path. This path current was calculated in A77, 0.01A. The power, in watts, dissipated in either of the 5,000 ohm resistors will be -
$$P = I^2 R = 0.01^2 \times 5000 = 0.5W \quad \text{(0.5W dissipated in each 5k}\Omega \text{ resistor)}$$

81. There will be equal power dissipated in both upper and lower branch.
To calculate the total power, calculate the power in either branch and double it.
$$P = \frac{V^2}{R} = \frac{150^2}{5,000 + 10,000} = \frac{22500}{15,000} = 1.5W \quad \text{Total power dissipated} = 3W.$$

82. Joining points A and B will have no effect on the overall resistance of the circuit of fig.21. Without the connection the effective resistance is that of the two series paths connected in parallel, this will give 7.5kΩ.
With A and B connected the two 5kΩ resistors are connected in parallel, having an effective resistance of 2.5kΩ. Also the two 10kΩ resistors are connected in parallel, having an effective resistance of 5kΩ. The circuit is now reconfigured as two resistors in series, one of 2.5kΩ and the other of 5kΩ. Total resistance - 7.5kΩ.

83. The power dissipated in a resistor is given by $P = I^2 R$
The current in either of the 10kΩ resistors is, from A77, 0.01A.
$$P = I^2 R = 0.01^2 \times 10,000 = 0.0001 \times 10,000 = 1W .$$
1W is the actual power dissipated by the resistor. In practice a resistor of 1.5W or 2W rating should be chosen for safety and reliability.

84. A 1kΩ resistor has a tolerance of 5% (5 parts in every 100, or 5Ω in 100Ω).
First calculate 5% of 1000Ω. $\quad 1000 \times \dfrac{5}{100} = 50\Omega.$
The resistor value may be between 1000 - 50 = 950Ω and 1000 + 50 = 1050Ω.

85. From the graph it can be seen that a current of 12A flows when 6V is applied.
Therefore by Ohm's Law, $R = \dfrac{V}{I} = \dfrac{6}{12} = 0.5\Omega.$ Choosing any two points on the straight line graph would have given the same result.

86. It can be seen from the diagram that 20mA (0.02A) flows in R_1. Since it is stated that all resistors are the same value 20mA must also flow in R_2. The total circuit current must therefore be the sum of these two currents, i.e. 40mA (0.04A). 40mA will also flow in R_3 and R_4 since they are in series.

87. Since the p.d. across R_3 is 10v, and 40 mA (0.04A) flows in it, the resistance of R_3 may be calculated. $R_3 = \dfrac{V_{R3}}{I} = \dfrac{10}{0.04} = 250\Omega .$ All the resistors in the circuit are 250Ω, see A86. The effective resistance of R_1 and R_2 in parallel is 125Ω, this is in series with R_3 and R_4, both 250Ω. *Continued -*

The total circuit resistance is therefore ;-
$R_T = R_{1,2} + R_3 + R_4 = 125 + 250 + 250 = 625\Omega$.
The current flowing in the circuit is 0.04A, therefore; the supply voltage-
$V = I \times R = 0.04 \times 625 = 25V$.

88. R_2 and R_3 are in series and of equal value. They are connected across an unknown supply voltage. If 50V is measured across R_3 there must also be 50V across R_2. Now, since the sum of the individual p.d.s in the series circuit equals the applied p.d, the applied p.d. must be 100V. The current measured on ammeter A1 is the total current in the circuit, which is the sum of the two branch currents.

$$I_1 = \frac{V}{R_1} = \frac{100}{100} = 1A$$

$$I_2 = \frac{V}{R_2 + R_3} = \frac{100}{50 + 50} = \frac{100}{100} = 1A.$$

$$I_T = I_1 + I_2 = 1 + 1 = 2\ amps.$$

89. Power dissipated in R_2. $P_{R_2} = I_2^2 R_2 = 1^2 \times 50 = 50W.$

90. Power dissipated in R_3. $P_{R_3} = I_2^2 R_3 = 1^2 \times 50 = 50W.$

91. R_2 and R_3 in series can be replaced by a single 100Ω resistor in parallel with R_1, 100Ω. The effective resistance of the combination is 50Ω. The total power dissipated by the circuit is therefore :- $P_T = \frac{V^2}{R_T} = \frac{100^2}{50} = \frac{10,000}{50} = 200W.$
The current reading on ammeter A2 will be 1A (see answer 88).

92. With R_3 disconnected no current will flow in the R_2,R_3 branch of the circuit, hence no power will be dissipated there. The only power dissipated will be in R_1.
$P_{R_1} = I_1^2 R_1 = 1^2 \times 100 = 100W.$
The current reading on ammeter A2 will be zero.

93. R_3 disconnected. Voltmeter in position on diagram fig.24. Since it was stated that the voltmeter had very high resistance and its effects could be ignored, it will read 100V. See also A53.

94. If R_1 is disconnected there will be no current flowing in it and no power dissipated. The only power dissipated will be in R_2 and R_3. The total power decreases.

2. Alternating Current and Wavelength

In this section we will -
1. calculate the frequency and period of a sine wave.
2. calculate the Peak, RMS and average values of a sine wave.
3. convert frequency to wavelength.

Frequency
The frequency; measured in hertz (*Hz*), of a waveform, is the number of complete cycles of the waveform occurring in one second.

Period
The period of a waveform is the time, measured in seconds, to complete one cycle of the waveform.

It therefore follows, that if 50 complete cycles of a sinusoidal waveform occur in 1 second, then one cycle of the waveform must occur in $\frac{1}{50}$ of a second or (0.02s).

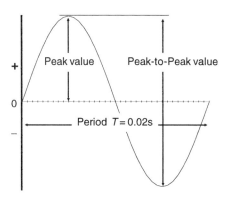

Fig.1 Showing one complete cycle of waveform occurring in 0.02 seconds.

Period and frequency are related by the formulae :-

$$T = \frac{1}{f}$$

$$f = \frac{1}{T}$$

Where :-
f = Frequency in Hertz (*Hz*).
T = Periodic time of waveform in seconds.

Peak and Peak-to-Peak Values
The peak, and peak-to-peak amplitudes of a sinusoidal waveform are shown in fig.1.

The peak value is the maximum value of voltage or current. It is measured either positive or negative with respect to the zero reference.

The peak-to-peak value of a sinewave is twice the peak value because a sinewave is symmetrical about its x axis. Other waveforms need not necessarily be symmetrical and would need to be measured on an oscilloscope.

2 - 1

RMS Values

R.m.s. values are the most common method of expressing alternating voltages and currents.

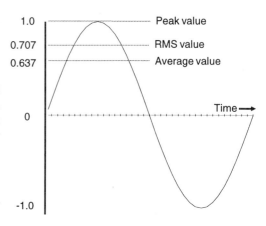

The r.m.s. (root-mean-square), or effective value of a sinusoidal voltage or current; is that value of a direct voltage or current which causes the same amount of power dissipation (heat) in a given resistor.

The r.m.s. value of a sinusoidal voltage or current waveform is 70.7% or 0.707 of its maximum or peak value, see fig.2.

R.m.s. voltages and currents are denoted by E or V and I.

Fig.2 Showing Peak, RMS, and Average values.

Formulae to remember :-

$V_{rms} = 0.707\ V_{pk} = 0.707 \times V_{pk}$

$I_{rms} = 0.707\ I_{pk} = 0.707 \times I_{pk}$

$V_{pk} = 1.414\ V_{rms} = 1.414 \times V_{rms}$

$I_{pk} = 1.414\ I_{rms} = 1.414 \times I_{rms}$

Where :-
V_{rms} = RMS Voltage.
V_{av} = Average voltage.
V_{pk} = Peak voltage.
I_{rms} = RMS Current.
I_{av} = Average Current.
I_{pk} = Peak current.

Average Values

The average value of a sinusoidal waveform is the mean value taken over one half cycle. The average is taken over half a cycle because the average over a full cycle is zero.
The average value for the sine wave is 0.637 or 63.7% of its peak or maximum value. Average values are often considered in connection with rectifier and battery charging circuitry.
Average values are denoted by the symbols E_{av} or V_{av} for voltage and I_{av} for current.

Formulae to remember :-

$V_{av} = 0.637\ V_{pk} = 0.637 \times V_{pk}$

$I_{av} = 0.637\ I_{pk} = 0.637 \times I_{pk}$

$V_{pk} = 1.57\ V_{av} = 1.57 \times V_{av}$

$I_{pk} = 1.57\ I_{av} = 1.57 \times I_{av}$

Alternating Current and Wavelength

Points to note.

1. The r.m.s. value is defined as the square *root* of the *mean* value of the *squares* of the instantaneous values taken over one complete cycle.
2. Alternating voltages and currents are normally expressed in r.m.s. values.
3. Normally, unless marked otherwise, the majority of a.c. measuring instruments will indicate the r.m.s. value of a sinusoidal alternating voltage or current.
4. A sinusoidal alternating current of $10A_{rms}$ ($14.14A_{pk}$) will produce the same amount of heat in a given resistor as a direct current of 10A.
5. A steady direct current of 10A flowing in a given resistor will cause the resistor to get hotter than a sinusoidal alternating current with a peak value of 10A.
6. When an a.c. voltmeter, calibrated in r.m.s. reads 10 volts, there will be a maximum voltage of 14.14 volts across its terminals (assuming a sinusoidal waveform).
7. The r.m.s. value of a sinusoidal waveform is known as the effective value because it has the same heating effect as a direct current or voltage of that value.

Frequency/Wavelength

Radiation from an antenna may be specified in terms of frequency f, or wavelength λ.

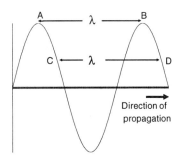

Fig.3 The wavelength is the distance in metres between two points of equal amplitude on successive cycles of the wave. E.g. A - B or C - D.

If the radiated signal has a frequency, f hertz (Hz), then f complete cycles will leave the antenna every second. The radiated signal travels at 3×10^8 m/s. Therefore, when the antenna has been radiating for one second, the surrounding electromagnetic field will extend to a distance of 3×10^8 metres.

It follows that f complete cycles occupy a distance of 3×10^8 metres, with 1 cycle occupying a distance of $\dfrac{3 \times 10^8}{f}$ metres. This distance is the wavelength (λ).

Frequency/wavelength conversion is essential in the design of antennas and matching stubs. Also broadcast receivers, having dials calibrated in wavelength, can be read or recalibrated in frequency.

Formulae to remember:-

$$\lambda = \frac{v}{f} = \frac{3 \times 10^8}{f} \quad or \quad \frac{300 \times 10^6}{f}$$

$$f = \frac{v}{\lambda} = \frac{3 \times 10^8}{\lambda} \quad or \quad \frac{300 \times 10^6}{\lambda}$$

Where :-
λ = Wavelength in metres.
v = velocity of radio waves (m/sec).
f = frequency in hertz (Hz).

Alternating Current & Wavelength

1. **The frequency of an alternating voltage or current is determined by:-**
   a) the number of complete cycles occurring in 1 second.
   b) the earths rotation.
   c) the generator voltage.
   d) the generator output power.

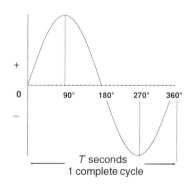

2. **The waveform shown in fig.4 is a-**
   a) sawtooth wave
   b) stationary wave.
   c) speech wave.
   d) sine wave.

Fig.4

3. **1000 complete cycles of the waveform shown in fig.4 occur in 1 second. What is the frequency of the waveform?**
   a) 0.01Hz   b) 1Hz   c) 1kHz   d) 10kHz

4. **The period 'T' of a waveform is-**
   a) the time taken for the wave to travel from A to B.
   b) the time taken for 1000 complete cycles of the waveform.
   c) the time required to complete one cycle of the waveform, measured in seconds.
   d) the period required for a damped oscillation to decay to zero.

5. **The sine wave of fig.4 could have been generated by one of the following-**
   a) an alternator.
   b) a 9V battery and a reversing switch.
   c) a nicad battery and a length of feeder.
   d) a d.c. generator.

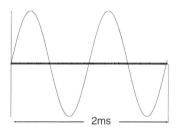

6. **Sine waves can also be generated by :-**
   a) an a.c. battery and a silicon diode.
   b) a negative feedback amplifier.
   c) a transistor L/C oscillator.
   d) a square wave multivibrator.

Fig.5

7. **What is the period 'T' of the waveform shown in fig.5?**
   a) 0.002ms   b) 2ms   c) 1ms   d) 10ms

8. **What is the frequency of the waveform shown in fig.5?**
   a) 200kHz   b) 2kHz   c) 1kHz   d) 0.1kHz

9. The period 'T' of a waveform is 2ms.
   What is the frequency?
   a) 500Hz
   b) 1kHz
   c) 2000Hz
   d) 10kHz

10. The period 'T' of a waveform is 1μs.
    What is the frequency?
    a) 500kHz
    b) 1MHz
    c) 2MHz
    d) 10MHz

11. **A sine wave will repeat itself every :-**
    a) 90°
    b) 180°
    c) 270°
    d) 360°

12. **Which of the following pairs of terms describe the amplitude of a sine wave?**
    a) VHF-inductive.
    b) Sine-capacitive.
    c) Peak-r.m.s.
    d) VSWR-RFI.

13. **The peak value of a sine wave is 1.4V. What is the r.m.s. Value?**
    a) 2.8V
    b) 1.4V
    c) 1.0V
    d) 0.707V

14. **The r.m.s. value of a sine wave is 70.7V. What is the peak value?**
    a) 280V
    b) 140V
    c) 100V
    d) 70.7V

15. **Referring to fig.6. A 200V d.c. power supply provides the power to a 50 Ω non-inductive load.**
    What would the peak voltage of sine-wave generator, G, need to be to provide the same power in the load as the d.c. supply.
    a) 282V
    b) 200V
    c) 141V
    d) 70.7V

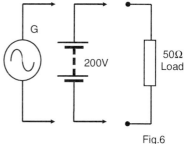

Fig.6

16. **A sinusoidal voltage is measured on an oscilloscope. Its peak value is 10V. What is its r.m.s. value?**
    a) Zero
    b) 5V
    c) 7.07V
    d) 20V

17. **500,000 complete cycles of R.F. energy leave an antenna in 0.5 seconds. What is the frequency of the carrier wave?**
    a) 1MHz
    b) 500kHz
    c) 50kHz
    d) 2MHz

18. An alternating voltage of r.m.s. value 230V has a peak value of-
    a) 162.6V   b) 250V
    c) 325V   d) 460v

19. An alternating voltage of 300V r.m.s. is connected across a pure
    resistance of 6000Ω. What is the r.m.s. current?
    a) 2.8A   b) 1.4A
    c) 1A   d) 0.05A

20. When an alternating supply is connected across a non-inductive resistor-
    a) the current and voltage will be in phase.
    b) the current will lag the voltage by 9°.
    c) the current will lead the voltage by 90°.
    d) there will be a 180° phase shift.

21. An alternating voltage of 325V peak is applied to a non-inductive load of
    10kΩ (10,000 ohms). What is the peak value of current that flows?
    a) 32.5mA   b) 230mA
    c) 325mA   d) 707mA

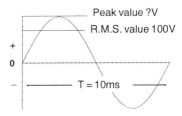

Fig.7

22. The sine wave shown in fig.7 has a
    peak-to-peak value of-
    a) 282V   b) 325V
    c) 200V   d) 141V

23. The frequency of the sine wave fig.7 is-
    a) 10Hz   b) 100Hz
    c) 1000Hz   d) 10,000Hz

24. What is the peak value of the voltage, fig.7, 2.5ms after the start of a cycle?
    a) +141V   b) +241V
    c) -100V   d) +70.7V

25. The average value of a sine wave is-
    a) 2 × V r.m.s.   b) 0.707 × V r.m.s.
    c) 2 × V peak.   d) 0.637 × V peak.

26. The abbreviation 'R.M.S. ' stands for-
    a) root mean square.
    b) resistive mean sum.
    c) reactive maximum sine.
    d) reactive mean standard.

27. **The waveform shown in fig.8, has a peak or maximum value of 10 amps. What value of direct current would be needed to provide the same heating effect in a purely resistive load?**

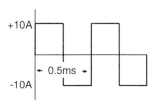

Fig.8

   a) 7.07A   b) 10A
   c) 14.1A   d) 28.2A

28. **A square wave can be shown to consist of :-**
   a) fundamental frequency plus second harmonic.
   b) fundamental frequency with no harmonics.
   c) even harmonics with no fundamental frequency.
   d) fundamental frequency plus an infinite number of odd harmonics.

29. **The fundamental frequency of the waveform shown in fig.8 is-**
   a) 500Hz   b) 1000Hz   c) 2000Hz   d) 4000Hz

30. **The 3rd harmonic of the waveform shown in fig.8 is-**
   a) 1.5kHz   b) 3kHz   c) 6kHz   d) 12kHz

31. **The 7th harmonic of the waveform shown in fig.8 is-**
   a) 7kHz   b) 14kHz   c) 21kHz   d) 28kHz

32. **Fig.9 shows two voltage waveforms of the same amplitue and frequency, they differ in-**
   a) phase and velocity.
   b) phase only.
   c) wavelength and velocity.
   d) none of the above apply.

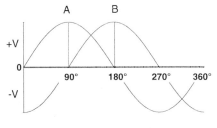

Fig.9

33. **The phase difference between the two waveforms shown in fig.9 is :-**
   a) 360°   b) 300°
   c) 180°   d) 90°

34. **Referring to the 2 waveforms, A and B fig.9, it may be said that-**
   a) A leads B by 90°. b) A lags B by 90°.
   c) B lags A by 180°. d) A lags B by 45°.

35. **The period 'T' of a sinusoidal waveform is 0.2ms. What is the frequency?**
   a) 500Hz (0.5kHz)   b) 1000Hz (1kHz)
   c) 5000Hz (5kHz)   d) 50000Hz (50kHz)

36. The period 'T' of a sinusoidal waveform is 0.25ms.
    How many complete cycles of the wave occur in 1 second?
    a) 500   b) 1000   c) 4000   d) 8000

37. A sine wave generator has a frequency of 2MHz.
    What is the time taken by each cycle of the output voltage?
    a) 0.1ms   b) 0.001ms   c) 0.0001ms   d) 0.5μs

38. The domestic a.c. mains has a frequency of 50Hz.
    What is the period 'T' of the waveform?
    a) 0.02s (20ms)   b) 0.05s (50ms)
    c) 0.2s (200ms)   d) 0.5s (500ms)

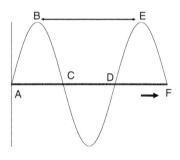

39. The wavelength of the wave shown in fig.10,
    may be described as the-
    a) length of time taken for the wave to travel
       from points A to C.
    b) average amplitude of fluctuations.
    c) distance between two identical points
       on successive cycles of the wave,
       such as B and E.
    d) velocity at which points A to C of the wave
       pass a given reference point.

Fig.10

40. If the frequency of a wave is known, the wavelength may be calculated by
    one of the following formulae-
    a) $\lambda = \dfrac{f}{3 \times 10^8}$ b) $\lambda = \dfrac{f}{300 \times 10^6}$ c) $\lambda = \dfrac{3 \times 10^6}{f}$ d) $\lambda = \dfrac{3 \times 10^8}{f}$

41. A radio station is listed as broadcasting on a wavelength of 208 metres,
    but your receiver is calibrated in frequency (kHz).
    To what frequency should the receiver be tuned?
    a) 1.442kHz   b) 14.4MHz   c) 1442.3kHz   d) 624kHz

42. It is typical of your luck, to be given the frequency of a transmission,
    l0.5MHz, when your receiver has its dial marked in metres.
    To what wavelength will you tune the receiver for this transmission?
    a) 28.57m   b) 14.29m   c) 7.14m   d) 3150m

43. The wavelength of a transmission is 24cm (0.24m).
    What is the frequency?
    a) 1250MHz   b) 240MHz   c) 125MHz   d) 24MHz

Alternating Current & Wavelength

44. The frequency of a transmission is 2400MHz. What is the wavelength?
a) 0.24m (24cm)   b) 0.125m (12.5cm)
c) 0.05m (5cm)   d) 1.25m (125cm)

45. Given the following list of frequencies, calculate the wavelengths.

Frequency	Wavelength	Frequency	Wavelength
a) 1.875MHz	____	g) 15.0MHz	____
b) 2.0MHz	____	h) 21.0MHz	____
c) 3.75MHz	____	i) 28.0MHz	____
d) 4.0MHz	____	j) 30.0MHz	____
e) 5.0MHz	____	k) 150.0MHz	____
f) 10.0MHz	____	l) 428.6MHz	____

46. Given the wavelength, calculate the frequency of the following.

Wavelength	Frequency	Wavelength	Frequency
a) 1500m	____	g) 40m	____
b) 498m	____	h) 37.5m	____
c) 207m	____	i) 18m	____
d) 100m	____	j) 5m	____
e) 50m	____	k) 3m	____
f) 30m	____	l) 1m	____

Answers - Alternating Current and Wavelength

				45		46	
1 a	16 c	31 b					
2 d	17 a	32 b		a	160m	a	200kHz
3 c	18 c	33 d		b	150m	b	602kHz
4 c	19 d	34 a		c	80m	c	1449kHz
5 a	20 a	35 c		d	75m	d	3MHz
6 c	21 a	36 c		e	60m	e	6MHz
7 c	22 a	37 d		f	30m	f	10MHz
8 c	23 b	38 a		g	20m	g	7.5MHz
9 a	24 a	39 c		h	14.28m	h	8MHz
10 b	25 d	40 d		i	10.7m	i	16.66MHz
11 d	26 a	41 c		j	10m	j	60MHz
12 c	27 b	42 a		k	2m	k	100MHz
13 c	28 d	43 a		l	70cm	l	300MHz
14 c	29 c	44 b					
15 a	30 c						

2-9

1. The frequency of an alternating current or voltage is determined by the number of complete cycles that occur in a time of 1 second. 1 cycle equals 360 degrees.

2. The waveform shown is a sinusoidal waveform (abbreviated sinewave). Typical sinewaves are that of the domestic a.c. electric mains - frequency 50Hz, audio frequency test tones and transmitter carrier waves. Any distortion of a sinewave will give rise to harmonic frequencies in the spectrum of the wave.

3. The frequency of a periodic waveform is the number of complete cycles that occur in 1 second. If 1000 complete cycles of a waveform occur in 1 second, then that frequency is 1000Hz, or 1kHz. Similarly, 1,000,000 cycles = 1MHz.

4. The period, or periodic time of a waveform is the time taken to complete one cycle. I.e. If a waveform has a frequency of 100Hz, there are 100 complete cycles of that waveform occurring in 1 second, therefore; 1 cycle of the waveform is generated in $1/100^{th}$ of a second (0.01s).

5. Alternators are electromechanical generators. They are used in power stations to supply 50Hz a.c. mains, motor vehicles for battery charging, and also bicycle lighting.

6. Valve or transistor oscillators employing quartz crystals, L/C tuned circuits or R/C phase shifting networks are normally used to generate the sinusoidal currents and voltages used in electronic and radio circuits.

7. The period T is the time taken to complete 1 cycle of the waveform. From fig.5 it can be seen that 2 complete cycles have occurred in 2ms, therefore; the time taken to complete 1 cycle of the waveform is 1ms (0.001s or 1×10^{-3}s).

8. $f = \dfrac{1}{T} = \dfrac{1}{0.001} = 1000Hz$ or $1kHz.$

9. Period = 2ms (0.002s or 2×10^{-3}s) $\quad f = \dfrac{1}{T} = \dfrac{1}{0.002} = 500Hz.$

10. Period = 1µs (0.000001s or 1×10^{-6}s) $f = \dfrac{1}{1 \times 10^{-6}} = 1 \times 10^{6}Hz = 1MHz.$

11. One complete cycle is divided into 360°. The cycle starting at zero will reach its first maximum value at 90°, pass through zero at 180°, reach a maximum negative value at 270° and return to zero at 360° to start a new cycle.

12. The amplitude of a current or voltage sinusoidal waveform is normally quoted in r.m.s. values unless stated otherwise. Peak, peak-to-peak, average, and instantaneous values are also used to describe the amplitude.

13. $V_{r.m.s.} = 0.707\ V_{pk} = 0.707 \times V_{pk} = 0.707 \times 1.414 = 1V.$

14. $V_{pk} = 1.414\ V_{r.m.s.} = 1.414 \times 70.7 = 100V.$

15. The peak a.c. value of the generator is higher than the r.m.s. or effective value, which is represented in fig.6 by the 200V battery. To cause the same heating effect in the load, as the d.c. supply, the generator peak output voltage will need to be higher than the d.c. supply.
$V_{pk} = 1.414 V_{r.m.s.} = 1.414 \times 200 = 282 V.$

16. $V_{r.m.s.} = 0.707 V_{pk} = 0.707 \times V_{pk} = 0.707 \times 10 = 7.07 V.$

17. The frequency of a wave is the number of complete cycles occurring in 1 second. In this case 500,000 complete cycles occur in 0.5s (one half of a second). Therefore; in one second twice that amount occur; 1,000,000 (1MHz).

18. $V_{pk} = 1.414 V_{r.m.s.} = 1.414 \times 230 = 325 V.$

19. Since the load is pure resistance we are able to apply Ohm's Law to the a.c. circuit :- $I = \dfrac{V}{R} = \dfrac{300}{6000} = 0.05A$ or $50mA.$

20. When an a.c. supply is connected across a circuit that does not contain reactance, either inductive or capacitive, and is purely resistive, the current and voltage are in phase.

21. $I_{pk} = \dfrac{V_{pk}}{R} = \dfrac{325}{10,000} = 0.0325A$ or $32.5mA.$

22. Calculate the peak value and double it.

$V_{pk} = 1.414 V_{r.m.s.} = 1.414 \times 100 = 141.4 V.$ $\therefore$ $V_{p-p} = 2 \times 141.4 = 282.8 V.$

23. $f = \dfrac{1}{T} = \dfrac{1}{10 \times 10^{-3}} = \dfrac{10^3}{10} = 100 Hz.$

24. Since one complete cycle (360°) occurs in 10ms, a quarter of a cycle must occur in 2.5ms (90°), this is the first maximum (positive) value. You have already calculated the peak value required in A22. +141.4 V.

25. The average value of a sine wave is :- 0.637 of its peak value. ($0.637 V_{pk}$) Average values are taken over one half cycle, because the average of a complete cycle is zero. Average values are not used as much as r.m.s. values.

26. The r.m.s. (root mean square) value of an alternating current or voltage, is the 'square root of the mean value of the squares of the instantaneous values taken over one complete cycle.' An r.m.s. alternating current having the same numerical value as a direct current will cause the same heat dissipation in a given resistor.

27. The rectangular waveform of 10A will deliver the same power to a resistive load as a steady direct current of the same value.

28. It can be graphically shown that the fundamental frequency plus an infinite number of odd harmonics produce a square wave.

29. $f = \dfrac{1}{T} = \dfrac{1}{0.5 \times 10^{-3}} = \dfrac{10^3}{0.5} = \dfrac{1000}{0.5} = 2000\ Hz\ \ or\ \ 2kHz.$

30. The 3rd harmonic is $3 \times fundamental = 3 \times 2000 = 6000Hz\ \ or\ \ 6kHz.$

31. The 7th harmonic is $7 \times fundamental = 7 \times 2000 = 14{,}000Hz\ \ or\ \ 14\ kHz.$

32. There is only a phase difference between these two waves.

33. The phase difference is 90°.

34. Waveform A is seen leading B by 90°.

35. $f = \dfrac{1}{T} = \dfrac{1}{0.2 \times 10^{-3}} = \dfrac{1 \times 10^3}{0.2} = \dfrac{1000}{0.2} = 5000Hz\ \ or\ \ 5kHz.$

36. $f = \dfrac{1}{T} = \dfrac{1}{0.25 \times 10^{-3}} = \dfrac{1 \times 10^3}{0.25} = \dfrac{1000}{0.25} = 4000Hz\ \ or\ \ 4kHz.$

37. $T = \dfrac{1}{f} = \dfrac{1}{2 \times 10^6} = 0.5 \times 10^{-6}s\ \ or\ \ 0.5\mu s.$

38. $T = \dfrac{1}{f} = \dfrac{1}{50} = 0.02\ s\ \ or\ \ 20\ ms.$

39. The wavelength is the distance between two identical points on successive cycles of the wave.

40. $\lambda = \dfrac{3 \times 10^8}{f}$ using the formula $\lambda = \dfrac{300 \times 10^6}{f}$ is useful when f is in MHz.

41. $f = \dfrac{300 \times 10^6}{\lambda} = \dfrac{300 \times 10^6}{208} = 1.4423 \times 10^6 Hz\ \ or\ \ 1442.3kHz.$

42. $\lambda = \dfrac{300 \times 10^6}{10.5 \times 10^6} = 28.57m.$

43. $f = \dfrac{300 \times 10^6}{\lambda} = \dfrac{300 \times 10^6}{0.24} = 1250 \times 10^{6Hz}\ \ or\ \ 1250MHz\ or\ 1.250GHz.$

44. $\lambda = \dfrac{300 \times 10^6}{f} = \dfrac{300 \times 10^6}{2400 \times 10^6} = 0.125m\ \ or\ \ 12.5cm.$

45,46. Answers given in key on page 2-9

3. Capacitance

In this section we will calculate -
1. charge and energy stored in a capacitor.
2. effective capacitance of series and parallel circuits.
3. time constants.

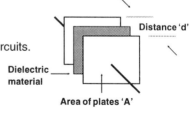

Distance 'd'

Dielectric material

Area of plates 'A'

Fig.1 $C \propto \dfrac{KA}{d}$

Symbol for capacitor —||—

Capacitance

Capacitance C is the measure of the ability of a conductor or a capacitor to store a charge of electricity.

A capacitor can be formed by two metal plates or conductors, see fig.1, separated by an insulator or 'dielectric'. Typical relative permittivities, 'K', of dielectric materials are :- Air 1, Paper 2, Mica 5, Glass 8, and ceramics 10 or higher.

Points to note.

1. Capacitance is the ability of a conductor to store a charge of electricity.
2. The unit of capacitance is the *FARAD*. However, the farad is too large a unit for most purposes. The more practical units are the microfarad μF ($10^{-6}F$), the nanofarad nF ($10^{-9}F$), and the picofarad pF ($10^{-12}F$).
3. A capacitor has a capacitance of 1 farad when a charge of 1 coulomb raises its potential by 1 volt.
4. Three factors affecting capacitance are shown in fig.1. Distance between the plates 'd', the area of the plates 'A', and the relative permittivity (dielectric constant) 'K' of the insulating material between the plates.
5. An increase in plate area 'A' increases the capacitance.
6. An increase in distance 'd' between the plates reduces the capacitance.
7. Electrical energy is stored in the electrostatic field between the plates.
8. The charge 'Q', developed on the plates of a capacitor is proportional to the applied voltage. Doubling the applied voltage V will double the charge Q.
9. The *relative permittivity,* or *dielectric constant* 'K' of a material, is the ratio of the capacitance of a capacitor employing that material as a dielectric to that of a similar capacitor employing air or a vacuum as a dielectric, 'K' = 1.
10. An air dielectric ($K = 1$) capacitor, having a capacitance of 100pF, will have a capacitance of 500pF if mica ($K = 5$) is substituted for the dielectric.
11. The *dielectric strength* of a dielectric material is a measure of the ability of that material to withstand electrical pressure (volts) across it.
12. Warning! Always discharge large value or high voltage capacitors through a suitable resistor. Avoid short-circuiting them.
13. Capacitors are normally classified by their dielectric material.

Capacitance

Charge on a capacitor $Q = CV$ coulombs.

Energy stored in a capacitor $W = \dfrac{CV^2}{2}$ joules.

Where :-
Q = Charge in coulombs.
C = Capacitance in farads.
V = P.d. in volts.
W = Energy in joules.

Capacitors in Parallel

Fig.2 shows 3 capacitors connected in parallel.
The total or effective capacitance C_T is :-

$$C_T = C_1 + C_2 + C_3 + \cdots C_N$$

C_T = Total capacitance of the circuit.
C_N = The Nth capacitor in the circuit.

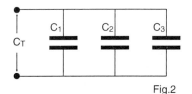

Fig.2

Points to note (parallel).

1. Adding capacitors in parallel increases the total capacitance C_T because the combination acts as a single capacitor with a greater plate area.
2. The total capacitance of parallel connected capacitors is always greater than the largest value capacitor.
3. Capacitors are connected in parallel to achieve a higher capacitance.
4. The p.d. across each capacitor, fig.2 is the same for each.
5. The charge taken by each capacitor depends on its capacitance and applied voltage ($Q = C\,V$).

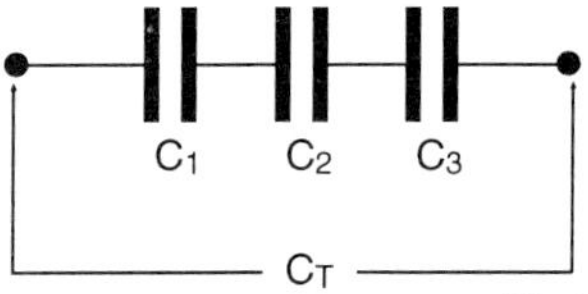

Capacitors in Series

Fig.3 shows 3 capacitors connected in series.
The total or effective capacitance C_T, for any number of capacitors connected in series is :-

$$\frac{1}{C_T} = \frac{1}{C_1} + \frac{1}{C_2} + \frac{1}{C_3} + \cdots \frac{1}{C_N}$$

When there are only two capacitors connected in series the following formula may be used:-

$$C_T = \frac{C_1 \times C_2}{C_1 + C_2}$$

When capacitors of equal value are connected in series, the effective capacitance C_T is given by:-

$$C_T = \frac{\textit{Value of one capacitor}}{\textit{Number of capacitors}}$$

Fig.3

Points to note (series).

1. Connecting capacitors in series is equivalent to increasing the distance between the plates; hence the total, or effective capacitance decreases, and is less than the smallest individual value of capacitance.
2. Connecting capacitors in series increases the breakdown voltage rating.
3. The voltage across each capacitor in the series circuit is inversely proportional to its capacitance. The lowest value capacitor having the largest voltage across it.
4. The charging current is the same in all parts of a series circuit, therefore, each capacitor acquires the same charge, 'Q'.

Capacitance

R & C in Series

Fig.4 shows a capacitor connected in series with a resistance. The capacitor will take a definite time to charge. The charging time will depend on the value of C and R.

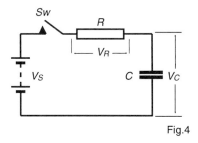

Fig.4

Consider the capacitor C initially uncharged. When the switch Sw is closed, there will be an initial flow of charging current, limited by the resistance R. The voltage across the capacitor V_C will begin to rise, rapidly at first, and then slowing down more and more as V_C approaches V_S. The current flow will decrease as V_C increases, and when the voltage across the capacitor V_C is equal to the supply voltage V_S, no further current will flow, and the voltage V_R will be zero. As the voltage V_C opposes the supply voltage, it can be considered as a 'back e.m.f.'.

Time Constant

Fig.5 shows the voltage across the capacitor increasing exponentially. After a certain time T, the voltage across the capacitor Vc, reaches 63% of its final value. This time, T, is called the *time constant* of the circuit, and is given by the formula $T = CR$. Where T = time constant in seconds, C = capacitance in farads, and R = resistance in ohms.

A capacitor is, for most practical purposes, considered fully charged after a time equal to $5CR$ seconds, i.e. 'five time constants.'

The charged capacitor can be discharged through a resistor, the discharge curve will be the opposite of the charge curve, provided that the same resistor is used. On discharge the voltage across the capacitor will fall to 37% of its initial value in time T, 'one time constant'. The capacitor can be considered fully discharged in $5T$ seconds, 'five time constants'.

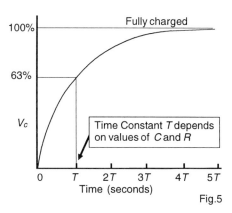

Fig.5

Points to note.

1. The initial charging current $I = \dfrac{V}{R}$

2. The final charging current is zero.

3. The voltage across the capacitor reaches 63% of its final voltage in CR seconds.

4. An increase in R and/or C will increase the time constant.

5. A decrease in R and/or C will decrease the time constant.

6. The capacitor may be considered fully charged or discharged in $5CR$ seconds.

Capacitance

1. The unit of capacitance is the-
   a) Henry
   b) Joule
   c) Coulomb
   d) Farad

2. Fig.6 shows a parallel plate capacitor. When the distance 'd' is increased, the capacitance will-
   a) increase.
   b) decrease.
   c) remain the same.
   d) increase slightly.

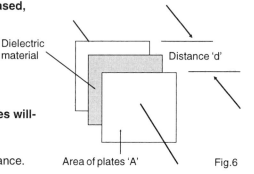

Dielectric material

Distance 'd'

Area of plates 'A'

Fig.6

3. Increasing the area of the plates will-
   a) increase the capacitance.
   b) decrease the capacitance.
   c) have no effect on the capacitance.
   d) allow direct current to pass.

4. The working voltage of a capacitor is dependent upon the-
   a) area of the plates.
   b) thickness of the plates.
   c) dielectric strength of the insulating material and the distance 'd' between the plates.
   d) thickness of the wires connected to the plates.

5. The value of capacitance of the capacitor shown in fig.6 may be increased by-
   a) reducing the area of the plates and increasing the distance 'd'.
   b) placing it in a vacuum.
   c) using pure silver for the dielectric.
   d) using mica for the dielectric and decreasing the distance 'd' between the plates.

6. Which type of capacitor has the greatest capacity per unit volume?
   a) Mica
   b) Air spaced
   c) Oil filled
   d) Electrolytic

7. Considering cost and standard practice, what type of capacitor would be the most suitable for smoothing a 250V d.c. power supply?
   a) Mica
   b) Air spaced
   c) Oil filled
   d) Electrolytic

8. Capacitors are normally classified by-
   a) the material used for the dielectric.
   b) their volume to capacitance ratio.
   c) their working voltage.
   d) their rated ripple current.

Capacitance

9. A typical value for a silver mica capacitor, used for tuning the R.F. stages of a V.H.F. receiver operating at a frequency of 145MHz, may be about-
   a) 0.001pF b) 10pF c) 10µF d) 100µF

10. The formula for the charge 'Q' coulombs, on a capacitor is-
    a) $Q = CV$ b) $Q = 2CV$ c) $Q = 4CV$ d) $Q = 8VC$

11. The energy 'W', stored in the field of a capacitor is given by-
    a) $W = CV$ b) $W = \dfrac{C V^2}{2}$ c) $W = CV$ d) $W = VC$

12. The unit of capacitance is rather a large unit to use, so a smaller and more practical unit is used, this is the-
    a) microhenry b) microcoulomb c) microjoule d) microfarad

13. One microfarad (1µF) is equal to-
    a) 1×10^{-3}F b) 1×10^{-6}F c) 1×10^{-9}F d) 1×10^{-12}F

14. Two picofarads (2pF) are equal to-
    a) 2×10^{-15}F b) 2×10^{-12}F c) 2×10^{-9}F d) 2×10^{-6}F

15. A capacitor with a value of 0.001µF, receives a charge of 1µC. What is the p.d. across the plates?
    a) 10V b) 100V c) 1000V d) 1500V

16. What quantity of charge 'Q' coulombs will produce a potential difference of 200V across the plates of a 5µF capacitor?
    a) 1000µC b) 100µC c) 10µC d) 1.0µC

17. A 2µF capacitor is charged to a p.d. of 1000 volts across its plates. What is the energy, in joules, stored in the capacitor?
    a) 100J b) 20J c) 10J d) 1J

18. A 1000pF capacitor is charged to a p.d. of 1000V. What is the energy stored in the capacitor and the charge in coulombs?
    a) 0.0005J / 1µC b) 0.005J / 10µC
    c) 10J / 50C d) 25J / 2C

19. What is the total or effective capacitance of the circuit shown in fig.7?
    a) 2µF b) 4µF
    c) 8µF d) 16µF

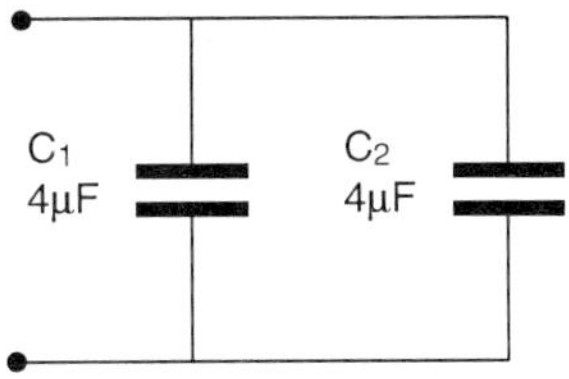

C_1 4µF C_2 4µF

Fig.7

20. What is the total capacitance of the
circuit shown in fig.8?
   a) 0.101μF
   b) 10.1μF
   c) 1101μF
   d) 111μF

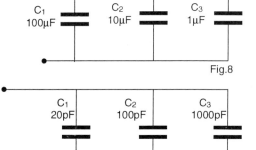

Fig.8

21. The effective capacitance of
the circuit shown in fig.9 is-
   a) 1,120pF
   b) 1,220pF
   c) 18pF
   d) 10pF

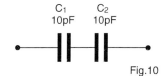

Fig.9

22. The total effective capacitance of
the series circuit shown in fig.10 is-
   a) 100pF
   b) 200pF
   c) 10pF
   d) 5pF

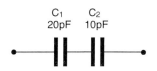

Fig.10

23. The total capacitance of the circuit
shown in fig.11 is-
   a) 200pF
   b) 30pF
   c) 15pF
   d) 6.66pF

Fig.11

24. The total capacitance of the circuit
shown in fig.12 is-
   a) 200,000pF
   b) 2100pF
   c) 95.23pF
   d) 9.523pF

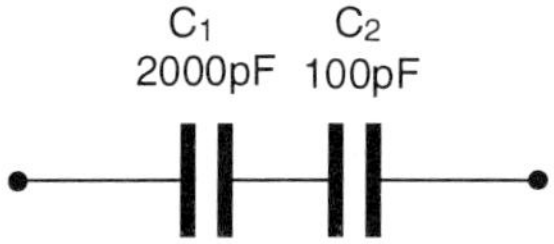

Fig.12

25. What is the total capacitance of the
circuit shown in fig.13?
   a) 3.64μF
   b) 5.32μF
   c) 38μF
   d) 1600μF

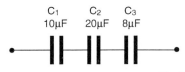

Fig.13

Capacitance

26. The total capacitance of the circuit shown in fig.14 is-
    a) 2.5µF
    b) 5µF
    c) 10µF
    d) 25µF

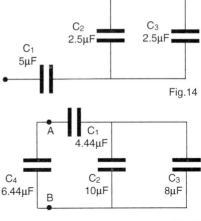

Fig.14

27. What is the total capacitance of the circuit shown in fig.15, measured across points A - B?
    a) 302.2µF
    b) 30.22µF
    c) 12.22µF
    d) 10µF

Fig.15

28. C_x, in fig.16 is a variable air spaced capacitor. To what value would it have to be adjusted to make the total capacitance across A - B equal 30pF?
    a) 20.625pF   b) 17.375pF
    c) 12.625pF   d) 9.375pF

29. To what value would C_x have to be adjusted to make the total capacitance at A - B fig.16, equal to 109.375pF?
    a) 79.375pF   b) 92pF
    c) 96.75pF   d) 100pF

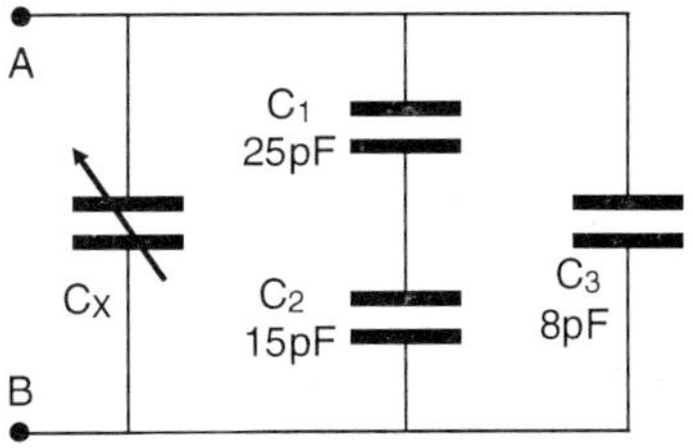

Fig.16

30. The total capacitance of the circuit shown in fig.17 is-
    a) 20µF
    b) 88µF
    c) 12.8µF
    d) less than 1µF

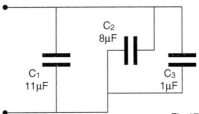

Fig.17

31. The plates of high quality, air spaced, variable capacitors used in high power stages of transmitters may have rounded edges and no sharp corners or projections, this is to-
    a) assist air flow for cooling.
    b) reduce losses due to corona discharge.
    c) prevent injury to the operator.
    d) bypass lightning strikes on the antenna.

32. When a capacitor is charged via a
   resistor, as shown in fig.18, the
   charging current, *I* -
   a) decreases exponentially.
   b) increases exponentially.
   c) decreases to 37% of the initial
      value and stops.
   d) decreases to 63% of the initial
      value and stops.

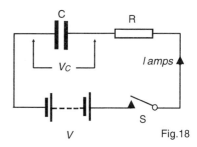

Fig.18

33. Referring to fig.18. When capacitor 'C' is charged via resistor 'R' , the
   voltage across the capacitor increases as shown below in curve-

   a)   b)   c)   d)

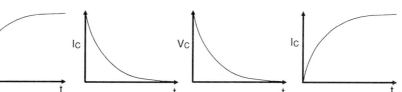

34. Referring to fig.18. When capacitor 'C' is charged via resistor 'R', the
   current in the circuit decreases as shown above in curve-

35. The 'time constant' of the C R circuit shown in fig.18 is the time taken for
   the capacitor to-
   a) fully charge.
   b) reach 98% of its full charge.
   c) reach 63% of its full charge.
   d) reach 37% of its full charge.

36. The 'time constant' of the C R circuit, fig.18, is given by the formula -

   a) $T = CR$ b) $T = \dfrac{R}{C}$

   c) $T = \dfrac{C}{R}$ d) $T = 1.414CR$

37. What is the time constant of the C R circuit shown in fig.19?
   a) 0.5 second.
   b) 1 second.
   c) 2 seconds.
   d) 10 seconds.

10kΩ   200μF   Fig.19

Capacitance

38. What is the time constant of the R C circuit shown in fig.20?
   a) 2 seconds.
   b) 10 seconds.
   c) 100 seconds.
   d) 200 seconds.

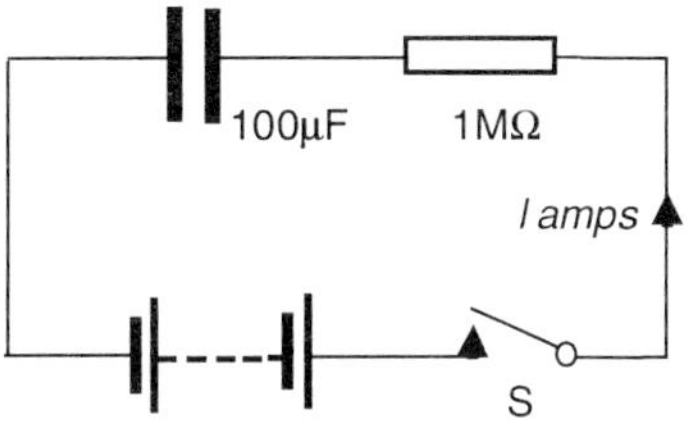

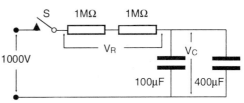

Fig.20

39. 200 seconds after switch 'S' fig.21 is closed, the p.d. across the capacitor will be about-
   a) 37 volts.
   b) 63 volts.
   c) 100 volts.
   d) zero.

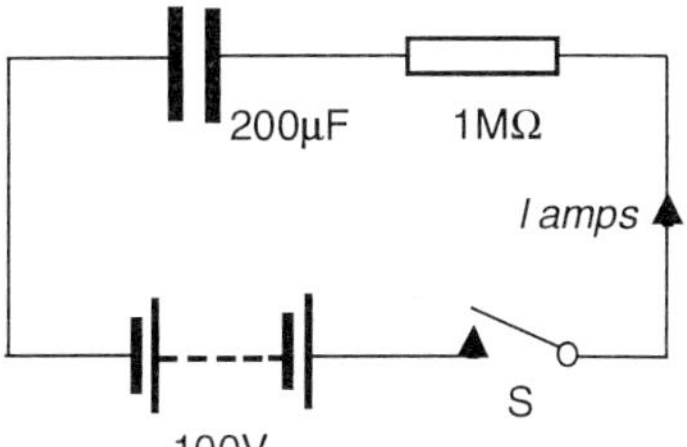

Fig.21

40. For practical purposes, a capacitor, when charged via a series resistor, may be considered fully charged in a time of-
   a) *CR* seconds   b) 2*CR* seconds
   c) 5*CR* seconds   d) 100*CR* seconds

41. What is the 'time constant' of the circuit shown in fig.22?
   a) 100 seconds.
   b) 400 seconds.
   c) 500 seconds.
   d) 1000 seconds.

Fig.22

42. What current will flow in the circuit shown in fig.22 at the instant switch 'S' is closed? It may be assumed that the supply has negligible internal resistance and that the capacitors are initially discharged.
   a) 0.5mA   b) 0.63mA   c) 100mA   d) 500mA

43. Referring to fig.22 and assuming that the capacitors are initially discharged. What is the p.d. across the capacitors at the instant switch 'S' is closed?
   a) Zero   b) 370V   c) 630V   d) 1000V

44. Referring to fig.22 and assuming that the capacitors are initially discharged. What current will flow in the circuit 1000 seconds after switch 'S' has been closed?
   a) Zero   b) 0.185mA   c) 0.630mA   d) 1mA

45. Referring to fig.23 and assuming that the capacitor is initially discharged. What is the p.d. across the resistor the instant switch 'S' is closed?
   a) 500V   b) 370V   c) 63V   d) Zero

46. Referring to fig.23. With switch 'S' closed, the capacitor is charged via resistor 'R' for at least 5CR seconds. When a voltmeter with a sensitivity of 1000Ω/V is switched to the 1000V f.s.d. range and connected across points A - B, the meter reading will-

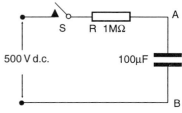

Fig.23

   a) rise rapidly to 500V and then fall slowly to 250V.
   b) rise rapidly to 500V and remain steady.
   c) rise slowly to 500V and remain steady.
   d) rise rapidly to 250V and then increase slowly to 500V.

47. Refer to fig.23. Initially switch 'S' is open and the capacitor fully discharged. The same voltmeter as in Q 46 is connected across the resistor R. When switch 'S' is closed, the voltmeter reading will-
   a) rise slowly to 500V and remain steady.
   b) rise rapidly to 250V and then increase slowly to 500V.
   c) rise slowly to 1000V and remain steady.
   d) rise rapidly to about 500V and gradually fall to zero.

48. A capacitor is able to-
   a) block a direct current.
   b) store a charge of electricity.
   c) maintain a charge for a period of time.
   d) all of above.

Answers - Capacitance

1	d	11	b	21	a	31	b	41	d
2	b	12	d	22	d	32	a	42	a
3	a	13	b	23	d	33	a	43	a
4	c	14	b	24	c	34	b	44	b
5	d	15	c	25	a	35	c	45	a
6	d	16	a	26	a	36	a	46	a
7	d	17	d	27	d	37	c	47	d
8	a	18	a	28	c	38	c	48	d
9	b	19	c	29	b	39	b		
10	a	20	d	30	a	40	c		

Answers - Capacitance

1. The unit of capacitance is the *farad* (Symbol F). The farad is too large for most practical purposes in electronics and radio, therefore smaller units are used. The microfarad μF (10^{-6}F), the nanofarad nF (10^{-9}F), and the picofarad pF (10^{-12}F).

2. The capacitance of a capacitor is inversely proportional to the distance between the plates; $c \propto \dfrac{1}{d}$ As the distance d between the plates increases, the capacitance decreases.

3. Capacitance is proportional to the area of the plates. The capacitance increases as the plate area increases.

4. The working voltage of a capacitor is dependent on the distance between the plates and also the dielectric, or insulating material between the plates, and the ability of that material to withstand the electrical pressure (volts) without breaking down.

5. Assume an air dielectric capacitor to have a capacitance of 1μF, substituting the dielectric material, air, for mica, which has a dielectric constant or relative permittivity of 5, the capacitance will increase by a factor of 5 to 5μF. Decreasing the distance between the plates will also increase the capacitance.

6. Electrolytic capacitors normally offer the highest capacitance per unit volume.

7. For PSU smoothing electrolytic capacitors are normally used. They are normally polarised and must be connected with the correct polarity or damage may result.

8. Capacitors are normally classified by their dielectric material. They are also specified by their capacitance, working voltage, tolerance and temperature range.

9. Capacitors in the range 1pF to 20pF are typical values found in VHF tuned circuits.

10. The charge Q coulombs, on the plates of a parallel plate capacitor is given by $Q = CV$.

11. The energy stored in the field of a capacitor is given by $W = \dfrac{CV^2}{2}$.

12. A practical unit of capacitance is the microfarad, (1μF = 1×10^{-6}F).

13. 1μF is $\dfrac{1}{1,000,000}$F or 1×10^{-6}F.

14. 2pF is $\dfrac{2}{1,000,000,000,000}$F or 2×10^{-12}F.

15. $Q = CV \quad \therefore \quad V = \dfrac{Q}{C} = \dfrac{1 \times 10^{-6}}{0.001 \times 10^{-6}} = \dfrac{1}{0.001} = 1000\,V.$

16. $Q = CV = 5 \times 10^{-6} \times 200 = 1000 \times 10^{-6} = 1000\mu C$ (*microcoulombs*).

17. $W = \dfrac{CV^2}{2} = \dfrac{2 \times 10^{-6} \times 1000^2}{2} = \dfrac{2 \times 10^{-6} \times 10^6}{2} = \dfrac{2}{2} = 1J$ (*1 joule*).

18. $W = \dfrac{CV^2}{2} = \dfrac{1000 \times 10^{-12} \times 1000^2}{2} = \dfrac{1000 \times 10^{-12} \times 10^6}{2} = 0.0005J.$

$Q = CV = 1000 \times 10^{-12} \times 1000 = 1 \times 10^{-6} = 1\mu C$ (*1 microcoulomb*).

19. The effective capacitance $C_T = C_1 + C_2 = 4 + 4 = 8\mu F.$

20. $C_T = C_1 + C_2 + C_3 = 100 + 10 + 1 = 111\mu F.$

21. The capacitors are connected in parallel.
$C_T = C_1 + C_2 + C_3 = 20 + 100 + 1000 = 1,120pF.$

22. $C_T = \dfrac{C_1 \times C_2}{C_1 + C_2} = \dfrac{10 \times 10}{10 + 10} = \dfrac{100}{20} = 5pF.$

23. $C_T = \dfrac{C_1 \times C_2}{C_1 + C_2} = \dfrac{20 \times 10}{20 + 10} = \dfrac{200}{30} = 6.66pF.$

24. $C_T = \dfrac{C_1 \times C_2}{C_1 + C_2} = \dfrac{2000 \times 100}{2000 + 100} = \dfrac{200,000}{2,100} = 95.23pF.$

25. Use the general formula for any number of capacitors in series.
$$\dfrac{1}{C_T} = \dfrac{1}{C_1} + \dfrac{1}{C_2} + \dfrac{1}{C_3} = \dfrac{1}{10} + \dfrac{1}{20} + \dfrac{1}{8} = \dfrac{4 + 2 + 5}{40} = \dfrac{11}{40}$$

Now $\dfrac{11}{40} = \dfrac{1}{C_T}$ $\therefore$ $C_T = \dfrac{40}{11} = 3.64\mu F.$

26. First calculate the effective capacitance, C_{eff}, of C_2 and C_3 in parallel.
$C_{eff} = C_2 + C_3 = 2.5 + 2.5 = 5\mu F.$
Next calculate the total capacitance, C_T, of C_1 in series with C_{eff}.
Use the formula for 2 capacitors in series :-
$$C_T = \dfrac{C_1 \times C_{eff}}{C_1 + C_{eff}} = \dfrac{5 \times 5}{5 + 5} = \dfrac{25}{10} = 2.5\mu F.$$

27. Calculate the effective capacitance of C_1, C_2 and C_3 as in the previous case. Careful study of the circuit will show that C_4 is connected in parallel with the effective capacitance of C_1, C_2 and C_3.
$$C_{1,2,3} = \dfrac{C_1 \times (C_2 + C_3)}{C_1 + (C_2 + C_3)} = \dfrac{4.44 \times (10 + 8)}{4.44 + (10 + 8)} = \dfrac{79.92}{22.44} = 3.56\mu F.$$

Continued $\Rightarrow$

Total capacitance C_T = (Effective capacitance of C_1,C_2,C_3) + C_4
Capacitance across A - B = 3.56 + 6.44 = 10 µF.

28. First calculate the total or effective capacitance of the circuit without C_X.
The circuit breaks down to C_1 and C_2 in series, with C_3 connected in parallel with them. Calculate the effective C of the series path, then add C_3.

$$C_T = \frac{C_1 \times C_2}{C_1 + C_2} + C_3 = \frac{25 \times 15}{25 + 15} + 8 = \frac{375}{40} + 8 = 9.375 + 8 = 17.375pF.$$

The effective capacitance of the fixed combination is 17.375pF. To make the total capacitance up to 30pF, capacitor C_X will need to be adjusted to 12.625pF.

29. Since the effective capacitance of the fixed combination is 17.375pF, and the required total capacitance is 109.375pF, the difference between these two values will give the value for C_X. 109.375 − 17.375 = 92pF

30. Inspecting this circuit closely, and redrawing if necessary, you will find that all three capacitors are connected in parallel.
$C_T = C_1 + C_2 + C_3 = 11 + 8 + 1 = 20µF.$

31. Capacitors used in high power RF stages are subject to high potentials.
The dimensions and spacing between the plates needs to be large enough to prevent breakdown. Corona discharge, visible as a blue glow in the dark, is due to high electric stress, occurring at sharp edges and corners; this may eventually cause complete breakdown. The edges are rounded to reduce this possibility.

32. Assuming the capacitor to be fully discharged 'empty', when the switch is closed there is an initial inrush of current, limited only by R. This initial current $I = \frac{V}{R}$
decays exponentially as the voltage across the plates of the capacitor increases.

33. Curve a) shows the voltage across the capacitor increasing exponentially with time.

34. Curve b) shows the capacitor charging current decreasing exponentially with time.

35. The time constant of the CR circuit is the time taken for the capacitor to reach 63% of the full charging voltage. I.e. if the charging voltage is 100V, the potential difference across the plates of the capacitor will reach 63V in 1 time constant.

36. The time constant of the CR circuit is given by $T = CR$. Where T is in seconds, C is in farads and R is in ohms.

37. $T = CR = 200 \times 10^{-6} \times 10 \times 10^3 = 2000 \times 10^{-3} = 2s.$

38. $T = CR = 100 \times 10^{-6} \times 1 \times 10^6 = 100s$

39. $T = CR = 200 \times 10^{-6} \times 1 \times 10^{6} = 200s$ The time constant of this circuit is 200s. This is the time take for the capacitor to reach 63% of the 100V charging supply. 63% of 100V = 63V.

40. It can be seen from the exponential curves that the charge rate slows down as the voltage on the capacitor approaches the charging voltage. A capacitor is considered for most practical purposes to be fully charged in a time of 5 time constants, $5CR$.

41. In this circuit we have 2 capacitors in parallel, their effective capacitance is 500μF. The effective resistance of the 2 resistors in series is 2MΩ. The equivalent circuit now consists of 2MΩ in series with 500μF.

$T = CR = 500 \times 10^{-6} \times 2 \times 10^{6} = 1000s$

42. With the capacitors fully discharged the initial charging current will be limited only by the R in the circuit, Ohm's Law applies.

$I = \dfrac{V}{R} = \dfrac{1000V}{2M\Omega} = \dfrac{1000}{2 \times 10^{6}} = 500 \times 10^{-6} = 500\mu A \ or \ 0.5mA.$

43. At the instant of switch-on the voltage across C is zero. But the current is maximum.

44. From A41 the time constant is 1000s. And from A42 the initial current is 500μA. The initial charging current (500μA) reduces to 37% of this value in $1CR$ (1000s).

$\therefore$ Current after $1000s = 500 \times \dfrac{37}{100} = 185\mu A.$

45. At the instant of switch-on 500V is developed across the resistor.

46. The capacitor is considered fully charged in $5CR$ seconds. It will have a p.d. of 500V across its plates. The voltmeter resistance is 1MΩ. When the voltmeter is connected across the fully charged capacitor it will initially read 500V. The capacitor will discharge through the meter resistance until its p.d. reaches 250V. This p.d. (250V) will be maintained across the 1MΩ meter resistance since it is in series with the 1MΩ resistor in the circuit.

47. At the instant the switch is closed the current in the circuit will be a maximum; limited by the circuit resistance, R, and there will be a maximum voltage developed across the resistor, in this case 500V. As the capacitor acquires a charge, and the voltage across the capacitor plates increases, the current in the resistor decreases, resulting in a decreasing voltage across the resistor. When the capacitor is fully charged, no further current will flow in the circuit, and there will be no voltage developed across the resistor.

48. Capacitors are used to block direct currents, store a charge of electricity for a period of time, smooth power supply units, and tune resonant circuits.

Top left to right, 1000pF, 150pF and 33pF silvered mica capacitors, 100µF 25 Volt and 1000µF 16 Volt electrolytics.
lower left to right, 0·001µF and 0.01µF ceramic types, polyester, tantalum, feedthrough and high voltage axial capacitors.

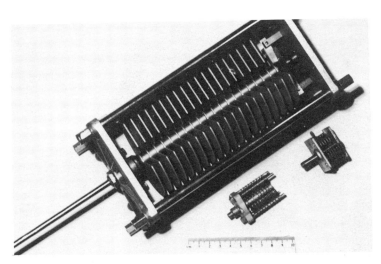

Above, variable air spaced capacitors. Top is a high voltage capacitor, suitable for medium to high power transmitters and antenna tuning units. also shown are two small variable air spaced capacitors for lower power applications.

Typical inductors. Top, coil wound on ferrite rod.
Lower left to right, self supporting VHF coil. Three small coils
with adjustment by means of ferrite slugs inside the formers.
465kHz Intermediate frequency (IF) transformer, slug tuned.
Approx: full size.

Variable inductor for high power applications such as transmitter
PA stages and antenna tuning units. Wound on porcelain or
ceramic former with silver plated wire of approx 14 SWG.
Coil length Approx 23cm. Coil dia: 7cm.

4. Inductance

In this section we will -
1. answer questions on inductance and inductors.
2. calculate the effective value of inductors in series.
3. calculate the effective value of inductors in parallel.
4. solve simple Time Constant problems.

a)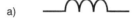

b)

c)

Fig.1 Inductor symbols.
a) Air-cored
b) Iron-cored
c) Dust-cored

Inductance

The inductance, or self-inductance of a circuit is that property of a circuit which opposes any change of current in that circuit. The symbol for inductance is L, and the unit is the henry (symbol H). Inductance is introduced into a circuit by means of a device called an inductor, or coil. Inductors may be used to oppose the flow of an alternating current whilst simultaneously passing direct, or steady current.

Inductance $L \propto \dfrac{N^2 A}{l}$

Where :-
L = Inductance in henrys.
N = Number of turns on inductor.
l = length of inductor.
A = Area of cross section.

Points to note.
1. An inductor has a self-inductance of 1 henry when a current changing at the rate of 1A/s (1 amp per second) induces a back-e.m.f. of 1 volt across it.
2. The henry can be divided into smaller units, the millihenry mH (10^{-3}H), and the microhenry μH (10^{-6}H).
3. Inductance is a property of an inductor. Any conductor possesses inductance.
4. Induction is the process of inducing voltage changes by changing magnetic flux.
5. Winding a conductor into a coil increases inductance.
6. Inserting an iron core into an inductor increases the inductance.
7. Inductance is proportional to the square of the number of turns, i.e. $L \propto N^2$ (doubling the number of turns over the same length increases the inductance four times).
8. Generally, squeezing the turns of a coil closer together will increase the inductance, and stretching the coil will decrease the inductance.
9. Inductors resist, or react, to changing currents, but, apart from their winding resistance, have no effect on unchanging currents, i.e. steady d.c.
10. Energy is stored in the magnetic field of the inductor.
11. Low frequency inductors usually employ laminated iron cores. Low power r.f. inductors usually employ dust-iron, ferrite or air cores, and may be self-supporting.
12. Due to the tendency of high frequency currents to concentrate near the surface, and less in the centre of a conductor, a phenomenon known as 'skin effect', high power r.f. inductors are normally self-supporting, air cored, and constructed from silver plated copper wire or tube. The coils may be of large diameter.

Inductance

Inductors in Series

When inductors are connected in series, with no mutual coupling between them, i.e. the magnetic field of either inductor does not cut the other, the total or effective inductance L_T of the series connected inductors is:-

$L_T = L_1 + L_2 + L_3 \ldots\ldots + L_N$

When two inductors are connected in series, and mutual inductance L_M exists between them, the direction of the coil windings, and the resulting magnetic fields due to the current in the coils will determine whether the mutual coupling increases or decreases the total, or effective inductance L_T. If the coils are connected series-aiding, fig.2, i.e. the magnetic fields are in the same direction, L_T increases. If the coils are series-opposing, fig.3, i.e. the magnetic fields are in opposite directions, L_T decreases.

Series-aiding :- $L_T = L_1 + L_2 + 2L_M$

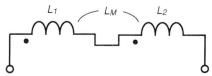

Series-opposing :- $L_T = L_1 + L_2 - 2L_M$

L_M = Mutual inductance in henrys.

Fig.2 Series-aiding

Points to note (series).

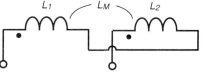

1. Inductors in series are additive, providing no mutual inductance exists between them.
2. When mutual inductance exists, the effective inductance is modified by the direction of the magnetic fields.

Fig.3 Series-opposing

3. If the fields are aiding, the effective inductance increases.
4. If the fields are opposing, the effective inductance decreases.
5. The spots on the coil symbols indicate the same direction of the windings.

Inductors in Parallel

Fig.4 shows 2 inductors connected in parallel.
This text will not consider the effects of mutual inductance for the parallel circuit.

For inductors in parallel :-
(With no mutual coupling.) $\dfrac{1}{L_T} = \dfrac{1}{L_1} + \dfrac{1}{L_2} + \dfrac{1}{L_3} + \ldots\ldots + \dfrac{1}{L_N}$

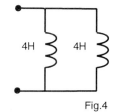

For two inductors only in parallel :-
(With no mutual coupling.) $L_T = \dfrac{L_1 \times L_2}{L_1 + L_2}$

Fig.4

Inductance

Time Constant

Fig.5 shows L and R connected in series. When the switch Sw is closed, position 1, the current I will not reach its final steady value immediately, instead it increases exponentially as shown in fig.6. The slow increase in circuit current is due to the self-inductance of the inductor opposing any change in the circuit current.

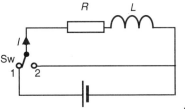

Fig.5

The *Time Constant*, T, of the circuit shown in fig.5, is the time taken for the current to reach 63% of its final steady ($I = \dfrac{V}{R}$) value.

The time constant $T = \dfrac{L}{R}$ seconds.

T = Time in seconds.
L = Inductance in henrys.
R = Resistance in ohms.

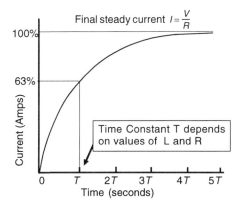

Fig.6. Showing growth of current in an inductor.

Points to note (Time Constant).

1. When the d.c. supply is connected, the final steady current $I = \dfrac{V}{R}$ (Ohm's Law).

2. An increase in R reduces the final current (Ohm's Law).
3. The current in the inductor reaches 63% of its final value in one time constant:-

    $T = \dfrac{L}{R}$ seconds.

4. The larger the L the greater the time constant.
5. The larger the R the smaller the time constant.
6. For practical purposes, the current reaches its final steady value in approximately five time constants ($5T$ seconds).
7. When the switch, Sw, fig.5, is moved to position 2, the collapsing magnetic field around the inductor causes a current to flow in the circuit that decays exponentially. This current will decay to 37% of the initial value in one time-constant, and fall practically to zero in a time equal to five time-constants (5T seconds).

Inductance

1. The unit of inductance is the -
   a) Henry   b) Farad   c) Flux   d) Joule

2. A practical inductor consists of a number of turns of wire, either self supporting or wound on a former. The effect of increasing the number of turns on the coil is to -
   a) increase the inductance.
   b) decrease the inductance.
   c) reduce the magnetic field.
   d) reduce the capacitance.

3. If an inductor has a length of 10cms, and comprises of 10 turns, the effect of stretching the 10 turns over a length of 20cms will be to -
   a) increase the inductance.
   b) reduce the inductance.
   c) triple the magnetic field.
   d) reduce the inductance to zero.

4. When an iron core is inserted in the centre of an inductor, the value of inductance-
   a) increases.   b) decreases.
   c) remains the same.   d) decreases to zero.

5. When a brass core is inserted in the centre of an inductor, the value of inductance-
   a) increases.   b) decreases.
   c) remains the same.   d) decreases to zero.

6. If the current flowing in an inductor changes at the rate of 1 Amp/second, and the voltage across its terminals is 1V, the value of the inductor is-
   a) 1µH   b) 1mH   c) 1H   d) 10H

7. When the current flowing in an inductor changes-
   a) a back e.m.f. is produced opposing the change causing it.
   b) a back e.m.f. is produced aiding the change causing it.
   c) the inductance value decreases.
   d) the magnetic field collapses.

8. When does a 10cm length of copper wire possess the property of inductance?
   a) When it is wound into a coil.   b) When it is silver plated.
   c) It is always inductive.   d) Never.

9. **Fig.7 shows 2 coils in close proximity so that the magnetic field of coil P cuts the turns of coil S. The meter M will deflect when-**
   a) the current I_P has reached its steady state condition.
   b) the current I_P does not vary.
   c) the current I_S is zero.
   d) there is a changing current in coil P.

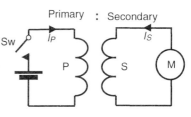

Fig.7

10. **When 2 coils are magnetically coupled as in fig.7, the e.m.f. induced in coil S, caused by a change of current in coil P, is due to-**
    a) mutual induction.
    b) self induction.
    c) bi-metallic conduction.
    d) electrostatic radiation.

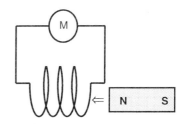

11. **Referring to fig.8. A bar magnet is moved in, and then out of the coil. The meter is a centre zero type. What deflection would you expect the meter to display?**
    a) Remain at zero as the induced currents oppose each other.
    b) The meter will deflect to the left and return to zero.
    c) The meter will deflect to the right and return to zero.
    d) The meter will deflect first to one side as the magnet is inserted and return to zero, it will then deflect to the other side as the magnet is withdrawn and then return to zero.

Fig.8

12. **Referring to fig.9. With switch 'Sw' closed, and under steady state conditions, i.e. no further current variation in the primary winding P-**
    a) there will be no deflection on the meter A.
    b) current I_S will flow anticlockwise.
    c) current I_S will flow clockwise.
    d) no current will flow in P.

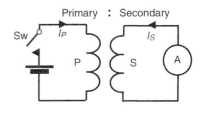

Fig.9

Inductance

13. Referring to fig.9. With switch 'Sw' closed and under steady state conditions, i.e. there is no further current variation taking place, the d.c. primary current I_P will be limited by the-
    a) resistance of the meter in the secondary circuit.
    b) resistance of the secondary winding S, in series with the meter resistance.
    c) resistance of the primary winding P in series with the internal resistance of the battery.
    d) joint resistance of the primary and secondary circuits.

14. The total inductance of two series connected inductors, with no mutual inductance between them is given by-
    a) $L_1 + L_2$ b) $\dfrac{L_1 + L_2}{L_1 \times L_2}$ c) $\dfrac{L_1 \times L_2}{L_1 + L_2}$ d) $\dfrac{L_1}{L_2}$

15. The total inductance of the two series connected inductors, shown fig.10, with no mutual inductance between them is-
    a) 3.33H
    b) 15H
    c) 50H
    d) 500H

Fig.10

16. The total inductance of 2 inductors connected in parallel with no mutual inductance between them is given by-
    a) $L_1 + L_2$ b) $\dfrac{L_1 + L_2}{L_1 \times L_2}$ c) $\dfrac{L_1 \times L_2}{L_1 + L_2}$ d) $\dfrac{L_1}{L_2}$

17. Assuming no mutual inductance, the total inductance of the two parallel connected inductors shown in fig.11 is-
    a) 1H
    b) 800mH
    c) 60mH
    d) 13.33mH

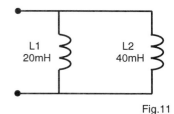

Fig.11

18. Assuming no mutual inductance, the total inductance of the circuit shown in fig.12 is-
    a) 200H
    b) 29H
    c) 27H
    d) 2H

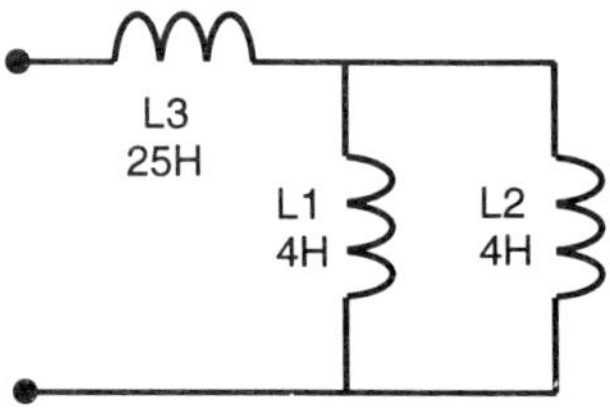

Fig.12

19. Assuming no mutual inductance, what is the total inductance of the circuit shown in fig.13?

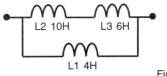

Fig.13

a) 240H
b) 20H
c) 12H
d) 3.2H

20. Referring to fig.14. Two series connected inductors of 5H and 15H respectively, are spaced so that the mutual inductance between them is 4H. What is the resulting inductance when they are connected in series aiding?

a) 20H
b) 24H
c) 28H
d) 12H

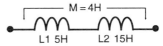

Fig.14

21. The two series connected inductors shown in fig.14 are now connected in series opposing, what is the effective inductance of this combination?

a) 20H   b) 24H   c) 28H   d) 12H

22. A typical value of inductance for a transmitter power supply smoothing choke would be about-

a) 10-100mH
b) 10-30H
c) 0.5-1H
d) 100-2000H

23. The coils used for tuning the RF signal stages of a VHF receiver would probably consist of-

a) about 4000 turns of thin silver plated copper wire.
b) about 100 turns of soft copper wire wound on a bundle of soft iron wires.
c) 1500 turns of very fine wire wound on a 10kΩ non-inductive resistor.
d) 2-8 turns of 18 s.w.g. silver plated copper wire, self supporting, and about 0.5-1cm in diameter.

24. A typical tuning coil used in a HF antenna tuning unit might consist of-

a) 4000 turns of cotton covered 36 s.w.g. wire.
b) 100 turns of copper wire wound on a bundle of soft iron wires.
c) about 50 turns of 18 s.w.g. silver plated copper wire wound on a 3 inch diameter ceramic former with tapping connections or a geared roller.
d) about 5 turns of 10 s.w.g. aluminium wire, wound on a cardboard former of 5 inch diameter with tapping points every turn.

25. A radio frequency choke (RFC), intended for operation at 100MHz, may consist of about 5 - 20 turns of 22 SWG insulated copper wire wound on a ferrite core a quarter inch in diameter and one inch long.
It may be used to -
a) block a direct current and pass the 100MHz signal.
b) pass a direct current and offer maximum impedance to the 100MHz signal.
c) trap slowly changing direct currents.
d) stabilze the oscillator supply current.

26. Two of the factors that contribute to the effective series resistance of a practical coil used at radio frequencies are-
a) construction of the former and insulation of the wire.
b) type of solder used and diameter of the turns.
c) resistivity of the copper used for the wire and the frequency of operation.
d) none of the above.

27. At high frequencies, the effective resistance of an inductor increases, this is due to-
a) the reactance of the stray capacity.
b) construction of the former.
c) rigidity of the turns of the coil.
d) skin effect.

28. A transmitting coil is constructed from 18 s.w.g. silver plated copper wire. Why is the wire silver plated?
a) To reduce the risk of skin infection if the operator is scratched.
b) To reflect incoming interference.
c) To make the wire easier to solder.
d) To reduce the surface, or skin resistance.

29. The term 'skin effect' refers to the way in which-
a) RF currents tend to travel out to the surface of a wire as the frequency is increased.
b) the surface of the wire oxidises causing decomposition of the coil.
c) infection sets in when a person is scratched by oxidised copper wire.
d) copper wire resists being soldered.

30. The time constant 'T' for the circuit shown in fig.15 is given by-
    a) $T = R/L$
    b) $T = RL^2$
    c) $T = L^2/R$
    d) $T = L/R$

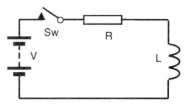

Fig.15

31. Refer to fig.15. The time constant of the R L circuit may be expressed as the-
    a) time taken for the current to reach 63% of its final steady value.
    b) time taken for the current to reach 37% of its final steady value.
    c) time taken for the current to reach maximum.
    d) power dissipated in one standard second.

32. Referring to fig.16. What is the time constant of the circuit?
    a) 40s
    b) 4s
    c) 0.4ms
    d) 0.25ms

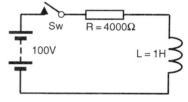

Fig.16

33. Referring to fig.16. If the 4000Ω resistor is replaced by one of 8000Ω. What is the time taken for the current in the inductor to reach 63% of its final steady value?
    a) 0.125ms   b) 0.25ms   c) 0.4ms   d) 2.5ms

34. Referring to fig.16. What current will flow in the circuit at the instant switch 'Sw' is closed?
    a) 25mA   b) 15.75mA   c) 9.25mA   d) Zero

35. Referring to fig.16. What will be the steady state current flowing in the inductor when switch 'Sw' has been closed for a period of at least 5 time constants?
    a) 400mA   b) 40mA   c) 25mA   d) 2.5mA

36. Referring to fig.16. Which one of the curves shown below represents the current in the inductor when switch 'Sw' is closed?

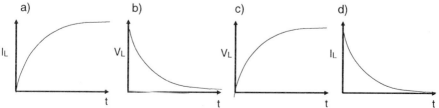

Answers - Inductance

1	a	11	d	21	d	31	a
2	a	12	a	22	b	32	d
3	b	13	c	23	d	33	a
4	a	14	a	24	c	34	d
5	b	15	b	25	b	35	c
6	c	16	c	26	c	36	a
7	a	17	d	27	d		
8	c	18	c	28	d		
9	d	19	d	29	a		
10	a	20	c	30	d		

1. The unit of 'self-inductance', usually abbreviated to inductance, symbol L, is the 'henry'. For practical use the henry may be divided into smaller units :- The millihenry (mH) = 0.001H or 10^{-3}H and the microhenry (μH) = 0.000001H or 10^{-6}H.

2. Increasing the number of turns increases the inductance.

3. Stretching the length of a coil will reduce the inductance. Squeezing the turns closer will increase the inductance . This procedure is often used in practice for coarse adjustment of tuned circuits.

4. The effect of inserting an iron or ferrite core into the inductor is to concentrate the magnetic field into the inductor, increasing the magnetic field that cuts the turns of the coil and inducing more voltage. The inductance is increased.

5. The use of a brass core will decrease the inductance.

6. A coil is said to have a 'self inductance' (inductance) of 1 henry, when a current in it, changing at the rate of 1A/s, produces an e.m.f. of 1 volt across its terminals.

7. When the current flowing in an inductor changes, the associated magnetic field (often referred to as lines of magnetic flux or lines of magnetic force) is also changing and cutting the coil producing it. This magnetic field induces a voltage (or 'back e.m.f.') in the coil which opposes the change causing it.

8. All conductors have some inductance, although in the case of short lengths of wire that may be very small. E.g. The inductance of the connecting wires on a capacitor may sufficient to cause that capacitor to resonate at VHF, this effect is made use of for suppression purposes. A radio station earthing wire/system may have a reactance of a fraction of an ohm to mains frequency currents, but several hundred ohms to high frequency currents due to its inductance.

9. When the switch is closed current flows in coil P, producing a changing magnetic field that cuts coil S. An e.m.f. is induced in coil S and a momentary deflection on the meter is observed. When the primary current reaches a steady, unchanging state there will be no current in the meter and no deflection.

10. When two coils are coupled in close proximity, so that a changing current in one coil induces an e.m.f. in the other, the coils are said to be mutually coupled. They possess mutual inductance. (This is the transformer principle.)

11. In this example of electromagnetic induction, the changing magnetic field produced by the lines of magnetic flux surrounding the bar magnet being moved in and out of a stationary coil, produce an e.m.f. which causes a current to flow in the meter circuit. When the magnet is inserted a deflection will be observed in one direction, when the magnet comes to rest there will be no deflection, and when the magnet is withdrawn, there will be a deflection in the opposite direction.
The magnitude of the induced voltage and current depends on - 1) The velocity of the magnet, 2) the strength of the magnet, and 3) the number of turns on the coil.

12. There will be no deflection on the meter. See answer 9.

13. Under steady state conditions, with no current changes producing magnetic field changes, there will be no opposing reaction from the inductor, and the current will reach its Ohm's Law value $I = \dfrac{V}{R}$. Where R is the combined resistance of the primary coil, the internal resistance of the battery, and the connecting wires.

14. For series connected inductors, with no mutual inductance (magnetic coupling between the coils), $L_T = L_1 + L_2$.

15. $L_T = L_1 + L_2 = 5 + 10 = 15H$.

16. For two inductors in parallel with no mutual coupling :- $L_T = \dfrac{L_1 \times L_2}{L_1 + L_2}$.

17. $L_T = \dfrac{L_1 \times L_2}{L_1 + L_2} = \dfrac{20 \times 40}{20 + 40} = \dfrac{800}{60} = 13.33H$.

18. Calculate the effective inductance of the parallel circuit and add the series inductor.
$$L_T = \left\{\frac{L_1 \times L_2}{L_1 + L_2}\right\} + L_3 = \left\{\frac{4 \times 4}{4 + 4}\right\} + 25 = \left\{\frac{16}{8}\right\} + 25 = 2 + 25 = 27H.$$

19. Treat this as a parallel circuit in which one of the branches is the sum of two inductors in series. $L_T = \dfrac{L_1 \times (L_2 + L_3)}{L_1 + (L_2 + L_3)} = \dfrac{4 \times (10 + 6)}{4 + (10 + 6)} = \dfrac{64}{20} = 3.2H.$

20. The existence of mutual inductance between coils either increases or decreases the total inductance, depending on whether the fields aid or oppose each other. For series aiding :-
$$L_T = L_1 + L_2 + 2L_M = 5 + 15 + (2 \times 4) = 5 + 15 + 8 = 28H.$$

Answers - Inductance

21. For series opposing :-

$L_T = L_1 + L_2 - 2L_M = 5 + 15 - (2 \times 4) = 5 + 15 - 8 = 12H.$

22. A typical power supply smoothing choke may be about 10 - 30H.

23. A VHF coil may be wound on a small insulated former having an adjustable high quality ferrite slug for tuning. Alternatively, it may be 2 - 8 turns self-supporting, silver plated copper wire.

24. An antenna tuning unit inductor may be constructed from 12 - 14 SWG copper wire, silver plated to resist corrosion and offer low skin resistance at high frequencies. It is likely to be wound in a spiral groove on a 3 - 4 inch dia ceramic tube which is rotated by a spindle at one end. The tapping point is variable via a jockey wheel which rides along the coil as it rotates.

25. An inductor, usually referred to as a choke, is used to offer a high impedance to alternating current and low resistance to direct current.

26,27,28,29. When high frequency currents flow in a conductor the current distribution over the cross section is not uniform, instead it is concentrated towards the surface. The higher the frequency the less current flows in the centre of the conductor. Since the whole cross section is not carrying a uniform current the loss becomes higher as frequency increases. This phenomenon is known as 'skin effect'. In order to reduce the losses at the surface of the conductor silver plating is employed. High power transmitters may use copper tube for the final stage tuning coils.

30,31. The time constant, given by the formula $T = \dfrac{L}{R}$ is the time taken for the current to reach 63% of its final steady value, $I = \dfrac{V}{R}.$

32. $T = \dfrac{L}{R} = \dfrac{1}{4000} = 0.00025s$ or $0.25ms$ or $250\mu s.$

33. $T = \dfrac{L}{R} = \dfrac{1}{8000} = 0.000125s$ or $0.125ms$ or $125\mu s.$

34. Due to the reaction of the inductor opposing change, there will be no current at the instant the switch is closed.

35. When the current in the circuit is no longer changing, the primary current is the Ohm's Law value, $I = \dfrac{V}{R} = \dfrac{100}{4000} = 0.25A$ or $25mA.$

36. When the switch is closed the current in the inductor builds up to its Ohm's Law value exponentially. The exponential curve is shown in a). The final steady value being reached in approximately 5 Time constants; $5 \times \dfrac{L}{R}.$

5. Capacitive Reactance

In this section we will :-
1. answer questions on capacitive reactance.
2. solve simple problems.

Capacitive Reactance X_C

Capacitive reactance X_C is the ability of a pure capacitor to resist the flow of alternating current. It can be considered analogous to resistance in a d.c. circuit; except that there is no energy or power dissipated in a pure capacitor. A pure capacitor has no loss associated with it. The unit of reactance X, is the ohm, symbol Ω.

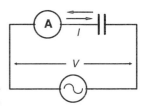

Fig.1 Capacitor in the a.c. circuit. The ammeter reads the amount of charge and discharge current.

Points to note.
1. No current flows in the dielectric between the plates of a pure capacitor.
2. The current I, measured in the capacitive circuit is due to the alternate charge and discharge of the capacitor, as shown by the arrows fig.1.
3. X_C is considered negative because the alternating voltage across the capacitor lags the current by 90°. See figs: 3 and 4.
4. X_C is inversely proportional to both capacitance and frequency, see fig.2.
5. In practice, most capacitors except electrolytic types can be regarded as pure.

Formulae to remember :-

$$X_C = \frac{1}{\omega C} = \frac{1}{2\pi f C}, \text{ and by transposition, } C = \frac{1}{2\pi f X_C} \text{ and } f = \frac{1}{2\pi C X_C}$$

$$I = \frac{V}{X_C} = \frac{V}{\frac{1}{\omega C}} = V\omega C$$

Where :-
X_c = Capacitive reactance (ohms)
$\omega = 2\pi f$.
C = Capacitance in farads.
f = Frequency in hertz.
I = Current in amps.

Fig.2 Reactance/frequency curve for capacitor.

Fig.3 Showing current waveform leading voltage waveform by 90°

Fig.4 Phasor diagram showing V lagging I by 90°

Capacitive Reactance

1. Opposition to the flow of alternating current in a pure capacitor is termed-
   a) capacitance.
   b) inductance.
   c) reactance.
   d) impedance.

2. In a pure capacitor the-
   a) voltage is in phase with the current.
   b) current is in phase with the voltage.
   c) current leads the voltage by 90°.
   d) voltage leads the current by 90°.

3. The reactance 'X_C' of a capacitor-
   a) remains constant with frequency.
   b) increases with increase in frequency.
   c) decreases with increase in frequency.
   d) none of the above.

4. The reactance of a pure capacitor may be found by applying the formula -
   a) $X_C = \dfrac{\omega C}{R}$
   b) $X_C = \dfrac{C}{R}$
   c) $X_C = \omega C$
   d) $X_C = \dfrac{1}{\omega C}$

5. The current flowing in a reactive circuit is given by-
   a) $I = \dfrac{V}{R}$
   b) $I = \dfrac{V}{X}$
   c) $I = \dfrac{X_C}{V}$
   d) $I = \dfrac{R}{X_C}$

6. The current flowing in a circuit consisting of pure capacitance only, is given by the formula-
   a) $I = V \omega C$
   b) $I = V f C$
   c) $I = f C R$
   d) $I = C V$

7. The symbol 'ω' represents the-
   a) actual value of reactance.
   b) wattless value of the power.
   c) angular velocity, and is equal to $2 \pi f$.
   d) 'Q' factor of the circuit, equal to $\dfrac{1}{\omega C R}$.

8. Capacitive reactance is considered-
   a) positive, the voltage leads the current by 90°.
   b) negative, the voltage lags the current by 90°.
   c) neutral, there is no phase change.
   d) antiphase, there is a 180°phase change.

Capacitive Reactance

9. The reactance/frequency curve for a capacitor is-

a)

b)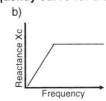

c)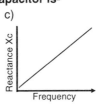

d)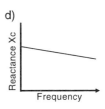

10. Which one of the waveforms shown below, represents the voltage and current when an alternating voltage is applied across a pure capacitor?

a)

b)

c)

d)

11. Which one of the following vector diagrams is representative of the voltage and current relationships in a circuit containing pure capacitance?

a)

b)

c)

d)

12. As the frequency applied to a practical capacitor is increased, the reactance decreases, until a frequency is reached at which the reactance begins to increase. What is the cause of this effect?
   a) Self inductance of the capacitor and its wires.
   b) Self capacitance of the capacitor and its wires.
   c) Frequency distortion within the capacitor.
   d) Negative temperature effects within the capacitor.

13. The leads of a capacitor may be cut to a certain length so that the capacitor becomes-
   a) parallel resonant at a certain frequency.
   b) super conductive at all frequencies.
   c) super inductive at all frequencies.
   d) series resonant at a certain frequency.

14. When a given value of capacitance is connected to a radio frequency generator, increasing the frequency will result in -
    a) rejection of medium frequency currents.
    b) an increase in circuit current.
    c) a decrease in circuit current.
    d) parasitic oscillations.

15. What is the reactance of a 1μF capacitor at a frequency of 800Hz?
    a) 19,999Ω   b) 9,999Ω   c) 199Ω   d) 99Ω

16. What is the reactance of a 1000μF capacitor at a frequency of 50Hz?
    a) 500Ω   b) 31.8Ω   c) 3.18Ω   d) 0.18Ω

17. What is the reactance of a 10pF capacitor at a frequency of 10MHz?
    a) 1591kΩ   b) 1592Ω   c) 1000Ω   d) 100Ω

18. At what frequency will a 2μF capacitor have a reactance of 100Ω?
    a) 796kHz   b) 796Hz   c) 2000Hz   d) 200Hz

19. A 1000pF capacitor has a reactance of 1000Ω when the applied signal has a frequency of-
    a) 159kHz   b) 159Hz   c) 1000kHz   d) 100Hz

20. A 2μF capacitor is connected across a 200V 50Hz supply.
    What current flows?
    a) 500mA   b) 250mA   c) 125mA   d) 100mA

21. A 10μF capacitor is connected across a 100V 100Hz supply.
    What current flows?
    a) 1.0A   b) 0.707A   c) 0.628A   d) 0.141A

22. A 0.5μF capacitor is connected across a 10V 5kHz supply.
    What current flows?
    a) 50mA   b) 141mA   c) 151mA   d) 157mA

23. The current flowing in a circuit consisting of pure capacitance only, is 1 amp.
    The applied voltage is 250 volts at a frequency of 100Hz.
    What is the value of the capacitor?
    a) 2.55μF   b) 3.22μF   c) 6.37μF   d) 10μF

Capacitive Reactance

24. **Which one of the four capacitors listed below has the lowest reactance at a frequency of 4000Hz (4kHz)?**
    a) 1µF 250V d.c.
    b) 0.05µF 800V d.c.
    c) 10,000pF 25V d.c.
    d) 4000pF 250V d.c.

25 **With the switch 'Sw' open, as in fig.5, the light bulb will :-**
    a) not light.
    b) glow at full brightness.
    c) glow at approximately half power.
    d) glow very dimly, just visible in a
       darkened room.

26 **When switch 'Sw' fig.5 is closed the lamp will :-**
    a) fail instantly.
    b) not light.
    c) glow at full brightness.
    d) instantly glow at full brightness and gradually extinguish.

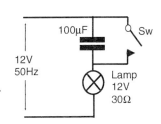

Fig.5

27. **Two capacitive reactances are connected in series.**
    Which formula will you use to calculate the total reactance X$_T$?
    a) $X_T = X_1 \times X_2$
    b) $X_T = X_1 + X_2$
    c) $X_T = (X_1 + X_2)^2$
    d) $X_T = \sqrt{X_1 + X_2}$

28. **For the values of capacitance and frequency given below, calculate the reactance.**

	Capacitance	Frequency	Reactance
a)	10µF	1000HZ	_____
b)	2µF	796Hz	_____
c)	1µF	10,000Hz	_____
d)	1000pF	1MHZ	_____
e)	680pF	10MHZ	_____
f)	250pF	50MHZ	_____
g)	100pF	100MHZ	_____
h)	10pF	150MHZ	_____
i)	5pF	200MHz	_____

Capacitive Reactance

29. For the values of reactance and frequency given below, calculate the capacitance.

Reactance X_C	Frequency	Capacitance
a) 1000Ω	10Hz	____
b) 1000Ω	1000Hz	____
c) 25Ω	10,000Hz	____
d) 10Ω	1MHz	____
e) 5Ω	10MHz	____
f) 100Ω	10MHz	____
g) 1000Ω	20MHz	____
h) 2900Ω	20MHz	____
i) 1000Ω	100MHz	____

30. For the values of capacitance and reactance given below, calculate the frequency.

Capacitance	Reactance X_C	Frequency
a) 10µF	100Ω	____
b) 10µF	1000Ω	____
c) 5µF	500Ω	____
d) 2µF	2000Ω	____
e) 1.5µF	6000Ω	____
f) 1µF	1000Ω	____
g) 0.5µF	75Ω	____
h) 1000pF	6280Ω	____
I) 470pF	10Ω	____

Answers - Capacitive Reactance

1	c	11	a	21	c	28		29		30	
2	c	12	a	22	d	a	15.9Ω	a	15.9µF	a	159Hz
3	c	13	d	23	c	b	99.97Ω	b	0.159µF	b	15.9Hz
4	d	14	b	24	a	c	15.9Ω	c	0.636µF	c	63.66Hz
5	b	15	c	25	c	d	159Ω	d	0.0159µF	d	39.78Hz
6	a	16	c	26	c	e	23.4Ω	e	3.183nF	e	17.68Hz
7	c	17	b	27	b	f	12.7Ω	f	159pF	f	159Hz
8	b	18	b			g	15.9Ω	g	7.95pF	g	4244Hz
9	a	19	a			h	106.1Ω	h	2.74pF	h	25.343kHz
10	a	20	c			i	159Ω	i	1.59pF	i	33.863MHz

Answers - Capacitive Reactance

1. Opposition to the flow of alternating current in a pure capacitor is *'reactance'*, symbol X_C. Reactance is similar to resistance in a d.c. circuit, and is measured in ohms, symbol Ω.

2. In a pure capacitor the current leads the voltage by 90°.

3. The reactance of a capacitor decreases as the applied frequency increases. At low frequencies a given capacitor may have a very high reactance, and will only pass a small current, while at high frequencies the reactance - opposition to current flow - decreases, and the current flow increases.

4. Capacitive reactance is given by the formula :- $X_C = \dfrac{1}{\omega C} = \dfrac{1}{2 \pi f C}$.

5. Current flow in the reactive circuit is :- $I = \dfrac{V}{X}$.

6. Current flow in a pure capacitor is
$$I = \frac{V}{X_C} = \frac{V}{\dfrac{1}{\omega C}} = V \omega C \quad (Where \ \omega = 2 \pi f \ ).$$

7. The symbol ω (omega) $= 2 \pi f$ is the angular velocity measured in radians.

8. Capacitive reactance is considered negative since the voltage lags the reference current phasor by 90°.

9. Curve a) is the reactance/frequency curve for the capacitor.

10. Waveform a) shows the current leading the voltage by 90°.

11. Phasor a) shows the current phasor leading the voltage phasor by 90°.

12,13. All conductors possess some inductance. The leads of a capacitor are therefore inductive. At high frequencies the inductive reactance of the leads may become higher than the reactance of the capacitor and the net reactance increases. When the reactance due to the capacitor X_C is equal to the inductive reactance X_L of the leads, the circuit becomes series resonant (it forms an acceptor circuit) and passes current very easily. This self resonant effect is useful in simple filter circuits for bypassing unwanted signals. The capacitor leads may be cut for a particular resonant frequency.

14. Increasing the frequency will result in an increase in current.

15. $X_C = \dfrac{1}{\omega C} = \dfrac{1}{2 \pi f C} = \dfrac{1}{2 \times \pi \times 800 \times 1 \times 10^{-6}} = \dfrac{10^6}{1600 \times \pi} = 199\Omega$.

16. $X_C = \dfrac{1}{\omega C} = \dfrac{1}{2 \pi f C} = \dfrac{1}{2 \times \pi \times 50 \times 1000 \times 10^{-6}} - \dfrac{10^6}{100,000 \times \pi} - 3.18\Omega$.

17. $X_C = \dfrac{1}{\omega C} = \dfrac{1}{2\pi f C} = \dfrac{1}{2\times\pi\times 10\times 10^6 \times 10\times 10^{-12}} = \dfrac{10^6}{200\times\pi} = 1592\Omega.$

18. $f = \dfrac{1}{2\pi C X_C} = \dfrac{1}{2\times\pi\times 2\times 10^{-6}\times 100} = \dfrac{10^6}{400\times\pi} = 796Hz.$

19. $f = \dfrac{1}{2\pi C X_C} = \dfrac{1}{2\times\pi\times 1000\times 10^{-12}\times 1000} = \dfrac{10^6}{2\times\pi} = 159.155kHz.$

20. $I = \dfrac{V}{X_C} = \dfrac{V}{\dfrac{1}{\omega C}} = V\omega C = 200\times 2\times\pi\times 50\times 2\times 10^{-6}$

$= 40,000\times\pi\times 10^{-6} = 0.125A \;(125mA).$

21. $I = \dfrac{V}{X_C} = \dfrac{V}{\dfrac{1}{\omega C}} = V\omega C = 100\times 2\times\pi\times 100\times 10\times 10^{-6}$

$= 200,000\times\pi\times 10^{-6} = 0.628A \;(628mA).$

22. $I = \dfrac{V}{X_C} = \dfrac{V}{\dfrac{1}{\omega C}} = V\omega C = 10\times 2\times\pi\times 5\times 10^3\times 0.5\times 10^{-6} = 0.157A \;(157mA).$

23. First calculate the reactance :- $X_C = \dfrac{V}{I} = \dfrac{250}{1} = 250\Omega$ and then :-

$C = \dfrac{1}{\omega X_C} = \dfrac{1}{2\times\pi\times f\times X_C} = \dfrac{1}{2\times\pi\times 100\times 250} = \dfrac{1}{50,000\times\pi} = 6.366\mu F.$

24. Ignore the voltage rating it has no effect on the reactance. The capacitor with the lowest reactance is the one with the largest capacitance, $1\mu F$. $X_C = 39.8\Omega.$

25. The lamp will light, although not at its full brightness. The reactance of the capacitor to the 50Hz supply is 31.8Ω. This has the effect of reducing the current in the circuit.

26. When the switch is closed the lamp will glow at full brightness since the capacitor is bypassed and the lamp will be working at its rated voltage.

27. For reactances in series the total reactance is the sum of the individual reactances. $X_T = X_1 + X_2$

28,29,30. Answers are given in the key. Use one of the following formulae :-

$$X_C = \dfrac{1}{2\pi f C} \qquad C = \dfrac{1}{2\pi f X_C} \qquad f = \dfrac{1}{2\pi C X_C}$$

6. Inductive Reactance

In this section we will :-
1. answer questions on inductive reactance.
2. solve simple problems.

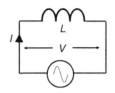
Fig.1 Showing an Inductor connected in an a.c. circuit.

Inductive Reactance X_L

Inductive reactance X_L is the ability of a pure inductor to resist the flow of alternating or changing current. It can be considered analogous to resistance in a d.c. circuit; except that no energy or power is dissipated by a pure inductor since all energy used in building up the magnetic field is returned to the circuit when the field collapses.

In practice an inductor has some resistance, mainly due to the material with which it is constructed, and some power will be dissipated. However, when this resistance is very low its effects may be neglected. The unit of reactance is the ohm.

Points to note.
1. X_L depends on both inductance and frequency, see fig.2.
2. An increase in frequency and/or inductance will increase X_L.
3. X_L is considered positive because the alternating voltage across the inductor leads the current by 90°. See figs. 3 and 4.

Formulae to remember :-

$$X_L = \omega L = 2\pi f L, \quad \text{and by transposition,} \quad L = \frac{X_L}{2\pi f} \quad \text{and} \quad f = \frac{X_L}{2\pi L}$$

The current in the circuit $I = \dfrac{V}{X_L} = \dfrac{V}{2\pi f L}$

Where :-
X_L = Inductive reactance (ohms)
$\omega = 2\pi f$.
L = Inductance in henrys.
f = Frequency in hertz.
I = Current in amps.

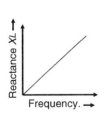

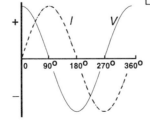

Fig.2 Reactance / Frequency curve for inductor. Showing X_L increasing with frequency.

Fig.3 Showing voltage waveform leading current waveform by 90°

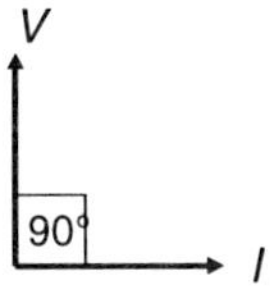

Fig.4 Phasor diagram showing V leading I by 90°

Inductive Reactance

1. Opposition to the flow of alternating current in a pure inductor is termed-
   a) inductance.
   b) resistance.
   c) reactance.
   d) impedance.

2. In a pure inductor, the-
   a) voltage is in phase with the current.
   b) current is in phase with the voltage.
   c) current leads the voltage by 90°.
   d) voltage leads the current by 90°.

3. The reactance 'X_L' of an inductor-
   a) remains constant with change in frequency.
   b) increases with increase in frequency.
   c) decreases with increase in frequency.
   d) is very high when direct currents are present.

4. The reactance 'X_L' of an inductor may be found by applying the formula-
   a) $X_L = 2 \pi f$
   b) $X_L = 2 \pi f L$
   c) $X_L = 2 f L$
   d) $X_L = 2 \pi^2 f^2 L$

5. The current flowing in a circuit consisting of pure inductance is given by-
   a) $I = \dfrac{V}{2 \pi f L}$
   b) $I = \dfrac{V}{2 f L}$
   c) $I = \dfrac{V^2}{2 f L}$
   d) $I = \dfrac{2 f L}{V^2}$

6. Inductive reactance is considered-
   a) positive, the voltage leads the current by 90°.
   b) negative, the voltage lags the current by 90°.
   c) cancelled, there is a 180° phase shift.
   d) neutral, there is no phase shift.

7. A pure inductor has a 50Hz, 100V supply connected across it, with the applied voltage leading the current by 90°. If the supply frequency is changed to 25Hz, the voltage will lead the current by-
   a) 270°
   b) 180°
   c) 90°
   d) 45°

8. Which one of the reactance/frequency characteristics shown below is representative of a pure inductor?

   a)
   b)
   c)
   d)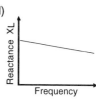

9. Which one of the waveforms shown below represents the voltage and current when an alternating supply is connected across a pure inductor?

a) 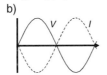   b) 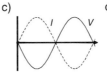   c) 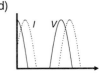   d)

10. Which of the following phasor diagrams is representative of a pure inductor?

a)   b)    c)   d)

11. A practical inductor becomes parallel resonant at a certain frequency, this is due to the-
   a) self inductance of low grade copper wire.
   b) self capacitance between the turns of the coil.
   c) impurities in the coil former.
   d) value of the applied voltage.

12. An air-cored inductor is connected in series with a lamp (light bulb) as shown in fig.5. In this condition the lamp glows at about half brightness.
What will happen if an iron core is inserted into the centre of the inductor?
   a) The lamp will glow brighter.
   b) The filament will vaporise instantly.
   c) The current will lead the voltage by 45°.
   d) The lamp's brightness will decrease.

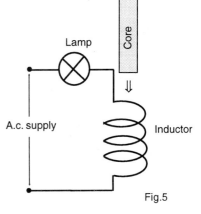

Fig.5

13. Referring to fig.5 above, and ignoring the iron core. What will happen if the supply frequency is increased? The voltage to remain the same.
   a) The lamp's brightness will decrease.
   b) The filament will vaporise instantly.
   c) The lamp will emit a 1kHz tone.
   d) The lamp will glow brighter.

14. What is the reactance of a pure inductor of 10 henrys, at a frequency of 50Hz?

   a) 3142Ω   b) 3.18Ω   c) 31.41Ω   d) 31.8Ω

15. What is the reactance of a 1 henry inductor at a frequency of 1000Hz?

   a) 6283Ω   b) 6.36Ω   c) 62.82Ω   d) 63.6Ω

16. What is the reactance of a 5mH (5 x 10^{-3}H) inductor at a frequency of 5MHz (5 x 10^{6}Hz)?

   a) 10kΩ   b) 15.7kΩ   c) 157.079kΩ   d) 125.6kΩ

17. What is the reactance of a 1mH inductor, given that ω = 5000 rad/sec?

   a) 5Ω   b) 50Ω   c) 500Ω   d) 5000Ω

18. Calculate the current flowing in a 20mH (20 x 10^{-3}H) inductor when it is connected across a 70.7V, 796Hz supply.

   a) 0.707A   b) 7.07A   c) 70.7A   d) 796mA

19. A 100mH inductor is connected across a 10V, 1000Hz (1kHz) supply. What current flows?

   a) 100mA   b) 15.9mA   c) 159mA   d) 1000mA

20. What is the reactance of a 15H inductor at a frequency of 50Hz?

   a) 4712.4Ω   b) 314.1Ω   c) 0.005Ω   d) 0.05Ω

21. A 15H inductor is connected across a 100V 50Hz supply. What current will flow?

   a) 0.0318A (31.8mA)   b) 0.005A (5mA)
   c) 0.021A (21mA)   d) 0.05A (50mA)

22. What value of inductor will be required to produce a reactance of 1000Ω at a frequency of 1000Hz?

   a) 0.159H (159mH)   b) 0.001H (1mH)
   c) 0.0159H (15.9mH)   d) 0.0001H (0.1mH)

23. A 0.159H (159mH) inductor is connected across a 100V 1000Hz supply. What current flows?

   a) 0.1A (100mA)   b) 0.159A (159mA)
   c) 1.59A   d) 159A

24. At what frequency will a 500mH choke have a reactance of 2000Ω?

   a) 6.36Hz   b) 63.6Hz   c) 636.6Hz   d) 10,000Hz

Inductive Reactance

25. At what frequency will a 0.5H coil have a reactance of 314.16Ω?
    a) 1570Hz   b) 157Hz   c) 50Hz   d) 100Hz

26. A 20V 50Hz supply is connected across an inductor of 500mH.
    What current will flow?
    a) 1A (1000mA)   b) 0.127A (127mA)
    c) 2.5A (2,500mA)   d) 0.1A (100mA)

27. What is the reactance of a 2mH inductor at a frequency of 1MHz?
    a) 62.83Ω   b) 6,283Ω   c) 12,566Ω   d) 20,000Ω

28. An inductor has a reactance of 314.159Ω at a frequency of 50Hz.
    What is the value of the inductor?
    a) 0.5H   b) 1H   c) 314.195H   d) 1.57H

29. For the values of inductance and frequency given below,
    calculate the reactance.

Inductance	Frequency	Reactance
a) 10H	1000Hz	_____
b) 1H	5kHz	_____
c) 0.5H	5kHz	_____
d) 200mH	1MHz	_____
e) 200mH	100Hz	_____
f) 100mH	50Hz	_____
g) 1mH	10MHz	_____
h) 1µH	100MHz	_____
i) 1µH	150MHz	_____

30. For the values of reactance and frequency given below,
    calculate the inductance.

Reactance	Frequency	Inductance
a) 400Ω	100kHz	_____
b) 20kΩ	1MHz	_____
c) 10kΩ	5MHz	_____
d) 1000Ω	5kHz	_____
e) 250Ω	5000Hz	_____
f) 5000Ω	10MHz	_____
g) 50Ω	5MHz	_____
h) 200Ω	20MHz	_____
i) 100Ω	2MHz	_____

31. For the values of inductance and reactance given below, calculate the frequency.

Inductance	Reactance	Frequency
a) 10H	100Ω	____
b) 2H	1000Ω	____
c) 0.1H	1000Ω	____
d) 0.01H	2500Ω	____
e) 1000µH	100Ω	____
f) 318µH	1000Ω	____
g) 200µH	1000Ω	____
h) 1µH	100Ω	____
i) 1µH	20Ω	____

Answers - Inductive Reactance

1 c	11 b	21 c	29		30		31	
2 d	12 d	22 a	a	62.8kΩ	a	0.63mH	a	1.59Hz
3 b	13 a	23 a	b	31.4kΩ	b	3.183mH	b	79.57Hz
4 b	14 a	24 c	c	15.7kΩ	c	318.3µH	c	1591.55Hz
5 a	15 a	25 d	d	1.256MΩ	d	31.8mH	d	39.79Hz
6 a	16 c	26 b	e	125.6Ω	e	7.96mH	e	15.9kHz
7 c	17 a	27 c	f	31.4Ω	f	79.5µH	f	500.49kHz
8 c	18 a	28 b	g	62.8kΩ	g	1.59µH	g	795.8kHz
9 a	19 b		h	628.3Ω	h	1.59µH	h	15.9MHz
10 d	20 a		i	942.4Ω	i	7.95µH	i	3.183MHz

Answers - Inductive Reactance

1. Opposition to the flow of alternating current in a pure inductance is *'reactance'* X_L. Reactance is measured in ohms, symbol Ω.

2. In a pure inductor voltage leads the current by 90°.

3. The reactance of an inductor increases as frequency increases.

4. Inductive reactance is given by the formula:- $X_L = \omega L = 2\pi f L$.

5. The current flow in a pure inductor:- $I = \dfrac{V}{X_L} = \dfrac{V}{\omega L} = \dfrac{V}{2\pi f L}$.

6. Inductive reactance is considered positive since voltage leads the current by 90°.

7. For pure inductance the voltage will lead the current by 90° irrespective of the frequency.

8. Reactance/frequency curve c) shows reactance increasing with frequency.

9. Waveform a) shows the voltage across a pure inductor (solid line), leading the current (broken line) by 90°.

10. Phasor (or vector) diagrams are used to show the direction and magnitude of voltages and currents in a.c. circuits. phasor diagram d) shows the voltage V leading the current I by 90°. (Consider the vectors to rotate anticlockwise.)

11. The self capacitance, or distributed capacitance between the turns of an inductor form a parallel L/C circuit, resonant when $X_L = X_C$.

12. The effect of inserting the iron core into the inductor is to increase the inductance of the inductor. This in turn increases the reactance (a.c. resistance), reducing the amount of current passed. The lamp reduces in brightness depending on how far the core is inserted into the coil.

13. The inductive reactance of the coil will increase as the frequency increases, this will reduce the current in the circuit and the brightness of the lamp will decrease.

14. $X_L = \omega L = 2\pi f L = 2 \times \pi \times 50 \times 10 = 1000\pi = 3142\Omega$.

15. $X_L = \omega L = 2\pi f L = 2 \times \pi \times 1000 \times 1 = 2000\pi = 6283\Omega$.

16. $X_L = \omega L = 2\pi f L = 2 \times \pi \times 5 \times 10^6 \times 5 \times 10^{-3} = 50 \times \pi \times 10^3 = 157k\Omega$.

17. $X_L = \omega L = 5000 \times 1 \times 10^{-3} = 5\Omega$.

18. $I = \dfrac{V}{X_L} = \dfrac{V}{2\pi f L} = \dfrac{70.7}{2 \times \pi \times 796 \times 20 \times 10^{-3}} = \dfrac{70.7}{100.028} = 0.707A \; (approx)$.

19. $\quad I = \dfrac{V}{X_L} = \dfrac{V}{2\,\pi\,f\,L} = \dfrac{10}{2 \times \pi \times 1000 \times 100 \times 10^{-3}} = \dfrac{10}{200\,\pi} = 0.0159A \;\; (15.9mA).$

20. $\quad X_L = \omega\,L = 2\,\pi\,f\,L = 2 \times \pi \times 50 \times 15 = 1500\,\pi = 4712\Omega \;\; (4.7k\Omega \; approx).$

21. $\quad I = \dfrac{V}{X_L} = \dfrac{V}{2\,\pi\,f\,L} = \dfrac{100}{2 \times \pi \times 50 \times 15} = \dfrac{100}{4712} = 0.021A \;\; (21mA).$

22. $\quad X_L = 2\,\pi\,f\,L.$ by transposition $L = \dfrac{X_L}{2\,\pi\,f}.$

$$L = \dfrac{X_L}{2\,\pi\,f} = \dfrac{1000}{2 \times \pi \times 1000} = \dfrac{1}{2 \times \pi} = 0.159H \,(159mH).$$

23. $\quad I = \dfrac{V}{X_L} = \dfrac{V}{2\,\pi\,f\,L} = \dfrac{100}{2 \times \pi \times 1000 \times 0.159} = \dfrac{100}{999} = 0.1A \;\; (approx).$

24. $\quad X_L = 2\,\pi\,f\,L.$ by transposition $f = \dfrac{X_L}{2\,\pi\,L}.$

$$f = \dfrac{X_L}{2\,\pi\,L} = \dfrac{2000}{2 \times \pi \times 500 \times 10^{-3}} = \dfrac{2000}{\pi} = 636.6Hz.$$

25. $\quad f = \dfrac{X_L}{2\,\pi\,L} = \dfrac{314.16}{2 \times \pi \times 0.5} = \dfrac{3.146}{1 \times \pi} = 100Hz.$

26. $\quad I = \dfrac{V}{X_L} = \dfrac{V}{2\,\pi\,f\,L} = \dfrac{20}{2 \times \pi \times 50 \times 500 \times 10^{-3}} = \dfrac{20}{\pi} = 0.127A \;\; (127mA).$

27. $\quad X_L = 2\,\pi\,f\,L = 2 \times \pi \times 1 \times 10^6 \times 2 \times 10^{-3} = 4000\,\pi = 12.56k\Omega.$

28. $\quad L = \dfrac{X_L}{2\,\pi\,f} = \dfrac{314.159}{2 \times \pi \times 50} = 1H.$

29,30,31. Answers are given in the key. Use one of the following formulae :-

$$X_L = 2\,\pi\,f\,L \qquad L = \dfrac{X_L}{2\,\pi\,f} \qquad f = \dfrac{X_L}{2\,\pi\,L}$$

7. Impedance

In this section we will:-
1. study the effects of L and R in series.
2. study the effects of C and R in series.
3. calculate impedance, voltage and current in the series L R and C R circuit.

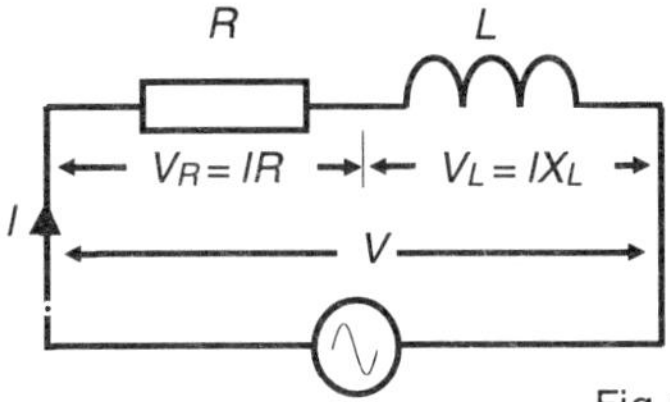

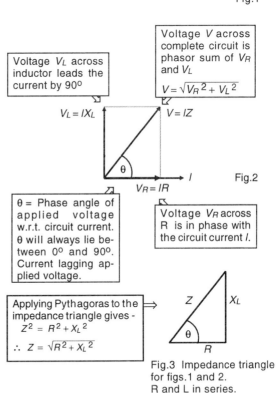

Fig.1

Impedance Z

Impedance, symbol Z, measured in ohms, is the total opposition to current flow in a circuit where resistance R and reactance X are combined.

X may be inductive reactance X_L, or capacitive reactance X_C.

Voltage V_L across inductor leads the current by 90°

Voltage V across complete circuit is phasor sum of V_R and V_L

$$V = \sqrt{V_R{}^2 + V_L{}^2}$$

$V_L = IX_L$

$V = IZ$

$V_R = IR$

R and L in Series

Fig.1 and 2 show the voltage and current relationships in the series R and L circuit.

In this case the applied voltage leads the circuit current by the phase angle θ. For the RL circuit shown the phase angle is always positive.

θ = Phase angle of applied voltage w.r.t. circuit current. θ will always lie between 0° and 90°. Current lagging applied voltage.

Fig.2

Voltage V_R across R is in phase with the circuit current I.

The Impedance Triangle

Fig 3 shows the impedance Z, with its two components, X and R represented by a right angle triangle (The impedance triangle). The angle θ is the phase angle.

The sides of the triangle are obtained by dividing the voltages V, V_R and V_L in fig.2 by the current, which is common throughout the series circuit.

Applying Pythagoras to the impedance triangle gives -
$$Z^2 = R^2 + X_L{}^2$$
$$\therefore Z = \sqrt{R^2 + X_L{}^2}$$

Fig.3 Impedance triangle for figs.1 and 2. R and L in series.

Power in the a.c. L R and C R circuit

The reactive components L and C do not dissipate power. Power is dissipated solely by the resistance R.

The $P = VI$ formula is only good if the generator current and voltage are in phase. The true power may be found by applying the formula $P = I^2 R$ when the current and resistance are known.

7-1

Impedance

R and C in series

Figs 4 and 5 show voltage and current relationships in the series R C circuit. In this case the applied voltage V lags the circuit current by the phase angle θ.

For the RC circuit shown, the phase angle is always negative.

The Impedance Triangle

Fig 6 shows the impedance Z, with its two components, X and R represented by a right angle triangle (The impedance triangle).

The angle θ is the phase angle. The sides of the triangle are obtained by dividing the voltages V, V_R and V_C in fig.5 by the current, which is common throughout the series circuit.

R L and C in Series

For R L and C in series :-

$$Z = \sqrt{R^2 + (X_L - X_C)^2}$$

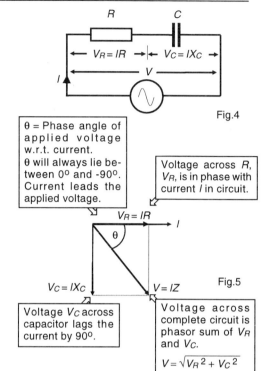

θ = Phase angle of applied voltage w.r.t. current.
θ will always lie between 0° and -90°. Current leads the applied voltage.

Voltage across R, V_R, is in phase with current I in circuit.

Voltage V_C across capacitor lags the current by 90°.

Voltage across complete circuit is phasor sum of V_R and V_C.

$$V = \sqrt{V_R^2 + V_C^2}$$

Fig.4

Fig.5

Formulae to remember:-

R and L in series	R and C in series
$Z^2 = R^2 + X_L^2$	$Z^2 = R^2 + X_C^2$
$\therefore Z = \sqrt{R^2 + X_L^2}$	$\therefore Z = \sqrt{R^2 + X_C^2}$
$V = \sqrt{V_R^2 + V_L^2}$	$V = \sqrt{V_R^2 + V_C^2}$
$I = \dfrac{V}{Z}$	$I = \dfrac{V}{Z}$
$\theta = Tan^{-1}\dfrac{X_L}{R}$	$\theta = Tan^{-1}\dfrac{X_C}{R}$
R, L and C in series	
$Z = \sqrt{R^2 + (X_L - X_C)^2}$	

Fig.6 Impedance triangle for figs.4 and 5. R and C in series.

Impedance

1. The opposition to current flow in a circuit consisting of resistance and reactance is called -
   a) reactance.
   b) impedance.
   c) resonance.
   d) reluctance.

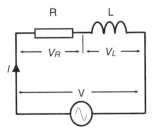

Fig.7

2. The current *I*, flowing in *R*, fig.7 is -
   a) in phase with V_R.
   b) leading V_R by 90°.
   c) lagging V_R by 90°.
   d) 180° out of phase with V_R.

3. The voltage V_L, across the inductor shown in fig.7-
   a) leads *I* by 90°.
   b) lags *I* by 90°.
   c) is in phase with *I*.
   d) is 180° out of phase with *I*.

4. The voltage, V_L, across the inductor in fig.7 is given by-
   a) $V_L = I \omega L$
   b) $V_L = V \omega L$
   c) $V_L = \omega^2 C^2 L^2$
   d) $V_L = 2\omega L$

5. The applied voltage *V*, in fig.7, is given by the-
   a) vector division of V_R and V_L.
   b) vector product of V_R and V_L.
   c) vector sum of V_R and V_L.
   d) product of *I* and V_L.

6. What is the formula for the impedance of the series circuit shown in fig.7?
   a) $Z = \sqrt{R^2 + X_L^2}$
   b) $Z = R^2 + X_L^2$
   c) $Z^2 = \sqrt{R^2 + X^2}$
   d) $Z = R^2 + X L^2$

7. Which of the phasor diagrams shown below is representative of the circuit shown in fig.7?

   a)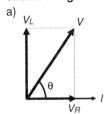
   b)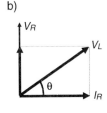
   c)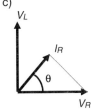
   d)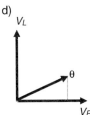

8. From the phasor diagram, an 'impedance triangle' can be constructed, this will take the form-

a)

b)

c)

d)

9. From whose formula for right-angled triangles was the general formula for impedance developed? (See also Q 6 and Q 8 for a clue.)
   a) Taurus
   b) Sir Henry Wood
   c) Sagittarius
   d) Pythagoras

10. The phase angle of the circuit shown in fig.8 is given by the formula-

   a) $\theta = \tan^{-1} \dfrac{X_L}{R}$

   b) $\theta = \tan^{-1} \dfrac{L}{R}$

   c) $\theta = \tan^{-1} \dfrac{R}{X_L}$

   d) $\theta = \tan^{-1} \dfrac{X_L}{L}$

11. What is the impedance Z, of the circuit shown in fig.8?
    a) 240Ω
    b) 0.24Ω
    c) 50Ω
    d) 800Ω

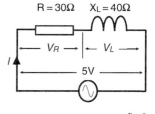

fig.8

12. What is the current, I, flowing in the circuit of fig.8?
    a) 20.8mA
    b) 20.8A
    c) 100mA
    d) 6.25mA

13. What is the phase angle of the circuit shown in fig.8?
    a) 53.13°
    b) 27.31°
    c) 90°
    d) 27.57°

14. Referring to Q 13. The phase angle you chose indicates that the-
    a) applied voltage leads the current by 53.13°
    b) applied voltage leads the current by 27.31°
    c) current flowing in the circuit leads V by 90°
    d) current flowing in the circuit leads V by 27.57°

Impedance

15. Referring to fig.8. What is the voltage V_R developed across the 30Ω resistor?
    a) 5V   b) 4V   c) 3V   d) 2V

16. Referring to fig.8. What is the voltage V_L developed across the inductor?
    a) 5V   b) 4V   c) 3V   d) 2V

17. What is the impedance of fig.9?
    a) 42.4Ω   b) 60Ω
    c) 900Ω   d) 600Ω

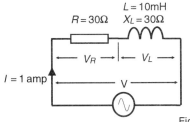

Fig.9

18. Referring to fig.9.
    What is the supply frequency?
    a) 477.4Hz   b) 796Hz
    c) 954Hz   d) 1592Hz

19. Referring to fig.9. What is the
    voltage developed across the
    10mH inductor when I = 1 amp?
    a) 3V   b) 30V
    c) 90V   d) 900V

20. Calculate the voltage V_R across the resistor fig.9.
    a) 3V   b) 30V
    c) 42.4V   d) 60V

21. Referring to fig.9. Calculate the applied voltage V.
    a) 30V   b) 40V
    c) 42.4V   d) 90V

22. The voltage leads the current in the circuit of fig.9 by an angle depending
    on the ratio of X_L and R. This angle is calculated using the formula -

    $\theta = \tan^{-1} \dfrac{X_L}{R}$. What is the phase angle of the circuit shown in fig.9?

    a) 30°   b) 45°   c) 60°   d) 90°

23. The impedance of the series R C circuit shown in fig.10, is given by-
    a) $Z = R^2 + X_C^2$
    b) $Z = \sqrt{R^2 + X_C^2}$
    c) $Z^2 = \sqrt{R^2 + X_C^2}$
    d) $Z = R^2 + X_C^2$

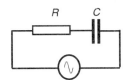

Fig.10

7 - 5

24. The phase angle of the RC circuit shown in fig.11 is given by-

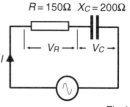

$R = 150\Omega$ $X_C = 200\Omega$

Fig.11

a) $\theta = \tan^{-1} \dfrac{X_C}{R}$

b) $\theta = \tan^{-1} \dfrac{C}{R}$

c) $\theta = \tan^{-1} \dfrac{R}{C}$

d) $\theta = \tan^{-1} CR$

25. Which one of the phasor diagrams shown below is representative of the circuit shown in fig.11?

a)

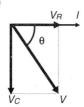

b)

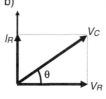

c)

d)

26. From the phasor diagram chosen in Q 25 above, an impedance triangle may be constructed. Which of the triangles shown below is the impedance triangle for the series RC circuit?

a)

b)

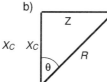

c)

d)

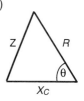

27. The voltage across the capacitor, V_C, in fig.11 -
   a) lags the current by 90°.
   b) leads the current by 90°.
   c) is in phase with the current.
   d) is 180°out of phase with the current.

28. Calculate the impedance of the circuit shown in fig.11. Where $R = 150\Omega$ and $X_C = 200\Omega$.
   a) 50Ω b) 173.2Ω
   c) 187Ω d) 250Ω

Impedance

29. A circuit consisting of *R* and *C* in series has an impedance of 1000Ω. The series resistor has a resistance of 707Ω. Calculate the capacitive reactance X_C.
    a) 1707Ω
    b) 1000Ω
    c) 707Ω
    d) 293Ω

30. A 16µF capacitor, connected in series with a 200Ω resistor, is connected across a 250V 50Hz supply. What is the impedance *Z* of the circuit?
    a) 418.3Ω
    b) 318Ω
    c) 518Ω
    d) 282Ω

31. Referring to Q30 above. Calculate the supply current.
    a) 282.8mA
    b) 18.3mA
    c) 886mA
    d) 200mA

32. When a circuit consists of *L*, *C* and *R*, connected in series, see fig.12, the impedance '*Z*' of the circuit can be calculated from the formula-
    a) $Z = \sqrt{R^2 + (X_L - X_C)^2}$
    b) $Z = \sqrt{R + X}$
    c) $Z = \sqrt{R^2 + X_L^2 + X_C^2}$
    d) $Z = \sqrt{R + X^2}$

33. What is the impedance of the circuit shown in fig.12?
    a) 70.7Ω
    b) 100Ω
    c) 141.4Ω
    d) 200Ω

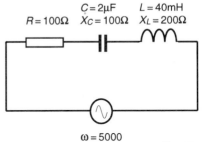

$C = 2\mu F$ $L = 40mH$
$R = 100\Omega$ $X_C = 100\Omega$ $X_L = 200\Omega$

34. See fig.12. Given that ω = 5000, calculate the frequency.
    a) 1591Hz
    b) 1000Hz
    c) 796Hz
    d) 400Hz

ω = 5000

Fig. 12

35. Referring to the circuit shown in fig.13, calculate the following-
    a) X_C
    b) Z
    c) frequency
    d) phase angle
    e) *I*
    f) V_R
    g) V_C
    h) Power dissipated in the circuit.

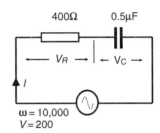

400Ω   0.5µF

$V_R \rightarrow$ $\leftarrow V_C \rightarrow$

ω = 10,000
V = 200

Fig.13

36. Referring to the circuit shown in fig.14,
    calculate the following-
    a) X_L
    b) Z
    c) frequency
    d) phase angle
    e) I
    f) V_R
    g) V_L
    h) Power dissipated in the circuit.

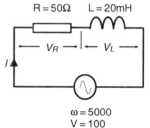

R = 50Ω   L = 20mH

V_R — | — V_L

I

ω = 5000
V = 100

Fig.14

Answers - Impedance

1 b	13 a	25 a	35		36	
2 a	14 a	26 c	a	200Ω	a	100Ω
3 a	15 c	27 a	b	447.2Ω	b	111.8Ω
4 a	16 b	28 d	c	1.592kHz	c	796Hz
5 c	17 a	29 c	d	-26.56°	d	63.4°
6 a	18 a	30 d	e	0.447A	e	0.894A
7 a	19 b	31 c	f	178.8V	f	44.7V
8 a	20 b	32 a	g	89.4V	g	89.4V
9 d	21 c	33 c	h	80W	h	40W
10 a	22 b	34 c				
11 c	23 b					
12 c	24 a					

Answers - Impedance

1. Opposition to alternating current flow in a circuit consisting of resistance and reactance is 'impedance' Z. The unit of impedance is the ohm, symbol Ω.

2. In an a.c. circuit the current and voltage are in phase in a pure resistor.

3. In a pure inductor the voltage V_L leads the current I by 90°.

4. Similar to Ohm's Law $V = I\,R$, the voltage $V_L = I\,X_L = I\,\omega L$ Where $\omega = 2\pi f$.

5. The voltage across the series circuit of fig.7 is the phasor sum of V_R and V_L :-
    $$V = \sqrt{V_R{}^2 + V_L{}^2}$$

6. $Z = \sqrt{R^2 + X_L{}^2}$

7. Since the voltage V_R and the current are in phase they are drawn in the same direction. The voltage V_L is leading the current by 90°. Phasor V is the applied voltage, leading the current by angle θ which depends on the ratio of X_L and R.

8, 9. Impedance triangle a) is developed from the phasor diagram of Q7 by dividing V, V_L and V_R by the current I, i.e :- $Z = \dfrac{V}{I}$, $X_L = \dfrac{V_L}{I}$ and $R = \dfrac{V_R}{I}$.
    Pythagoras' Theorem for the solution of right-angled triangles is used.
    The square on the hypotenuse (in this case impedance Z) is equal to the sum of the squares on the other two sides (X_L and R).
    $$Z^2 = R^2 + X_L{}^2 \quad \therefore\ Z = \sqrt{R^2 + X_L{}^2}\ .$$

10. $\theta = \tan^{-1}\dfrac{Reactance}{Resistance} = \tan^{-1}\dfrac{X_L}{R} = \tan^{-1}\dfrac{\omega L}{R} = \tan^{-1}\dfrac{2\pi f L}{R}.$

11. $Z = \sqrt{R^2 + X_L{}^2} = \sqrt{30^2 + 40^2} = \sqrt{900 + 1600} = \sqrt{2500} = 50\Omega\ .$

12. Using Ohm's Law for the a.c. circuit, $I = \dfrac{V}{Z} = \dfrac{5}{50} = 0.1A$ *or* $100mA.$

13. $\theta = \tan^{-1}\dfrac{X_L}{R} = \tan^{-1}\dfrac{40}{30} = \tan^{-1} 1.33 = 53.13°.$

14. For an inductive circuit the voltage leads the current. In this case by 53.13°.

15. $V_R = I\,R = I \times R = 0.1 \times 30 = 3V$

16. $V_L = I\,X_L = I \times X_L = 0.1 \times 40 = 4V$
    As a check on A15 and A16 the vector sum of V_R and V_C should equal the applied voltage. $V = \sqrt{V_R{}^2 + V_L{}^2} = \sqrt{3^2 + 4^2} = \sqrt{25} = 5V.$ ✓

17. $Z = \sqrt{R^2 + X_L{}^2} = \sqrt{30^2 + 30^2} = \sqrt{900 + 900} = \sqrt{1800} = 42.4\Omega\ .$

Answers - Impedance

18. At first glance there is no indication of frequency on the diagram, however, the reactance X_L depends on frequency, so we can transpose the reactance formula to give frequency. $X_L = 2\pi f L$ Transposing for frequency :-

$$f = \frac{X_L}{2\pi L} = \frac{30}{2\times\pi\times 10\times 10^{-3}} = \frac{30\times 10^3}{20\times\pi} = 477.4Hz.$$

19. $V_L = I X_L = I \times X_L = 1 \times 30 = 30V.$

20. $V_R = I R = I \times R = 1 \times 30 = 30V.$

21. $V = \sqrt{V_R{}^2 + V_L{}^2} = \sqrt{30^2 + 30^2} = \sqrt{1800} = 42.4V.$

    The same result could have been obtained by application of Ohm's Law :-
    $V = I Z = 1 \times 42.4 = 42.4V.$ (Applied voltage.)

22. $\theta = \tan^{-1}\dfrac{X_L}{R} = \tan^{-1}\dfrac{30}{30} = \tan^{-1} 1 = 45°.$

23. $Z = \sqrt{R^2 + X_C^2}.$

    Minus sign indicates negative angle for a capacitor.

24. $\theta = \tan^{-1}\dfrac{X_C}{R} = \tan^{-1} -\dfrac{1}{\omega C R}$

25. Phasor a) shows the applied voltage V lagging the current by the phase angle θ.

26. Impedance triangle c) is developed from the phasor diagram of Q25 by dividing V, V_C and V_R by the current I, i.e. $Z = \dfrac{V}{I}$, $X_C = \dfrac{V_C}{I}$ and $R = \dfrac{V_R}{I}$.

27. The voltage across the capacitor V_C lags the current I by 90°.

28. $Z = \sqrt{R^2 + X_C{}^2} = \sqrt{150^2 + 200^2} = \sqrt{62500} = 250\Omega.$

29. From $Z^2 = R^2 + X_C{}^2$ transpose for X_C $\therefore X_C{}^2 = Z^2 - R^2$
    Taking the root of both sides -
    $X_C = \sqrt{Z^2 - R^2} = \sqrt{1000^2 - 707^2} = \sqrt{500,151} = 707\Omega$ (approx).

30. $Z = \sqrt{R^2 + X_C{}^2} = \sqrt{R^2 + \left(\dfrac{1}{2\pi f C}\right)^2} = \sqrt{200^2 + 199^2} = 282\Omega$ (approx).

31. $I = \dfrac{V}{Z} = \dfrac{250}{282} = 0.886A$ or $886mA.$

32. $Z = \sqrt{R^2 + (X_L - X_C)^2}$

33. $Z = \sqrt{R^2 + (X_L - X_C)^2} = \sqrt{100^2 + (200 - 100)^2} = \sqrt{20,000} = 141.4\Omega.$

Answers - Impedance

34. $\omega = 2\pi f$, therefore, by transposition :- $f = \dfrac{\omega}{2\pi} = \dfrac{5000}{2\pi} = 796Hz.$

35a) $X_C = \dfrac{1}{\omega C} = \dfrac{1}{10,000 \times 0.5 \times 10^{-6}} = \dfrac{10^6}{5000} = 200\Omega.$

b) $Z = \sqrt{R^2 + X_C{}^2} = \sqrt{400^2 + 200^2} = \sqrt{200,000} = 447.2\Omega.$

c) $\omega = 2\pi f$, $\therefore f = \dfrac{\omega}{2\pi} = \dfrac{10,000}{2\pi} = 1592Hz$ (1.592kHz).

d) $\theta = \tan^{-1}\dfrac{X_C}{R} = \tan^{-1} - \dfrac{200}{400} = \tan^{-1} -0.5 = -26.56°$

e) $I = \dfrac{V}{Z} = \dfrac{200}{447} = 0.447A$ (447mA).

> Negative angle for a capacitor

f) $V_R = IR = 0.447 \times 400 = 178.8V.$

g) $V_C = IX_C = 0.447 \times 200 = 89.4V.$

h) Since power is only dissipated in the resistance, using the formula $P = I^2R$ will give the true power. $P = I^2R = 0.447^2 \times 400 = 79.96W.$
Alternatively true power $= VI\cos\theta = 200 \times 0.447 \times \cos 26.56° = 79.96W$

36a) $X_L = \omega L = 5000 \times 20 \times 10^{-3} = 100\Omega.$

b) $Z = \sqrt{R^2 + X_L{}^2} = \sqrt{50^2 + 100^2} = \sqrt{12,500} = 111.8\Omega.$

c) $\omega = 2\pi f$, $\therefore f = \dfrac{\omega}{2\pi} = \dfrac{5000}{2\pi} = 796Hz.$

d) $\theta = \tan^{-1} - \dfrac{X_L}{R} = \tan^{-1}\dfrac{100}{50} = \tan^{-1} 2 = 63.4°$

e) $I = \dfrac{V}{Z} = \dfrac{100}{111.8} = 0.894A$ (894mA).

f) $V_R = IR = 0.894 \times 50 = 44.7V.$

g) $V_L = IX_L = 0.894 \times 100 = 89.4V.$

h) Since power is only dissipated in the resistance, using the formula $P = I^2R$ will give the true power. $P = I^2R = 0.894^2 \times 50 = 40W.$
Alternatively true power $= VI\cos\theta = 100 \times 0.894 \times \cos 63.4° = 40W.$

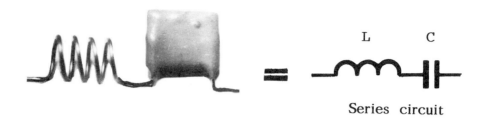

L   C

Series circuit

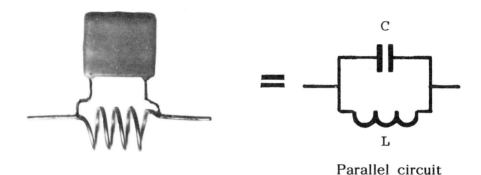

C

L

Parallel circuit

Above. A practical application of a tuned circuit, the tank
circuit of a 100 watt VHF transmitter. Showing coil and
capacitor. The valve anode leads are also shown.

8. Resonance

In this section we will deal with :-
1. series resonance.
2. parallel resonance.
3. selectivity, bandwidth and Q.

Resonant Circuits
Circuits containing L and C connected in series or parallel, and tuned to resonance, are commonly used for tuning oscillators, radio receivers and transmitters, and in filters capable of selecting one particular frequency from a whole band of frequencies.

Resonance is a condition occurring in both series and parallel $L\,C$ circuits. It occurs when the inductive reactance X_L is equal in magnitude and opposite in sign to the capacitive reactance X_C. In this condition X_L and X_C cancel.

For resonance $X_L = X_C$ or $2\pi f_r L = \dfrac{1}{2\pi f_r C}$

and by transposition $f_r = \dfrac{1}{2\pi\sqrt{L\,C}}$

The Series Resonant Circuit
In the series LCR circuit, fig.1, the impedance is minimum at resonance, $Z = R$, where R, in this case, is due to the resistance of the inductor. In practice, capacitors, except electrolytic types, are usually considered pure, i.e. possessing no loss.

Fig.2 shows the relationship between X_L, X_C and the resonant frequency. In the series circuit, see fig.3, maximum current flows at resonance.

High voltages are likely to be developed across the reactive components L and C, these voltages may far exceed the supply voltage V_S. This 'voltage magnification' effect is referred to as the 'Q' of the circuit.

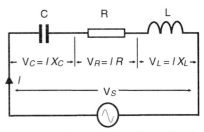

Fig.1 showing LC and R in series.

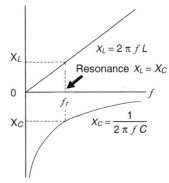

Fig.2 Reactance/frequency curves. Resonance occurs when $X_L = X_C$.

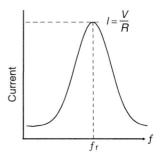

Fig.3 Current response curve of series circuit. Showing current maximum at resonance.

Resonance

Points to note (series circuit)

1. At resonance $X_L = X_C$. The reactances cancel. The net reactance is zero.
2. At resonance the series circuit is resistive. (R is low.)
3. At resonance the circuit current is limited only by the series resistance.
4. The lower the value of R, the sharper will be the response curve of fig.3.
5. The voltage developed across the reactive components can be higher than the supply voltage. This is *Voltage Magnification*. Refer to Q Factor.
6. At resonance all the supply voltage is developed across R. $\therefore$ $V_R = V_S$.
7. The voltage across the capacitor, $V_C = I\,X_C$.
8. The voltage across the inductor, $V_L = I\,X_L$.
9. The series circuit passes current easily at the resonant frequency.
10. A series resonant circuit is often referred to as an 'Acceptor Circuit'.
11. The value of R has no effect on the resonant frequency of the series circuit.
12. The series circuit is capacitive below resonance, inductive above resonance.

The Parallel Resonant circuit

Fig.4 shows a circuit consisting L & C connected in parallel. R represents the resistance of the inductor and is usually very small compared with X_L.

At the resonant frequency, with pure L and C connected in parallel, i.e. no resistance R present, the reactive branch currents I_C and I_L are equal in magnitude and opposite in sign, therefore they cancel, their vector sum is zero and the supply current I_S is zero.

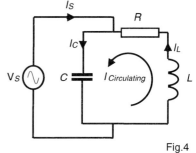

Fig.4

Since there is an applied voltage and no supply current I_S flowing in the external circuit the impedance must be infinite.

In the practical circuit, fig.4, some power is dissipated by the resistance R, therefore, the supply current I_S, at resonance, will no longer be zero, but a minimum value to replace the power dissipated by R.

There will, however, be a maximum circulating current within the closed LC circuit due to the initially established charge on the capacitor, or magnetic field of the inductor, causing a repeated interchange of energy between L and C. This circulating current is higher than the supply current.

The impedance of the parallel circuit at resonance is referred to as the dynamic resistance, R_D, and given by :-

$$R_D = \frac{L}{C\,R}\,.\quad \text{The supply current } I_S = \frac{V_S}{R_D}\,.\quad \text{Magnification factor } Q = \frac{\omega L}{R}\,.$$

The circulating current, I_{circ}, maximum at resonance, is equal to $Q \times I_S$.

Resonance

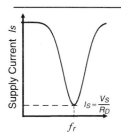

⇐ Fig.5 Current/frequency response curve for a parallel circuit. Showing dip in supply current I_S at resonance, indicating high impedance.

Fig.6 Impedance/frequency response ⇒ curve for the parallel circuit. Showing impedance is maximum at resonance.

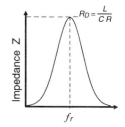

Points to note (parallel circuit)

1. Resonance occurs when $X_L = X_C$
2. At resonance $I_L = I_C$. I_L lags V_S by $90°$ and I_C leads V_S by $90°$. Therefore both I_L and I_C cancel, resulting in minimum supply line current.
3. At resonance the supply current I_S is minimum.
4. At resonance the circulating current I_{circ} is maximum.
5. At resonance the circulating current is greater than the supply current.
6. At resonance the circulating current $I_{circ} = Q \times I_S$.
7. At resonance the parallel tuned circuit has maximum impedance.
8. Reducing R, fig.4, sharpens the response curve (Q increases).
9. Increasing R, fig.4, broadens the response curve (Q Decreases).
10. When R is small compared with X_L, the resonant frequency, f_r, is calculated using the same formula as the series circuit.
11. The parallel tuned circuit is sometimes referred to as a *'rejector'* or *'tank'* circuit.
12. Increasing the L/C ratio increases the dynamic resistance R_D.
13. Use is made of the selective properties of parallel tuned circuits in filters, wavetraps, RF and IF amplifiers, radio receivers and transmitters, and the frequency determining elements of many types of oscillator.
14. The parallel circuit is inductive below resonance, capacitive above resonance.

Selectivity, Bandwidth & Q

Selectivity is the ability of a tuned circuit to respond to the frequency or band of frequencies to which it is tuned, whilst at the same time having poor response to frequencies either side of this frequency or band.

The bandwidth of a tuned circuit is the separation, either side of maximum response, by which the output has fallen to 0.707 (70.7%) of the maximum value (often referred to as the *half power bandwidth or -3dB bandwidth*). See fig.7.

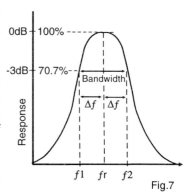

Fig.7

$$Bandwidth\ (B/W) = \frac{f_r}{Q} \quad \text{and} \quad Q = \frac{f_r}{B/W} = \frac{f_r}{2\Delta f}$$

Resonance

The Q factor (magnification factor or quality factor) of a tuned circuit is a measure of its selectivity.

A high Q indicates high selectivity and narrow bandwidth (B/W). A low Q indicates less selectivity and wide bandwidth, see fig.8.

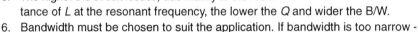

Fig.8 Typical response curves.
High and low Q resonant circuits.

Points to note (selectivity, bandwidth and Q)
1. Q of a resonant circuit is a measure of its selectivity.
2. High Q circuits have good selectivity and narrow B/W.
3. Low Q circuits have poor selectivity and wide B/W.
4. Bandwidth and Q depend on R and the ratio of L to C.
5. The higher the circuit losses, due mainly to the resistance of L at the resonant frequency, the lower the Q and wider the B/W.
6. Bandwidth must be chosen to suit the application. If bandwidth is too narrow - (high Q), the sidebands of a wanted transmission may be attenuated.
7. If the B/W is too wide, unwanted frequencies will be passed as well as the wanted.
8. The bandwidth of a parallel tuned circuit can be increased by damping the circuit with shunt resistance, however, this will lower the Q.
9. For parallel circuits a high resistance source is required for minimum damping, high Q, and narrow bandwidth.
10. For series circuits a low resistance source is necessary for high Q and narrow bandwidth.

Formulae to remember (resonant tuned circuits)

Series Resonance	Parallel Resonance
$f_r = \dfrac{1}{2\pi\sqrt{LC}}$	$f_r = \dfrac{1}{2\pi\sqrt{LC}}$ * When R is small.
$C = \dfrac{1}{4\pi^2 f_r^2 L}$	$C = \dfrac{1}{4\pi^2 f_r^2 L}$
$L = \dfrac{1}{4\pi^2 f_r^2 C}$	$L = \dfrac{1}{4\pi^2 f_r^2 C}$
$Q = \dfrac{\omega L}{R}$	$Q = \dfrac{\omega L}{R}$
$Q = \dfrac{V_L}{V_R}$	$Q = \dfrac{I_L}{I_S}$
$I_S = \dfrac{V_S}{R}$	$I_S = \dfrac{V_S}{R_D}$
$Z = R$	$R_D = \dfrac{L}{CR}$

Resonance

1. **The condition of resonance occurs when the-**
   a) inductive reactance X_L is equal to the capacitive reactance X_C and opposite in sign.
   b) losses in the circuit are confined to the inductor.
   c) resistance R and the reactance X cancel.
   d) resistance R and the reactance X add.

2. **Fig.9 shows a series LC circuit. The formula for the resonant frequency is given by -**
   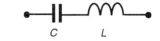
   a) $f_r = \sqrt{2\pi L C}$ b) $f_r = 2\pi X_C$
   c) $f_r = \dfrac{1}{4\pi^2 L^2}$ d) $f_r = \dfrac{1}{2\pi\sqrt{L C}}$ Fig.9

3. **What happens to the resonant frequency when the value of the capacitor is decreased?**
   a) It remains the same. b) It decreases.
   c) It increases.   d) It becomes super-resonant.

4. **If the value of the inductor in a series resonant circuit is increased, the resonant frequency-**
   a) remains the same.   b) decreases.
   c) increases.   d) damps to zero.

5. **Resonance occurs when-**
   a) $X_L = X_C$ b) $L R = C^2$
   c) $X_L = C^2 L^2$ d) $f^2 = R$

6. **A change in the resistance of R in the series circuit shown in fig.10 will -**
   a) decrease the resonant frequency.
   b) increase the resonant frequency.
   c) not effect the resonant frequency.
   d) cancel with X at resonance.
   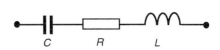

7. **At resonance, the impedance of the series circuit fig.10 is equal to -**
   a) the reactance of the inductor.
   b) the reactance of the capacitor.
   c) the series resistance R.
   d) $X_L + X_C + R$.

   Fig.10

8. At resonance, the impedance of the
   series circuit shown in fig.11 is-
   a) 500Ω   b) 50Ω
   c) 5Ω   d) 0.5Ω

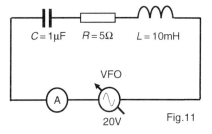

Fig.11

9. What is the resonant frequency
   of the circuit shown in fig.11?
   a) 500Hz   b) 796Hz
   c) 1592Hz   d) 15.92kHz

10. What is the resonant frequency of the circuit shown in fig.11 when
    the capacitor is changed to 4μF?
    a) 500Hz   b) 796Hz
    c) 1592Hz   d) 1.592Hz

11. The value of the capacitor shown in fig.11 is changed to 4μF.
    What is the circuit impedance at resonance?
    a) 500Ω   b) 200Ω
    c) 50Ω   d) 5Ω

12. Referring to fig.11. If the a.c. supply is 20 volts at the resonant
    frequency of the circuit, what current will flow in the 5Ω resistor?
    a) 40A   b) 20A
    c) 10A   d) 4A

13. Referring to fig.11. Increasing the value of R to 10Ω will -
    a) increase the resonant frequency.
    b) decrease the resonant frequency.
    c) increase the current flowing in the circuit at resonance.
    d) decrease the current flowing in the circuit at resonance.

14. Referring to fig.11. Reversing the connections to the inductor will -
    a) increase the resonant frequency.
    b) decrease the resonant frequency.
    c) not change the resonant frequency.
    d) stop all current flow at resonance.

15. The variable frequency oscillator shown in fig.11 is slowly swept through
    the resonant frequency of the tuned circuit.
    What will ammeter 'A' indicate as the signal passes through resonance?
    a) Nothing   b) A dip
    c) A peak   d) 6.284A

Resonance

16. In a series *LCR* circuit, the current at resonance is -
    a) maximum
    b) minimum
    c) zero
    d) 3.142A

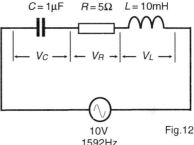

$C = 1\mu F$ $R = 5\Omega$ $L = 10mH$

$V_C \rightarrow$ | $V_R \rightarrow$ | $V_L \rightarrow$

10V
1592Hz

Fig.12

17. The resonant frequency of the circuit shown in fig.12 is 1592Hz. What is the current at resonance?
    a) 50A
    b) 5A
    c) 2A
    d) 1A

18. Referring to fig.12. The voltage V_R across the resistor at resonance is -
    a) 100V
    b) 10V
    c) 5V
    d) 1V

19. Referring to fig.12. The voltage V_L across the inductor at resonance is -
    a) 10mV
    b) 10V
    c) 20V
    d) 200V

20. Referring to fig.12. The voltage V_C across the capacitor at resonance is -
    a) 5V
    b) 10V
    c) 200V
    d) 1000V

21. The high voltages developed across the coil and capacitor shown in fig.12, are due to the -
    a) resistance of those particular components.
    b) temperature of those particular components.
    c) voltage ratings of those particular components.
    d) Q or magnification factor of the circuit.

22. The *Q* of the circuit shown in fig.12 is -
    a) 1
    b) 5
    c) 10
    d) 20

23. Referring to fig.12. At resonance, the voltage across the inductor V_L, and the capacitor V_C -
    a) cancel.
    b) add.
    c) multiply.
    d) square.

24. Referring to fig.12. If the value of *R* is halved, the voltages V_L and V_C will -
    a) halve.
    b) double.
    c) remain the same.
    d) decrease slightly.

8-7

25. If you construct the circuit shown in fig.12 as a practical circuit, would a 16V working capacitor be o.k.?
    a) Yes.
    b) No.
    c) Only just.
    d) Yes, if it is a tantalum.

26. Which one of the diagrams shown below represent the current/frequency response of a series tuned circuit?

a)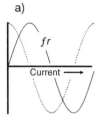
b)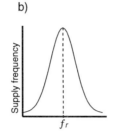
c)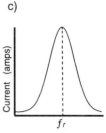
d)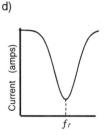

27. What is the current/voltage phase relationship across the resistor of fig.12?
    a) I and V are in phase.
    b) I and V are in anti-phase.
    c) I leads V by 90°.
    d) V leads I by 90°.

28. What is the relationship between the voltages that appear across the two reactive components L and C in fig.12?
    a) They are equal and in phase.
    b) They are equal and 180° out of phase.
    c) They are not equal, but are in phase.
    d) They are not equal and are 45° out of phase.

29. Which diagram below represents the impedance/frequency characteristic of a series tuned circuit?

a)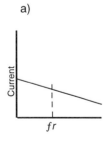
b)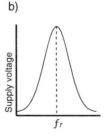
c)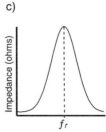
d)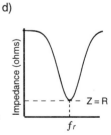

30. Using a high impedance voltmeter with a suitable frequency response for the circuit being measured, the Q factor of the circuit shown in fig.13 can be found by measurement of-

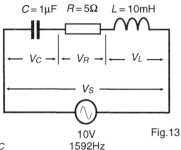

$C = 1\mu F$ $R = 5\Omega$ $L = 10mH$

10V
1592Hz
Fig.13

a) V_S and V_C and applying the formula $\dfrac{V_C}{V_S}$

b) V_S and V_C and applying the formula $\dfrac{V_S}{V_C}$

c) V_L and V_C and applying the formula $V_L - V_C$

d) V_L and V_C and applying the formula $V_L \times V_C$

31. The series resonant circuit is often referred to as -
   a) a deflector circuit.
   b) a rejector circuit.
   c) an acceptor circuit.
   d) a low pass filter.

32. Fig.14 shows a parallel tuned circuit. The formula for its resonant frequency is the same as for the series circuit as long as the losses are not too great. The impedance at resonance is -
   a) low.   b) high.
   c) zero.   d) equal to R.

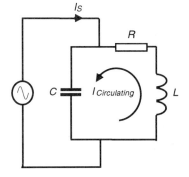

Fig.14

33. The impedance of a parallel tuned circuit at resonance (the Dynamic Resistance R_D) is given by -

a) $R_D = \dfrac{CR}{L}$ b) $R_D = \dfrac{L}{CR}$

c) $R_D = \dfrac{L}{2CR}$ d) $R_D = \dfrac{C}{\omega R}$

34. At resonance, the supply current, I_S of fig.14 will be -
   a) small.   b) large.
   c) zero.   d) equal to the circulating current.

35. Referring to fig.14. The circulating current in a good quality parallel resonant circuit will be-
   a) greater than I_S.   b) less than I_S.
   c) equal to I_S.   d) zero.

36. When the capacitor C, fig.15, has been charged with switch in position B, the switch is thrown to position A. Which waveform shown below is representative of the current I ?

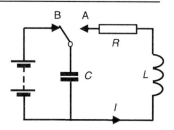

a)   b)   c)   d)   Fig.15

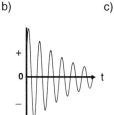 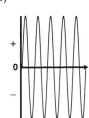 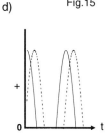

37. The damped oscillations that occur in the circuit of fig.15 will decay more rapidly if the-
   a) capacitor has a silver mica dielectric.
   b) inductor is wound on a glass former.
   c) value of the series resistor R is increased.
   d) value of the series resistor R is decreased.

38. Which one of the frequency response curves shown below is that of a parallel tuned circuit?

a)   b)   c)   d)

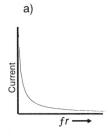 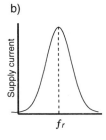 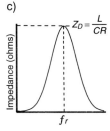 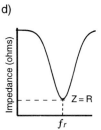

39. The main losses in a high quality parallel resonant tuned circuit are due to the-
   a) permittivity of free space surrounding the coil.
   b) quality of the dielectric material.
   c) Q factor of the capacitor.
   d) copper loss of the coil.

40. The parallel tuned circuit is often referred to as a -
a) gun circuit.
b) tank circuit.
c) bandpass filter.
d) bypass circuit.

41. The parallel tuned circuit is also sometimes referred to as -
a) an acceptor circuit.
b) a rejector circuit.
c) an injector circuit.
d) a deflector circuit.

42. In order that the highest possible voltage is developed across the parallel tuned circuit at the resonant frequency, the -
a) dynamic resistance of the circuit must be high.
b) dynamic resistance of the circuit must be low.
c) dynamic resistance of the circuit must be zero.
d) capacitor must have more loss than the inductor.

43. A parallel tuned circuit will be most selective when-
a) the capacitor is short-circuit.
b) supplied from a generator having a high internal impedance.
c) the source generator supply voltage is very high.
d) the circuit losses are high.

44. Referring to fig.16. Doubling the value of L, and halving the value of C will -
a) increase the resonant frequency of the circuit.
b) decrease the resonant frequency of the circuit.
c) not change the resonant frequency of the circuit.
d) increase the resonant frequency by a factor of 4.

45. What is the resonant frequency of the circuit shown in fig.16?
a) 503.3kHz
b) 50.33kHz
c) 5033Hz
d) 503.3Hz

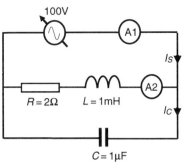

Fig.16

46. What is the dynamic resistance R_D of the circuit shown in fig.16?
a) 10Ω
b) 100Ω
c) 500Ω
d) 5000Ω

47. Referring to fig.16. What is the supply current I_S at the resonant frequency?
a) 0.2A
b) 0.5A
c) 1A
d) 5A

48. The power is supplied to the circuit of fig.16 from a variable frequency generator. If the generator is swept through the resonant frequency of the tuned circuit, the ammeter A1 will-
    a) peak at resonance.
    b) dip at resonance.
    c) zero at resonance.
    d) oscillate at resonance.

49. Referring to fig.16. When the variable frequency generator is swept through the resonant point of the circuit, ammeter A2 will -
    a) peak.
    b) dip.
    c) go to zero.
    d) oscillate.

50. The Q factor of the circuit of fig.16 may be derived from measurement of I_S and I_C, and applying the formula -
    a) $Q = I_C\, I_S$
    b) $Q = I_S + I_C$
    c) $Q = \dfrac{I_S}{I_C}$
    d) $Q = \dfrac{I_C}{I_S}$

51. The response curve of an $L\,C$ circuit is plotted and shown in fig.17. What is the Q of the circuit?
    a) 5
    b) 50
    c) 100
    d) 500

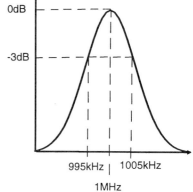

Fig.17

52. A circuit consisting of inductance and capacitance in series has a Q of 100, and a resonant frequency of 10MHz. What is the bandwidth of the circuit at the half power, or -3dB points?
    a) 100kHz
    b) 707kHz
    c) 1000kHz
    d) 10MHz

53. Increasing the resistive losses in a tuned circuit will -
    a) decrease the bandwidth.
    b) increase the bandwidth.
    c) notch the frequency response curve.
    d) cause regenerative feedback.

54. What is the Q factor of the response curve shown in fig.18?
    a) 78.33
    b) 47
    c) 470
    d) 0.012

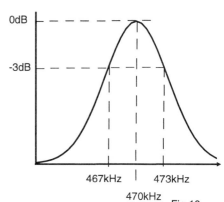

Fig.18

Resonance

55. **What is the resonant frequency of the circuit shown in fig.19?**
a) 3.98kHz
b) 7.95kHz
c) 15.915kHz
d) 31.83kHz

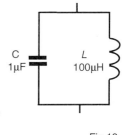

C
1μF

L
100μH

Fig.19

56. **Referring to fig.19. If the value of the capacitor is reduced to 0.25μF, the resonant frequency will be -**
a) doubled.
b) halved.
c) squared.
d) quartered.

57. **Referring to Q 56, the new resonant frequency will be -**
a) 31.83kHz
b) 7.95kHz
c) 63.66kHz
d) 3.98kHz

58. **Referring to fig.19. If the value of the inductor is increased to 400μH, the resonant frequency will be-**
a) doubled.
b) halved.
c) squared.
d) quartered.

59. **Referring to Q 58, the new resonant frequency will be -**
a) 31.83kHz
b) 7.95kHz
c) 63.66kHz
d) 3.98kHz

60. **The variable frequency generator shown in fig.20 is swept over a band of frequencies, and the RF ammeter 'A' shows a definite peak at a frequency of 10MHz.**
What might you expect to find inside the box?

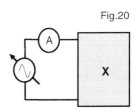

Fig.20

A

X

a) A series *LC* circuit resonant at 10MHz.
b) A parallel *LC* circuit resonant at 10MHz.
c) A 10MHz wideband *CR* series circuit.
d) A non-inductive resistor.

61. **If box X fig.20 contains a parallel tuned circuit, resonant at a frequency of 10MHz, what will be the indication on the RF ammeter, 'A', as the generator is swept through a frequency band centred on 10MHz?**
a) It will remain constant and not vary.
b) It will show a definite dip at 10MHz.
c) It will show a definite peak at 10 MHz.
d) It will start to oscillate at 10MHz.

Resonance

62. Given the required resonant frequency of a circuit, and the value of the chosen inductor L, it is possible to calculate the value of capacitance C required. Which formula will you use?

a) $C = \sqrt{2 \pi L C}$

b) $C = 2 \pi X_C f$

c) $C = \dfrac{1}{4 \pi^2 f_r^2 L}$

d) $C = \dfrac{1}{2 \pi \sqrt{L} R}$

63. A tuned circuit is required to resonate at a frequency of 796Hz. The inductor available has an inductance of 10mH. What value of capacitor will be required to bring the circuit to resonance?

a) 7.960pF   b) 3.99pF   c) 3.99µF   d) 39.9µF

64. With knowledge of the value of the capacitor C, and knowing the frequency of resonance, it is possible to calculate the value of the inductor L in a tuned circuit. Which formula should be used?

a) $L = \sqrt{2 \pi L C}$

b) $L = 2 \pi X_C f$

c) $L = \dfrac{1}{4 \pi^2 f_r^2 C}$

d) $L = \dfrac{1}{2 \pi \sqrt{C} R}$

65. A tuned circuit is resonant at a frequency of 1MHz. The value of the inductor L is unknown, but the capacitor C has a value of 159pF. Calculate the value of the inductor.

a) 100µH   b) 159.3µH   c) 1000µH   d) 159000µH

The following questions, not multiple choice, have been included for practice.

66. Given L and C, calculate f_r.

Capacitance	Inductance	Frequency
a) 3.5µF	10H	_____
b) 1µF	10H	_____
c) 1µF	750mH	_____
d) 0.5µF	250mH	_____
e) 0.15µF	175mH	_____
f) 10µF	10mH	_____
g) 5µF	20mH	_____

Resonance

67. Given f_r and L, calculate C.

Frequency	Inductance	Capacitance
a) 503.3Hz	100mH	_____
b) 251.64Hz	200mH	_____
c) 71.18Hz	500mH	_____
d) 56.27Hz	2H	_____
e) 50.329MHz	1µH	_____
f) 100.658MHz	0.5µH	_____
g) 11.254MHz	10µH	_____

68. Given f_r and C, calculate L.

Frequency	Capacitance	Inductance
a) 503.292kHz	100pF	_____
b) 450.158kHz	50pF	_____
c) 2.516MHz	20pF	_____
d) 5.033MHz	10pF	_____
e) 10.066MHz	5pF	_____
f) 20.132MHz	2.5pF	_____
g) 28.471MHz	2.5pF	_____

Answers - Resonance

1	a	21	d	41	b	61	b	67	a	1µF
2	d	22	d	42	a	62	c		b	2µF
3	c	23	a	43	b	63	c		c	10µF
4	b	24	b	44	c	64	c		d	4µF
5	a	25	b	45	c	65	b		e	10pF
6	c	26	c	46	c	66	a 26.9Hz		f	5pF
7	c	27	a	47	a		b 50.33Hz		g	20pF
8	c	28	b	48	b		c 183.7Hz	68	a	1mH
9	c	29	d	49	a		d 450.16Hz		b	2.5mH
10	b	30	a	50	d		e 982.325Hz		c	200µH
11	d	31	c	51	c		f 503.3Hz		d	100µH
12	d	32	b	52	a		g 503.3Hz		e	50µH
13	d	33	b	53	b				f	25µH
14	c	34	a	54	a				g	12.5µH
15	c	35	a	55	c					
16	a	36	b	56	a					
17	c	37	c	57	a					
18	b	38	c	58	b					
19	d	39	d	59	b					
20	c	40	b	60	a					

Answers - Resonance

1. The condition of resonance occurs in series or parallel LC circuits when the inductive reactance X_L, and the capacitive reactance X_C are equal in value but opposite in sign. Resonance occurs when $X_L = X_C$.

2. The resonant frequency is given by :- $f_r = \dfrac{1}{2\pi\sqrt{LC}}$.

3. Reducing the value of either L or C, or both, will increase the resonant frequency.

4. Increasing the value of either L or C, or both, will decrease the resonant frequency.

5. See A1, A2 above.

6. In the series circuit the value of the resistance will not affect the resonant frequency. It will, however, affect the Q, response curve and selectivity.

7, 8. At the resonant frequency, the reactances X_L and X_C cancel, and the impedance of the circuit equals the resistance $(Z = R)$. At resonance the circuit is at its lowest impedance and maximum current will flow. From the diagram it will be seen that when X_L and X_C cancel, the impedance, $Z = R = 5\Omega$.

9. $f_r = \dfrac{1}{2\pi\sqrt{LC}} = \dfrac{1}{2\times\pi\times\sqrt{10\times10^{-3}\times1\times10^{-6}}} = \dfrac{10^4}{2\times\pi} = 1592Hz.$

10. Increasing the value of C will reduce the resonant frequency of the circuit. Increasing C four times, from $1\mu F$ to $4\mu F$ will reduce the reduce the resonant frequency by half. Substituting the figures in the formula :-

$f_r = \dfrac{1}{2\pi\sqrt{LC}} = \dfrac{1}{2\times\pi\times\sqrt{10\times10^{-3}\times4\times10^{-6}}} = \dfrac{10^4}{4\times\pi} = 796Hz.$

11. At resonance X_L and X_C cancel, and R remains. As before for this circuit $R = 5\Omega$.

12. From previous answers we see that at resonance :-

$Z = R = 5\Omega. \quad \therefore I = \dfrac{V}{R} = \dfrac{20}{5} = 4A.$

13. Increasing the value of R will decrease the current flowing in the circuit at resonance, it will also reduce the Q of the circuit, and reduce the voltages developed across L and C at resonance.

14. Since there is no mutual coupling between the coil or any other part of the circuit, reversing the inductor connections will not alter the resonant frequency.

15,16. The impedance of the series LCR circuit is at its lowest when tuned to resonance, therefore, a maximum current will flow and the meter will peak.

17. At resonance $Z = R = 5\Omega, \quad \therefore I = \dfrac{V}{R} = \dfrac{10}{5} = 2A.$

Answers - Resonance

18. Since both V_L and V_C cancel at resonance, the supply voltage 10V will be developed across the resistor.

19. The voltage across the inductor is given by :- $V_L = I X_L$

$$V_L = I X_L = I \omega L = 2 \times 2 \times \pi \times 1592 \times 10 \times 10^{-3} = 200V \ (approx).$$

20. The voltage across the capacitor is given by :- $V_C = I X_C$

$$V_C = I X_C = \frac{I}{\omega C} = \frac{2}{2 \times \pi \times 1592 \times 1 \times 10^{-6}} = \frac{10^6}{\pi \times 1592} = 200V \ (approx).$$

21, 22. From A18, 19, and 20, it can be seen that high voltages can be developed across the reactive components. These voltages can be much higher than the supply voltage. This effect is referred to as voltage magnification, or Q.
The Q of this circuit can be found by using the formula $Q = \dfrac{V_L}{V_R} = \dfrac{200}{10} = 20$.

23. At resonance the voltages V_L and V_C are equal, but they are opposite in sign (polarity or phase) so they cancel.

24. Halving the value of R will allow twice the amount of current at the resonant frequency to pass, therefore, the voltages V_L and V_C will double, i.e. from 200V to 400V.

25. Don't be fooled by the 10V supply, the voltage across both L and C is $Q \times V_S$, and both components must be rated accordingly. A 16V capacitor will not do.

26. Curve c) shows the current/frequency response of the series LC circuit. The current increases to a maximum value at resonance.

27. The current and voltage across the resistor are in phase.

28. The voltages V_L and V_C, developed across the reactive components are equal, $V_L = V_C$. However, they are 180° out of phase and cancel.

29. Curve d) shows the impedance frequency characteristic of the series tuned circuit. The lowest impedance being at the resonant frequency when $Z = R$.

30. At resonance, the ratio of V_L or V_C to that of the supply V_S (or V_R) will give the magnification factor of the circuit. $\therefore \ Q = \dfrac{V_C}{V_S}$

31. The series resonant circuit is often referred to as an acceptor circuit due to its ability to pass or accept signals about its tuned frequency, and reject all others.

32. In practice, provided that the reactance of L and C are at least 10 times greater than the resistance R, the effect of R on the resonant frequency can be ignored. The impedance of the parallel tuned circuit at resonance, referred to as the *dynamic resistance* 'R_D' is high.

Answers - Resonance

33. Unlike the series circuit, the impedance of the parallel circuit at resonance is high, it is referred to as the dynamic resistance 'R_D'. $R_D = \dfrac{L}{CR}$.

34, 35. A high quality, low loss, parallel resonant circuit is generally characterised by a high circulating current I_{CIRC} and low supply current I_S. The supply current is sometimes referred to as the top-up current. $Q = \dfrac{I_{Circulating}}{I_{Supply}}$.

36, 37. When the charged capacitor is switched to position A, there is an oscillatory interchange of energy between the capacitor and the electromagnetic field of the inductor. Waveform b) shows the resulting current in the form of a damped oscillation. Increasing R will introduce more loss into the circuit and the oscillation will decay more rapidly. In an ideal case, with no loss present, waveform c) would result; however, this is not practical.

38. Curve c) shows impedance increasing with frequency up to its maximum value, where $R_D = \dfrac{L}{CR}$, above this the impedance decreases as shown.

39. The main cause of loss in an air core radio frequency tuned circuit is copper loss due to the resistance of the coil. The coil resistance increases with frequency due to the RF currents tending to flow in the surface of the conductor rather than the whole cross section. This is 'skin effect.'

40, 41. Due to its ability to store oscillatory energy, the parallel tuned circuit is referred to as a tank 'circuit.' When its high impedance characteristic is used, the parallel circuit is referred to as a rejector circuit since it rejects or blocks currents at or near the resonant frequency.

42. Due to its high R_D, the parallel resonant circuit needs a high resistance source for high Q, maximum selectivity, and sharp voltage peak at resonance.

43. The parallel tuned circuit will be most selective when supplied by a generator having a high internal impedance. The series tuned circuit will be most selective when supplied by a generator having a low internal impedance.

44. Doubling L and halving C will have no effect on the resonant frequency of the circuit.

45. $f_r = \dfrac{1}{2\pi\sqrt{LC}} = \dfrac{1}{2\times\pi\times\sqrt{1\times10^{-3}\times1\times10^{-6}}} = \dfrac{10^4}{1.987} = 5033Hz.$

46. $R_D = \dfrac{L}{CR} = 1\times\dfrac{10^{-3}}{1\times10^{-6}\times2} = 500\Omega.$

47. $I_S = \dfrac{V_S}{R_D} = \dfrac{100}{500} = 0.2A.$

48. Ammeter A1 is measuring the supply current. As the frequency is swept through the resonant point of the circuit, the supply current will dip due to the high dynamic resistance R_D of the parallel circuit at resonance.

49. The circulating current, within the closed LC circuit will peak at resonance.

50. $Q = \dfrac{Circulating\ current}{Supply\ current} = \dfrac{I_{Circulating}}{I_{Supply}} = \dfrac{I_C}{I_S}$.

51. The Q and bandwidth, B/W, of a tuned circuit may be determined from its response or selectivity curve. The bandwidth of the selectivity curve is measured between the half power (-3dB or 70.7%) points on the curve as shown.

From the curve :- $B/W = 1005kHz - 995kHz = 10kHz$

$$Q = \frac{f_r}{B/W} = \frac{1MHz}{10kHz} = \frac{1,000,000}{10,000} = 100.$$

52. Since from A51, $Q = \dfrac{f_r}{B/W}$ by transposition

$$B/W = \frac{f_r}{Q} = \frac{10MHz}{100} = \frac{10,000,000}{100} = 100,000Hz\ or\ 100kHz.$$

53. Increasing the losses, usually due to the R of the inductor, will flatten the response curve and increase the B/W.

54. $Q = \dfrac{f_r}{B/W} = \dfrac{470kHz}{473kHz - 467kHz} = \dfrac{470kHz}{6kHz} = \dfrac{470,000}{6,000} = 78.33.$

55. $f_r = \dfrac{1}{2\pi\sqrt{LC}} = \dfrac{1}{2\times\pi\times\sqrt{100\times10^{-6}\times1\times10^{-6}}} = \dfrac{10^6}{20\times\pi} = 15.915kHz.$

56, 57. Reducing the value of either C or L will always increase the resonant frequency. A four times reduction in C (or L) will double the resonant frequency. Therefore, the frequency calculated in A55 will be doubled. 31.83kHz

58, 59. Increasing the value of either L or C will always decrease the resonant frequency. A four times increase in L (or C) will halve the resonant frequency. Therefore, the frequency calculated in A55 will be halved. 7.95kHz.

60. A series tuned circuit has a very low Z at its resonant frequency. Therefore, as the frequency of the signal generator is swept through the resonant point of the circuit a maximum current will flow and the ammeter will show a peak.

61. A parallel tuned circuit has a very high dynamic resistance R_D at its resonant frequency. Therefore, the supply current will dip as the frequency of the signal generator passes through the resonant point of the circuit.

62. Transposing $f_r = \dfrac{1}{2\pi\sqrt{LC}}$ for C gives $C = \dfrac{1}{4\pi^2 f_r^2 L}$

63. $C = \dfrac{1}{4\pi^2 f_r^2 L} = \dfrac{1}{4\times\pi^2\times 796^2\times 10\times 10^{-3}} = 3.99\mu F$

64. $L = \dfrac{1}{4\pi^2 f_r^2 C}$

65. $L = \dfrac{1}{4\pi^2 f_r^2 C} = \dfrac{1}{4\times\pi^2\times(1\times 10^{-6})^2\times 159\times 10^{-12}} = 159\mu H$

The answers to the following questions are found in the key.

66. Use the formula :- $f_r = \dfrac{1}{2\pi\sqrt{LC}}$

67. Use the formula :- $C = \dfrac{1}{4\pi^2 f_r^2 L}$

68. Use the formula :- $L = \dfrac{1}{4\pi^2 f_r^2 C}$

9.Transformers and Power Supplies

This section will cover -
1. the transformer, step-up, step down and impedance matching.
2. half-wave and full-wave rectification.
3. smoothing and voltage stabilisation.

The Transformer

Transformers are used in radio and electronic equipment to increase or decrease alternating voltages, couple and tune r.f. signals, and match source to load impedances. They *will not* produce, or operate on, direct currents or voltages.

In its basic form a transformer consists of two or more coils, electrically insulated from each other and coupled by mutual induction.

When an alternating current in one coil (the primary) changes, it creates a changing magnetic field that induces a voltage in a second coil (the secondary). To ensure that as much of the magnetic field (or flux) as possible cuts the secondary coil, the coils are wound on a common core. In the case of power and audio frequencies the core is usually laminated iron, whilst at radio frequencies the core may be air, iron dust or ferrite. Power transformers for radio frequency work are normally air cored.

Transformer losses are mainly due to :-
a) resistance of windings (Copper Loss).
b) core not completely demagnetising after the current falls to zero. (Hysteresis).
c) eddy currents flowing in the core.

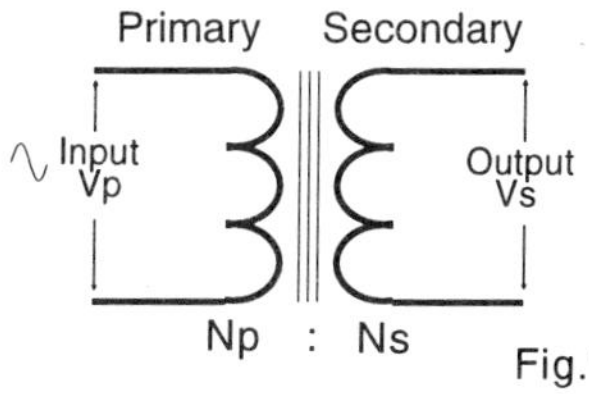

Fig.1

Turns Ratio and Voltage Ratio.

Assume a perfect transformer with no losses, i.e, all the lines of magnetic flux generated by the primary winding cut the secondary winding. When the turns of the primary winding (Np), and the turns of the secondary winding (Ns), are equal, the turns ratio is 1:1, and the voltage induced across the secondary (Vs) will be the same as that applied to the primary (Vp).

If there are twice as many turns on the secondary as on the primary (a *step-up* transformer), the secondary voltage will be twice the applied primary voltage.

If the turns on the secondary are half of those on the primary (a *step-down* transformer), the secondary voltage will be half of the applied primary voltage.

It follows that :-
$$\frac{V_p}{V_s} = \frac{N_p}{N_s} \qquad \therefore \quad V_s = V_p \times \frac{N_s}{N_p} \qquad or \quad V_p = V_s \times \frac{N_p}{N_s}$$

$$V_p\, I_p = V_s\, I_s \qquad \therefore \quad \frac{V_p}{V_s} = \frac{I_s}{I_p} \qquad and \quad I_p = I_s \times \frac{V_s}{V_p}$$

9-1

Transformers and Power Supplies

Impedance Matching

Since the load impedance connected across the secondary is reflected back to the primary, the transformer is also suitable for matching source and load impedances to ensure maximum power transfer.

Transformers can be used to match audio output stages to loudspeakers, r.f. power amplifier stages to antennas, antennas to small signal r.f. amplifiers, and microphones to audio amplifiers.

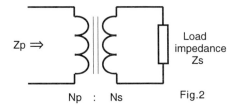

Fig.2

Np : Ns

Where :-
Zp = Primary impedance.
Zs = Secondary load impedance.
Np = Number of turns on primary.
Ns = Number of turns on secondary.

When the load Zs is connected across the secondary terminals of the transformer, fig.2, the impedance looking into the primary terminals is given by :-

$$Z_p = \left(\frac{N_p}{N_s}\right)^2 \times Z_s$$

The turns ratio required for transforming a given load impedance to that required by a source for optimum operation is given by :-

$$\frac{N_p}{N_s} = \sqrt{\frac{Z_p}{Z_s}}$$

Points to note.
1. Direct current will not pass from primary to secondary of a transformer.
2. Operation on a.c. only.
3. Transformers can be step-down, step-up, or a 1:1 ratio for isolation.
4. The voltage ratio is the same as the turns ratio.
5. The current ratio is the inverse of the voltage ratio.
6. A transformer does not generate power.
7. Power is transferred from primary to secondary by electromagnetic induction.
8. In a perfect transformer the output power equals the input power.
9. Transformers can be designed to operate from mains frequencies up to s.h.f, although they may look completely different.
10. A thin earthed copper screen may be placed in manufacture between the primary and secondary windings to reduce mains borne interference, and also to prevent direct contact between the primary and secondary windings in the event of an insulation breakdown fault. The screen must not form a short-circuit turn.

Power supplies

Power may be supplied to radio and electronic equipment by batteries made up of primary or secondary cells, connected in series or parallel to provide the required voltage and current; or, by means of an a.c. mains power supply unit (PSU).

Typical voltages required are:- ±3 to ±15Vdc for logic circuits, 6 to 24Vdc for modern radio equipment, 200V to 3kVdc for valve radio transmitters and RF linear amplifiers, and 6 to 12Vac for valve heaters.

Transformers and Power Supplies

The Power Supply Unit (PSU)

The basic PSU consists of three parts. 1) The mains transformer, to convert the mains voltage to that required by the equipment. 2) The rectifier (usually one or more silicon diodes), to convert the a.c. to d.c. 3) A smoothing circuit to minimise the a.c. ripple superimposed on the d.c. output voltage. In addition, more sophisticated circuits will employ a regulator circuit to stabilise the output against load and supply line variations.

The half-wave rectifier circuit fig.3.

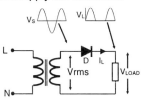

Diode D will conduct when the applied voltage V_{rms} drives the anode of the diode positive with respect to the cathode. The load current I_L will be a pulsating direct current.

The two waveforms of fig.3 show the voltage applied to the diode, and the load voltage, V_L. If the diode is reversed, a negative half-cycle will appear across the load. The diode current is equal to the load current, and the peak inverse voltage (PIV) across the diode equals the peak secondary voltage of the transformer, $1.4V_{rms}$. The output voltage waveform is shown in fig.6b. With the capacitor input filter of fig.7 connected between diode and load the PIV can rise to $2.8V_{rms}$.

Fig.3. The half-wave circuit. D conducts only during positive half-cycles, leaving a gap in the output voltage waveform.

The full-wave (bi-phase half-wave) circuit fig.4.

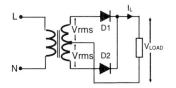

Diodes D1 and D2 conduct on alternate half cycles. The output voltage waveform is as fig.6c. The average direct current through each diode is one half of the total load current. The PIV across each diode is 2.8Vrms.

Fig.4. The full-wave circuit uses two half-wave circuits. A centre tapped transformer is required.

The full-wave bridge rectifier circuit fig.5.

Diodes D1 and D2 conduct on one half of the input cycle and diodes D3 and D4 on the other. The average direct current through each diode is one half of the total load current. The PIV for each diode is $1.4V_{rms}$. The output voltage waveform is shown in fig.6d.

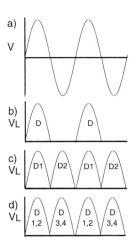

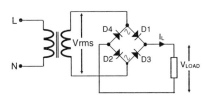

Fig.5 The full-wave bridge rectifier circuit using four diodes.

Fig.6 Showing input waveform a) and the output voltage waveforms VLOAD for -
b) half-wave.
c) full-wave biphase.
d) full-wave bridge.

The numbers of the conducting diodes are shown.

9 - 3

The filter circuit. The varying nature of the d.c. output voltage makes the circuits of figs 3,4,5 unsuitable for the majority of electronic and radio equipment. However; the output voltage can be smoothed by means of the low pass filter of fig.7. Here the input to the filter is the pulsating d.c. output of the half-wave circuit of fig.3; and the output of the filter is very

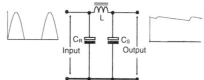

Fig.7. Capacitor input filter. Showing pulsating d.c. input and smoothed d.c. output waveforms.

much smoother with some 'ripple' on it. C_R (about 1,000 - 22,000µF) is the reservoir capacitor, it supplies current to the load when the diode is not conducting. C_S is the smoothing capacitor. The inductor L, usually referred to as a smoothing choke, presents a high impedance to the alternating ripple component of the waveform, and readily passes d.c. The filter may be used on both half-wave and full-wave circuits. The choke is sometimes replaced by a suitable resistor.

The practical full-wave circuit of fig.8 uses a centre tapped transformer and filter. It gives better regulation than the half-wave circuit.

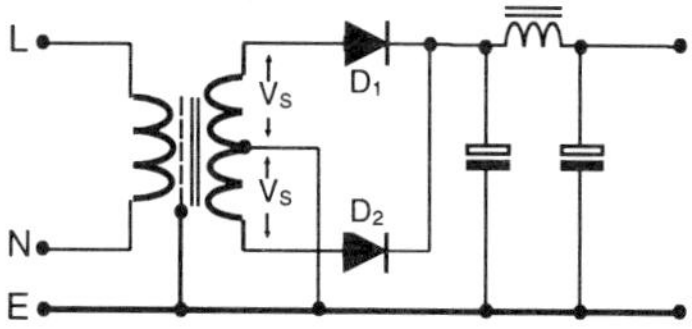

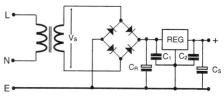

Fig.8

The stabilised supply produces an output voltage (with very little ripple) that remains constant when the supply voltage and load current are changing. Fig.9 shows a typical PSU using a three terminal regulator and a bridge rectifier.

Fig.9

Points to note.
1. All circuits shown, will, in practice, be fitted with mains supply fuses and double pole switches.
2. Ripple frequency (assuming 50Hz mains supply) for a half-wave circuit is 50Hz, and 100Hz for a full-wave circuit.
3. Diodes are often referred to as rectifiers when used in power supply applications.
4. Conducting silicon diodes have a voltage drop of about 0.65V across them.
5. The bridge rectifier may be made up of four individual diodes or purchased in a single encapsulated unit with four terminals.
6. Diodes may be connected in series to increase the PIV. Two 800V PIV diodes will withstand 1600V PIV. However; when connected in series they should be shunted with charge equalising resistors and transient suppression capacitors.
7. Bleed resistors should be fitted across high value PSU capacitors, particularly those used in high voltage supplies.
8. A simple, but effective voltage stabiliser can be constructed using a zener diode.
9. Ripple voltage depends on load current and value of smoothing components.

Transformers and Power Supplies

1. A transformer is constructed of two or more coils possessing-
   a) ferromagnetic bonding.
   b) eddy current losses.
   c) electrostatic coupling.
   d) mutual inductance.

2. The windings of a transformer introduce a loss, this is referred to as-
   a) feedback loss.
   b) hysteresis loss.
   c) eddy current loss.
   d) copper loss.

3. The two types of loss associated with a transformer core are-
   a) electromagnetic and ferromagnetic.
   b) inductive and capacitive.
   c) iron oxide and carbon.
   d) hysteresis and eddy current.

4. How could the core losses referred to in Q 3 above be reduced?
   a) By fitting an electrostatic screen between the two windings.
   b) By fitting a magnetic screen between the two windings.
   c) By reduction of the oxide and carbon levels in the core.
   d) By constructing the core of thin, insulated ferromagnetic laminations.

5. Transformer power losses cause-
   a) energy feedback into the mains.
   b) local neon signs to flicker.
   c) the load to overheat.
   d) the temperature of the transformer core and windings to increase.

6. A screen inserted between the primary and secondary of a transformer-
   a) must act as a short circuit turn to be effective.
   b) must not act as a short circuit turn.
   c) should be made of polythene.
   d) should be at least two wavelengths long at the mains frequency.

7. The screen of a transformer, when fitted, should be connected to-
   a) earth.
   b) H.T. positive.
   c) mains live.
   d) mains neutral.

8. What is the purpose of the transformer screen?
   a) It is a safety measure to isolate primary and secondary in event of a fault, and to provide an electrostatic screen to reduce mains-borne interference.
   b) It is to reduce the operating temperature of the transformer.
   c) It provides a low voltage reference source.
   d) It prevents the turns of the coils unwinding.

9. The voltage ratio between the primary and secondary of a transformer is-
   a) dependent on the supply current.
   b) directly proportional to the turns ratio.
   c) inversely proportional to the turns ratio.
   d) proportional to the turns ratio squared.

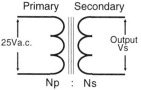

Primary   Secondary

Fig.10

10. The transformer shown in fig.10 has 100 turns on the primary, and 200 turns on the secondary. What is the secondary voltage?
   a) 12.5V   b) 25V
   c) 37.5V   d) 50V

11. A transformer has 600 turns on the primary and 2400 on the secondary. 960 volts is measured across the secondary. What is the primary voltage?
   a) 24V   b) 240V
   c) 600V   d) 2400V

12. A transformer has 3 times as many turns on the secondary as the primary. 230Va.c. is applied to the primary. What is the secondary voltage?
   a) 233V   b) 460V
   c) 690V   d) 920V

13. Assuming a perfect transformer, what power would be consumed when there is no load connected to the secondary?
   a) Zero   b) 100mW
   c) 10W   d) 1W

14. In addition to transforming voltages, a transformer can also be used for-
   a) reducing vibration in HF crystal oscillators.
   b) producing a highly stable reference frequency from the variable 50Hz supply.
   c) impedance matching.
   d) transforming d.c. voltages and currents.

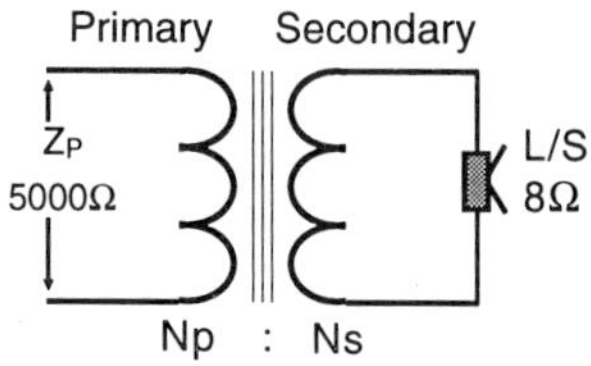

15. Referring to fig.11. What turns ratio is required to match 5000Ω to 8Ω?
   a) 25:1   b) 5000:8
   c) 625:1   d) 200:1

Primary   Secondary

Fig.11

16. An autotransformer-
   a) is only suitable for low current applications.
   b) is not suitable for low current applications.
   c) does not provide isolation between primary and secondary.
   d) has to be purchased on a special licence issued by the Ministry of Health.

Transformers and Power Supplies

17. Fig.12 shows a -
    a) voltage variable inductor.
    b) current variable inductor.
    c) step-up auto transformer.
    d) step-down autotransformer.

Fig.12

18. Fig.13 shows a-
    a) reactance variable transformer.
    b) oscillating transformer.
    c) step-up auto transformer.
    d) step-down autotransformer.

Fig.13

19. Referring to fig.14, the type of rectification is-
    a) quarter-wave.   b) half-wave.
    c) bi-phase.   d) full-wave.

20. The 'Peak Inverse Voltage' (PIV) across the diode in the circuit of fig.14 is-
    a) 100V   b) 141V
    c) 200V   d) 282V

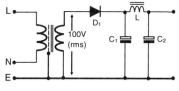

Fig.14

21. What is the output voltage of the power supply unit shown in fig.14 when there is no load connected?
    a) 100V   b) 141V   c) 200V   d) 282V

22. What working voltage would you select for the capacitors to be used in the filter circuit of fig.14?
    a) 70V   b) 100V   c) 200V   d) 1000V

23. What is the purpose of C1, C2 and L in the power supply unit shown in fig.14?
    a) They form the ripple filter or low pass filter for smoothing the rectified output. C1 is the reservoir capacitor.
    b) They form a voltage doubling circuit to make up for the loss in the rectifiers.
    c) They make up the voltage regulator.
    d) They provide the bias for the transformer.

24. If the power supply shown in fig.14 is supplying an audio amplifier and the capacitors go open circuit, what would be the most noticeable effect?
    a) The amplifier would radiate R.F. energy from its loudspeaker leads.
    b) The transformer would burn up.
    c) There would be a loud hum at the loudspeaker.
    d) The turntable, if used, would go into reverse.

9-7

25. If the single diode rectifier used in the circuit of fig.14, is substituted for two diodes in series, what will be the PIV across each diode?
    a) 100V   b) 141V
    c) 200V   d) 282V

26. The high value resistors fitted across the series connected diodes of fig.15 are to-

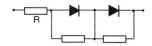

Fig.15

    a) pass more supply current to the load.
    b) assist the fuse to blow if the capacitors go faulty.
    c) equalise the reverse (or inverse) voltages, and are of equal value.
    d) bias the diodes into conduction.

27. Referring to fig.15. If fitted, the resistor 'R' is to-
    a) act as a current sensor to enable the current to be measured easily.
    b) prevent high peak inverse voltages destroying the diode.
    c) reduce the diode surge current to safe limits at switch-on.
    d) rectify the a.c. in advance of the diode.

28. Rectifier diodes will often be found with small capacitors fitted across them, as shown in fig.16. What is the reason?
    a) To increase the working voltage.
    b) To increase the rated current.
    c) To bypass rapid high voltage spikes or transients, which could damage the diode.
    d) To provide transformer protection should the diode go short circuit.

Fig.16

29. What type of rectification is employed in the power supply unit shown in fig.17?
    a) Quarter-wave.
    b) Half-wave.
    c) Three-quarter wave.
    d) Full-wave.

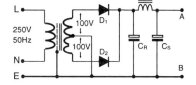

Fig.17

30. The PIV across each diode in fig.17 will be-
    a) 70.7V   b) 141V
    c) 200V   d) 282V

31. Under no-load conditions, the voltage measured across the reservoir capacitor, C_R, in fig.17 will be about-
    a) 70.7V   b) 100V
    c) 141V   d) 200V

32. Reversing the rectifiers and the capacitors shown in fig.17 will -
a) result in twice the available output current.
b) double the output voltage.
c) change the polarity of the output voltage, i.e. point 'A' will become negative.
d) enable the PSU to be operated from a d.c. source.

33. Fig.18 shows the circuit of a power supply.
What type of rectification does it use?
a) Quarter-wave.
b) Half-wave.
c) Full-wave bridge.
d) Quadro-phase.

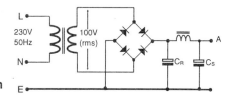

34. The PIV across each diode shown in fig.18 will be -
a) 63V   b) 100V
c) 141V   d) 282V

Fig.18

35. The polarity of the voltage at point 'A' in fig.18 is -
a) positive.   b) negative.
c) neutral.   d) negative 20V.

36. What is the ripple frequency of the full-wave rectifier circuits of 17 and 18?
a) 50Hz   b) 100Hz
c) 141Hz   d) 400Hz

37. The ripple voltage at the output of the power supplies shown in figures 14, 17 and 18, will be dependent upon the-
a) value of the capacitors and the load current.
b) power rating of the load.
c) stability of the mains supply.
d) material used for the transformer core.

38. Due to a supply failure in the a.c. mains, it has been decided to run the PSU of fig.19 off of a 200V direct current supply. The transformer is a 10:1 step down. What is the d.c. output voltage across terminals A and B when connected as shown?

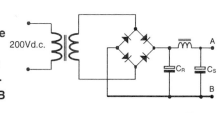

Fig.19

a) 200V   b) 100V
c) 20V   d) Zero

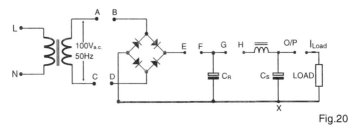

Fig.20

39. Fig.20 shows a PSU employing a full-wave bridge rectifier and capacitor input filter. Using an oscilloscope, which waveform from those shown below would you expect to see at points A-C?

a)   b)   c)   d)

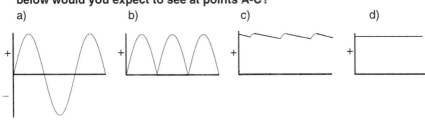

40. Referring to fig.20. When points A-B and C-D are linked, which one of the above waveforms would you expect to see on an oscilloscope connected across points E and X?

41. Referring to fig.20. A-B, C-D and E-F are linked. Which waveform, from those shown above, would you expect across points G and X?

42. Referring to fig.20. A-B, C-D, E-F, and G-H are linked. Which waveform, from those shown above, are you likely to see on an oscilloscope connected across the output terminals?

43. Referring to fig.20. With all the links connected. Which waveform, from those shown above, might be observed at the output terminals when a load is connected that draws the maximum rated current of the PSU?

44. The a.c. supply frequency to the PSU shown in fig.20 is 50Hz. What is the ripple frequency?
    a) 25Hz   b) 50Hz   c) 100Hz   d) 796Hz

45. Referring to fig.20. All the links and a 190Ω load are connected. The p.d. across the load is 95V. What is the current in the load?
    a) 0.25A   b) 0.5A   c) 1A   d) 2A

Transformers and Power Supplies

46. Point 'A' of the transformer shown in fig.21, is delivering the positive half cycle to the rectifier bridge. Which two diodes are conducting?
   a) D1 and D2   b) D3 and D4
   c) D1 and D3   d) D2 and D4

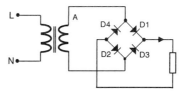

Fig.21

47. Which one of the bridge rectifier circuits shown below is correct?
   a)   b)   c)   d)

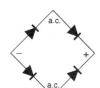   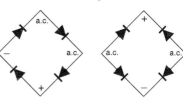

48. What is the circuit shown in fig.22?
   a) A voltage doubler.
   b) A current booster.
   c) A fuse protection device.
   d) A zener voltage stabiliser.

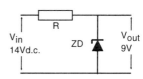

Fig.22

49. The difference between V_{in} and V_{out}, fig.22 is developed-
   a) across the resistor R.
   b) across the zener diode.
   c) across the load.
   d) in the secondary of the supply transformer.

50. Power supply design for the amateur is simplified by including box 'X' in the circuit shown in fig.23. What is box 'X'?
   a) A fixed-voltage integrated circuit regulator.
   b) An auto transformer.
   c) A non-linear 500 ohm carbon resistor.
   d) A thyratron, e.g. Mazda T41.

51. What is the function of box 'X' fig.23?
   a) To prevent oscillation in the bridge rectifier.
   b) To remove the negative half cycles from the input waveform.
   c) To remove supply system noise.
   d) To give a fixed and stabilised output voltage from an unregulated input voltage.

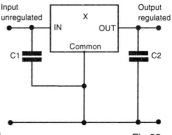

Fig.23

52. Referring to fig.24. Why has the zener diode been included in the circuit?

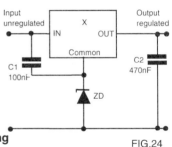

a) To maintain an even 'chip' temperature.

b) To increase the transformer current.

c) To increase the output voltage of the integrated circuit regulator.

d) To increase the rectifier power rating.

FIG.24

53. Why is it advisable to connect a decoupling capacitor close to the input terminal of the regulator, e.g. C1 in fig.23 and 24?

a) To increase the peak input voltage to the regulator.

b) To square the voltage available at the regulator output.

c) To improve the RF shielding of the silicon substrate.

d) To prevent high frequency instability.

54. Why is the decoupling capacitor at the output of the regulator fitted?

a) To bypass any negative half cycles present at the output.

b) To safeguard the user from electric shocks.

c) To reduce the output impedance to high frequency currents.

d) To reduce eddy currents in the transformer core.

55. The circuit shown in fig.25 is that of a typical-

a) series transistor voltage regulator.

b) common emitter voltage regulator.

c) shunt voltage regulator.

d) transistor test rig.

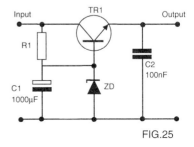

56. Referring to fig.25. Transistor TR1 can be regarded as-

a) a common emitter d.c. amplifier.

b) a collector follower d.c. amplifier.

c) an emitter follower d.c. amplifier.

d) a flip-flop circuit.

FIG.25

57. Where; and why; are bleed resistors fitted in power supplies?

a) Across the transformer to reduce damage due to lightning strikes.

b) Across the mains input to discharge antenna static.

c) Across the rectifiers to prevent destruction due to high voltage transients.

d) Across high value capacitors as a safety precaution to discharge them when the equipment is switched off, and to improve PSU regulation.

Answers - Transformers and Power Supplies

1 d	11 b	21 b	31 c	41 d	51 d
2 d	12 c	22 c	32 c	42 d	52 c
3 d	13 a	23 a	33 c	43 c	53 d
4 d	14 c	24 c	34 c	44 c	54 c
5 d	15 a	25 b	35 a	45 b	55 a
6 b	16 c	26 c	36 b	46 a	56 c
7 a	17 d	27 c	37 a	47 a	57 d
8 a	18 c	28 c	38 d	48 d	
9 b	19 b	29 d	39 a	49 a	
10 d	20 d	30 d	40 b	50 a	

1. When two coils, the primary and secondary, are placed so that the varying magnetic field surrounding the primary (caused by a varying current in that coil) produces and e.m.f. in the secondary, the two coils are inductively coupled. They are said to possess mutual inductance.

2. In a practical transformer the winding resistance introduces a loss which causes power dissipation in the form of heat. This loss is referred to as copper loss.

3,4. Hysteresis and eddy current losses cause heating in the transformer core. Transformer cores are designed to minimise these losses.

5. Power loss is power wasted, the wasted power being dissipated as heat in the winding and the core. Lost power is not available to do work.

6,7,8. Some transformers have a screen of copper foil between the primary and secondary windings. This screen must not form a short circuit turn or it will carry a large current, possibly overheat, and damage the transformer. The overlapping ends of the screen are insulated from one another. The screen is earthed. In the event of an insulation breakdown that could cause a contact between the windings, the faulty winding will be earthed via the screen. The screen also acts as an electrostatic shield to reduce mains-borne interference.

9. The ratio between primary and secondary voltage is proportional to the turns ratio. $\dfrac{V_p}{V_s} = \dfrac{N_p}{N_s}$

10. $\dfrac{V_p}{V_s} = \dfrac{N_p}{N_s}$ $\therefore V_s = V_p \times \dfrac{N_s}{N_p} = 25 \times \dfrac{200}{100} = 50V.$

11. $\dfrac{V_p}{V_s} = \dfrac{N_p}{N_s}$ $\therefore V_p = V_s \times \dfrac{N_p}{N_s} = 960 \times \dfrac{600}{2400} = 240V.$

12. Since the transformer has 3 times more turns on the secondary than the primary, the secondary voltage will be 3 times the applied primary voltage. I.e.-
$3 \times 230 = 690V.$

13. A perfect transformer, with no losses, will not consume power.

14. Transformers may be used to match impedances for maximum power transfer. E.g. Matching a low impedance microphone to high impedance amplifier, or matching a 75Ω feeder to a 50Ω antenna.

15. 5000Ω needs to be matched to 8Ω. What is the turns ratio of the transformer?

$$\frac{N_p}{N_s} = \sqrt{\frac{Z_p}{Z_s}} = \sqrt{\frac{5000}{8}} = \sqrt{625} = 25 \quad \text{The turns ratio is 25:1.}$$

16. There is no isolation between the input and output of an autotransformer.

17. Fig.12 is a step-down autotransformer.

18. Fig.13 is a step-up autotransformer.

19. Fig.14 shows a half-wave rectifier circuit employing a capacitor input filter for smoothing.

20. The peak inverse voltage PIV is the voltage developed across a diode in the non-conducting condition. In this case the capacitor will charge to the peak secondary voltage $100 \times 1.414 = 141.4V$ during the conducting half cycle. On the negative, non-conducting half cycle, the peak voltage at the anode of the diode will be -141.4V. The potential difference between the anode and cathode of the diode will therefore be 282V, the PIV.

21. With no load connected the capacitors will reach the peak value of the transformer secondary voltage $100 \times 1.414 = 141.4V$. When a load is connected to the power supply the voltage will drop depending on the load resistance. For low voltage PSUs the forward resistance of the diodes will need to be considered.

22. From A21 it is seen that the capacitors must withstand 141V. Building in a safety factor, and considering cost, capacitors rated at 200V will be suitable. The 1000V capacitor would be o.k. but unnecessarily expensive.

23. C1,C2 and L form a filter to smooth the pulsating d.c. at the output of the rectifier, which is useless for operating electronic equipment. C1 is the reservoir capacitor, it supplies the load when the diode is not conducting. L is the smoothing choke, it presents a high impedance to the a.c. ripple current and a low impedance to the d.c. load current. C2 is the smoothing capacitor, it has a low impedance to the a.c. ripple current and will not pass the d.c. load current.

24. With the reservoir and smoothing capacitor out of circuit any load will be fed from pulsating d.c. The effect in the case of audio equipment will be a loud hum.

25. Using two diodes in series will double the PIV rating over a single diode. In this case, since there is a PIV of 282V across the single diode, there will be 141V across each one when two diodes are connected in series.

26. The inverse voltage across series connected diodes does not divide equally, therefore; the diodes should be shunted by resistors to equalise the voltages.

27. At switch-on, the reservoir capacitor will initially draw a heavy charging current. Resistor R will reduce this current to a safe limit.

28. Diodes can be destroyed by high voltage spikes or transients on the supply. The diodes should be bypassed by capacitors, usually about $0.01\mu F$.

29. This circuit is the full-wave bi-phase circuit. This circuit requires a centre tapped transformer secondary. The PIV across each diode will be $2.8 \times V_{rms}$.

30. The PIV across each diode will be $2.8 \times V_{rms} = 2.8 \times 100 = 282V$.

31. With no load connected the voltage across C_R will reach the peak of the transformer secondary voltage; $100 \times 1.414 = 141.4\,V$. When a load is connected to the power supply the voltage will drop depending on the load resistance. For low voltage PSUs the forward resistance of the diodes will also need to be considered.

32. Reversing the diodes will result in a negative output voltage at 'A'. The electrolytic capacitors, C_R and C_S, since they are polarised types, will need to be reversed.

33. Fig.18 is a full-wave bridge circuit. The rectifier bridge may be constructed of four single diodes, or it may be an encapsulated unit. A heat sink may be required.

34. Each diode will have a PIV of 141V across it when not conducting.

35. The direction of the diode bridge gives a positive voltage at point A.

36. The ripple frequency of the full-wave circuit is double the supply frequency.

37. The smoothness, or amount of ripple voltage on the d.c. output depends on the values of the filter components and the current in the load. A light load (high resistance) will draw little current, and will have little effect on the ripple voltage. A heavy load (low resistance) will draw more current, increasing the ripple voltage. Larger capacitors, for a given load resistance, will reduce the ripple voltage.

38. There will be no output at A-B. A transformer will not operate from a d.c. supply.

39. The oscilloscope will display waveform a) 141V peak value.

40. The full-wave rectified, pulsating d.c. of waveform b) will be displayed.

41. Waveform d). The capacitor will charge up to the peak value of the transformer voltage and stay at that value since there is no discharge path.

42. Waveform d). Both capacitors will charge up to the peak value of the transformer voltage and stay at that value since there is no discharge path.

43. Waveform c). During the period when the rectified half cycles fall to zero the capacitors supply the load current. A high load current will result in the capacitors discharging more rapidly and an increase in ripple voltage will occur.

44. The ripple frequency is 100Hz.

45. $I = \dfrac{V}{R} = \dfrac{95}{190} = \dfrac{1}{2} = 0.5A.$

46. On the positive half cycle current flows from 'A', through D1, through the load, and returns to the transformer via D2.

47. The rectifier circuit shown at a) is correct.

48. Fig.22 is typical zener diode voltage stabiliser circuit.

49. The zener diode maintains a constant voltage across it, an increase in supply voltage will cause an increase in zener current (and vice versa). The difference between the zener voltage and the and supply voltage will be developed across the stabilising resistor R.

50,51. Fixed voltage integrated circuit regulators are in common use today. They simplify PSU design and provide a very stable output voltage when the supply voltage and load resistance change.

52. It is possible to increase the output voltage of the fixed voltage stabiliser by a fixed amount, by including a zener diode.

53. Decoupling capacitors should be connected to reduce the possibility of high frequency instability, which may result in poor regulation and cause interference.

54. The decoupling capacitor at the output of the regulator will present a low impedance path to any high frequency currents present at this point.

55. The simple zener diode voltage regulator of fig.22 is not suitable for regulation where high currents are concerned, therefore the series transistor voltage regulator, with it's base voltage stabilised by a zener diode offers better performance and higher current. The output voltage is about 0.6-0.7 volts lower than the zener voltage due to the voltage drop between the base and emitter.

56. The transistor acts as an emitter follower d.c. amplifier.

57. Bleed resistors are fitted across the high value capacitors in power supplies to ensue that they are discharged when the supply is switched off. Bleed resistors can also be employed to ensure better power supply regulation.

Typical power supply components. Top, rectifier diodes, medium
and high current. Middle. Full-wave bridge rectifiers.
Lower. Mains transformer and two electrolytic capacitors.

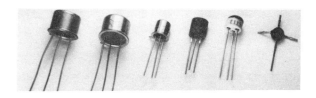

Top row. Typical power transistors.
Bottom row. Typical small-signal transistors.

10. Solid State Devices

This section will cover-
1. junction and zener diodes, NPN, PNP and field effect transistors.
2. basic transistor configurations:- common base, common emitter and common collector. Biasing and input and output impedances.
3. typical circuit configurations, audio and RF amplifiers, oscillators, frequency multipliers, mixers, demodulators and switches.

The semiconductor material

Solid state, or semiconductor devices, include diodes, transistors, and complex integrated circuits. The commonest semiconductor material is silicon (Si). Other materials such as germanium (Ge) are sometimes encountered. Silicon and germanium atoms have four electrons in their outer shell, which bond with the electrons in the outer shells of adjacent atoms to form a crystal lattice. Both materials in their pure state are poor conductors of electricity. In order to increase the conductivity of these materials, and make them suitable for the manufacture of semiconductor devices, a small and controlled amount of impurity is introduced (a process called *doping*).

The two types of semiconductor material used are:- 1) N-type (negative), in which the impurity atoms, typically phosphorous or arsenic, have 5 electrons in their outer shell, one more than the Si or Ge atoms of the base material. Hence, there is a surplus of electrons. And 2) P-type (positive), in which the impurity atoms - typically aluminium or boron - have 3 electrons in their outer shell, one less than the Si or Ge atoms of the base material, leaving a gap in the lattice, referred to as a hole. Holes carry a positive charge that can be filled by an electron. Both N-type and P-type materials are electrically neutral.

The junction diode

Fig.1 shows a diode formed by a P-N junction. There is no external voltage applied. At the junction there is a diffusion of electrons from the N-type material to the P-type material, and a similar diffusion of holes from the P-type material to the N-type material. The N-type material having lost some electrons assumes a positive charge, and repels further holes from the junction; while the P-type material, having acquired some electrons from the N-type assumes a negative charge, and repels further electrons from the junction. *(Like charges repel, unlike charges attract.)* A region depleted of all charge carriers is thus created at the PN junction, this is referred to as the depletion layer. The charges on either side of the junction create a potential barrier which can be regarded as a small internal battery.

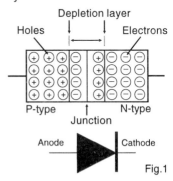

Fig.1

10 - 1

Solid State Devices

The forward biased diode

Fig.2 shows a forward biased diode. With an external battery connected as shown, electrons in the N-type material are attracted via the P-region to the positive terminal of the battery. Similarly holes in the P-region will move across the N-region to the negative terminal of the battery. Conduction will take place and current will flow when the potential of the external battery exceeds that of the barrier potential, approximately 0.7V for silicon (0.2V for germanium).

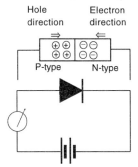

Fig.2 The forward biased diode.

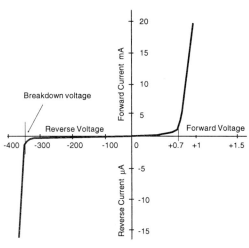

Fig.4 Typical silicon diode characteristic.

The reverse biased diode

Fig.3 shows the reverse biased diode. With the battery connected as shown, electrons in the N-region will be drawn away from the junction to the positive terminal of the battery and holes in the P-region will be drawn to the negative terminal causing the depletion layer to expand. Negligible current passes under this condition.

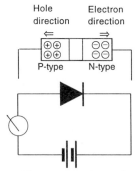

Fig.3 The reverse biased diode.

The rectifier diode

Since the diode only conducts in one direction it can be used to change alternating current to direct current, see section on power supplies.

The Zener diode

The Zener diode exploits the reverse voltage breakdown point of the diode so that it can be used as a voltage regulator.

The varactor, or variable capacitance diode

Operated in reverse bias, the width of the depletion layer increases with increase in voltage, this results in decreased capacitance between the P-N junction.

Solid State Devices

The Bipolar Transistor

There are two types of bipolar transistor, NPN and PNP. Both may be constructed from either silicon or germanium. However, both germanium and PNP types are not commonly used today. This text will deal mainly with NPN silicon types.

Figs.5 and 6 show the circuit symbols for both NPN and PNP transistors respectively, with their power source and bias connections.

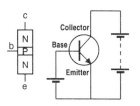

It can be seen from fig.5, that the NPN transistor is a region of P-type material sandwiched between two regions of N-type material. (For PNP this becomes N-type sandwiched between two P-type regions.) In the NPN circuit of fig.5 the base to emitter junction is forward biased, and current will flow in the base to emitter circuit when the bias voltage exceeds the barrier potential across the junction, approximately 0.7V for silicon. The base to collector junction is reverse biased.

Fig.5 The NPN transistor. The base to emitter junction is forward biased while the collector to base junction is reverse biased.

There are three modes of connection for transistor amplifiers, each one having a particular application. The modes are common emitter (CE), common base (CB), and common collector (CC) or emitter follower. Since the transistor is a three terminal device, common refers to the electrode common to both input and output signal current. The most frequently used mode of connection, giving both voltage and current gain is the common emitter circuit of fig.7.

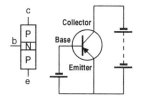

Fig.6 The PNP transistor. Note that the polarity of the batteries and the direction of the emitter arrow is the reverse of the NPN type of fig.5.

Basically the bipolar transistor is a current amplifying device, in which a small current flowing in the base-emitter circuit, I_B, causes a much larger current to flow in the collector-emitter circuit, I_C. From fig.7, and assuming the transistor to have a specified current gain, h_{FE} or 'β' of 100, a base current of 0.1mA (100μA) will result in a collector current of 10mA.

The static current gain for the common emitter amplifier is given by:

$$h_{FE} = \frac{Collector\ current}{Base\ current} = \frac{I_C}{I_B}$$

It follows that any small variations in base current will result in larger variations in collector current. If these small variations are caused by an alternating current superimposed on the steady d.c. bias current, larger variations in collector current occur, and the transistor is acting as a signal amplifier.

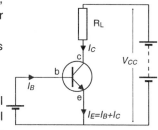

Fig.7 Basic circuit of the common emitter amplifier. Arrows show direction of conventional current.

Solid State Devices

The three basic transistor configurations

The three basic transistor configurations are shown.

The table below gives typical values of input and output impedance, and current, voltage and power gain.

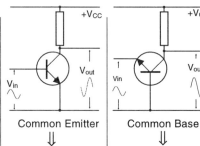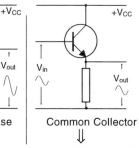

	Common Emitter	Common Base	Common Collector
Input Impedance	Medium 500Ω - 5kΩ	Low 30Ω - 500Ω	High 20kΩ - 1MΩ
Output Impedance	Medium 20kΩ -100kΩ	High 200kΩ - 500kΩ	Low 20Ω - 1kΩ
Voltage Gain	High 100 - 1000	High 50 - 1000	Less than 1 (<1)
Current Gain	High. β = 10 - 800	Low. α = Less than 1	High 10 - 800
Power Gain	High 5000 - 50,000	Medium 50 - 500	Medium 30 - 200
Typical uses	Most frequently used. Small signal RF amp: Audio class A amp:	Impedance matching, low Z to high Z. Stable RF amplification.	Impedance matching, high Z to low Z. Buffer amplifier.

The Practical Common Emitter Amplifier

Fig.8 shows a typical small signal class A amplifier. The input signal causes a small base current I_B to flow, this is multiplied by the current gain of the transistor and a larger collector current I_C flows in R_L. The output signal voltage is taken from the R_L/collector junction.

Bias and stabilisation is achieved by R_1, R_2, and R_E. Stabilisation will prevent *thermal runaway* occurring when the collector current I_C increases with junction temperature and leakage current. This effect is cumulative and the transistor can be rapidly destroyed.

Stabilising action of R_E - When I_C increases I_E also increases, and the voltage across R_E increases, reducing V_{BE} and base current I_B. This decreases I_C (and I_E). Similarly, a reduction in I_C will result in a reduction of p.d. across R_E and there will be an increase in V_{BE}, and I_B, I_C and I_E will rise. This results in a stable average value of I_C that does not increase with temperature. Capacitor C_E short-circuits resistor R_E for signal frequency currents, preventing negative feedback action reducing the amplifier gain.

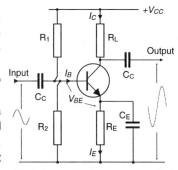

Fig.8 A practical common emitter amplifier circuit. With bias and stabilisation resistors shown. Also note 180° phase change between input and output signals.

The Field Effect Transistor (FET)

The FET is a semiconductor device, In its simplest form, shown in fig.9, the FET is a bar of N-type material (for an N-channel FET) with 2 regions of P-type material at the centre. The flow of current through the channel, from *drain* to *source* is controlled by an electric field set up in the channel by a voltage applied to the *gate*. The FET is a voltage controlled device and has a high input impedance similar to the triode valve.

The two types of FET are the Junction FET (JFET), and the Insulated Gate FET (IGFET). The Metal Oxide semiconductor FET (MOSFET) is a member of the IGFET family.

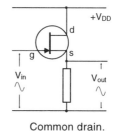

Fig.9 The N-channel JFET and circuit symbol.

The three basic FET configurations

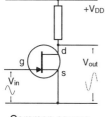

Common source.

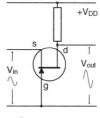

Common gate.

Common drain.

The Common Source JFET Voltage Amplifier

The load resistor R_L fig.10, converts the output current to an output voltage. The drain current I_D is controlled by the gate voltage. The gate and channel form a P-N junction which is normally reverse biased and therefore of high input resistance.

Automatic bias and d.c. stabilisation is provided by R_S and R_G. The current flowing in R_S develops a voltage across it, V_S, hence the source is positive with respect to ground. The gate current is negligible, and the gate held at ground potential (from a d.c. viewpoint) due to R_G. The gate is therefore biased negative with respect to source. If I_D rises, the gate bias voltage increases, reducing I_D. Capacitor C_S short-circuits resistor R_S for signal currents, preventing negative feedback action reducing the amplifier gain.

Capacitors C_C are the signal coupling capacitors, they will pass a.c. signals but not d.c.

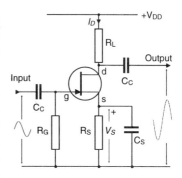

Fig.10 A practical common source N-channel JFET amplifier circuit. With bias and stabilisation resistors shown. Also note 180° phase change between input and output signals.

Classes of Operation

The three main classes of amplifier operation are class A, B and C. The classification referring to the portion of input cycle that causes collector current to flow in the transistor.

Class A operation. The transistor is biased so that collector current flows for the complete 360° of input cycle. Linear amplification will occur given suitable bias conditions so that the transistor operates on the linear part of its input/output curve. The output signal under class A conditions will be an amplified replica of the input signal. Collector current will flow when no input signal is present. Typical efficiency 25 - 35%.

Class B operation. The transistor is biased just at the cut-off point. Collector current flows for only 180° of the input cycle. This results in non-linear operation since only one half of the input cycle is amplified. For audio amplification, two transistors operating in class B push-pull are normally used, one amplifying the positive half cycle, and the second amplifying the negative half cycle. Single ended class B operation is used for SSB linear RF amplification, with a high Q tuned circuit in the output to restore the signal to a reasonably sinusoidal waveform. Typical efficiency 65%.

Class C operation. The transistor is biased beyond cut-of, and collector current flows for less than 180° of the input cycle. This results in non-linearity but high efficiency. Not suitable for audio amplification. Class C is normal for RF carrier wave amplification with a high Q tuned circuit in the output to restore the signal to a reasonably sinusoidal waveform. Typical efficiency 60 - 80%.

Digital and Linear Integrated circuits

The two types of integrated circuit in common use are digital and linear.

Digital ICs basically comprise a number (one or two - up to several thousand) of active on-off transistor switches, plus resistors and capacitors fabricated onto a small slice of silicon. They are used to control circuit functions such as computer operation and digital synthesisers.

Linear ICs are typically used in analogue RF and audio amplifier design, where the amplitude of a varying signal has to be amplified, as opposed to the switching logic (1 and 0) operation of the digital IC.

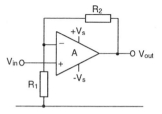

Fig.11 shows a typical linear IC operational amplifier. The gain is controlled by feeding a fraction of the output back to the minus (inverting) input of the device. The amplifier gain, $A_v = R_2/R_1$ (Approx). There is a 180° phase shift between the minus (inverting) input and the output, and a 0° phase shift between the plus (non-inverting) input and the output.

Fig.11 Typical non-inverting linear IC operational amplifier. The output voltage is in phase with the input signal.

1. The two main types of pure material used in the construction of semiconductors are-
   a) beryllium oxide and aluminium.
   b) gallium arsenide and copper.
   c) strontium and barium.
   d) silicon and germanium.

2. The semiconductor materials are manufactured by taking the pure materials described in Q 1 above and-
   a) mixing them with lead oxide at very high pressure.
   b) doping them with impurity elements.
   c) magnetising them to a high flux density.
   d) removing all their electrons.

3. N-type material-
   a) has a high potential across its faces.
   b) exhibits piezo electric properties.
   c) has an excess of electrons.
   d) has an excess of holes.

4. P-type material-
   a) has zero resistance.
   b) exhibits piezo electric properties.
   c) has an excess of electrons.
   d) has an excess of holes.

5. When a junction of P-type and N-type material is formed, a region virtually depleted of all charge carriers exists, this region is referred to as the-
   a) depletion layer.   b) neutral junction.
   c) carrier barrier.   d) contact junction.

6. The device that is formed by the P-N junction shown with its circuit symbol in fig.12 is a-
   a) triac.   b) diac.
   c) diode.   d) triode.

7. The device shown in fig.12 is-
   a) forward biased.
   b) reverse biased.
   c) rejecting.
   d) accepting.

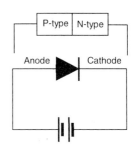

Fig.12

8. **Select the correct order for the four devices shown below.**

1)   2)   3)   4)

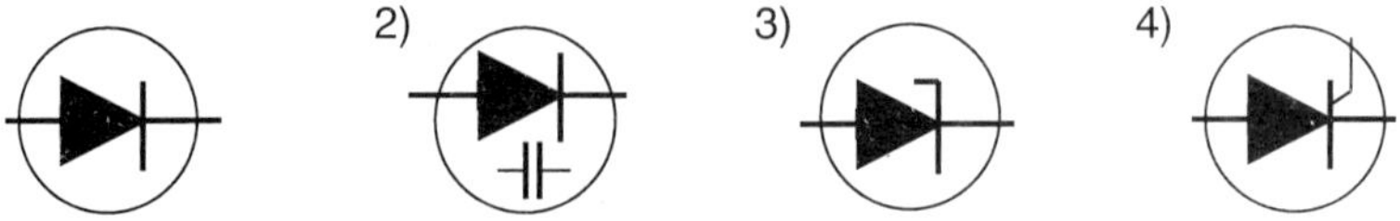

JD = Junction diode. VC = Vari-cap or Varactor diode.
ZD = Zener diode. Th = Thyristor.

a) 1 JD	b) 1 JD	c) 1 JD	d) 1 Th
2 VC	2 VC	2 Th	2 VC
3 ZD	3 Th	3 ZD	3 ZD
4 Th	4 ZD	4 VC	4 JD

9. **The junction diode-**
   a) is bidirectional.
   b) does not dissipate heat.
   c) amplifies small d.c. signals.
   d) passes current in one direction only.

10. **The varactor (or variable capacitance diode), is a device that-**
   a) exhibits variable capacitance for a varying d.c. applied control voltage.
   b) is normally used in voltage regulator circuits.
   c) is normally used to stabilise oscillator supply current.
   d) is tridirectional and used in control circuits.

11. **What is the purpose of the varactor diode in fig.13?**
   a) It stabilises the d.c. voltage.
   b) It reduces carrier harmonics.
   c) It damps all natural resonance.
   d) In conjunction with C1, L1, it determines the resonant frequency of the circuit.

12. **Referring to fig.13, what is the purpose of R_1 and C_2?**
   a) They limit the d.c. current in D_1.
   b) To ensure a constant d.c. supply at the diode.
   c) They decouple the control circuit from the oscillatory circuit.
   d) They prevent the control circuit current flowing in inductor L_1.

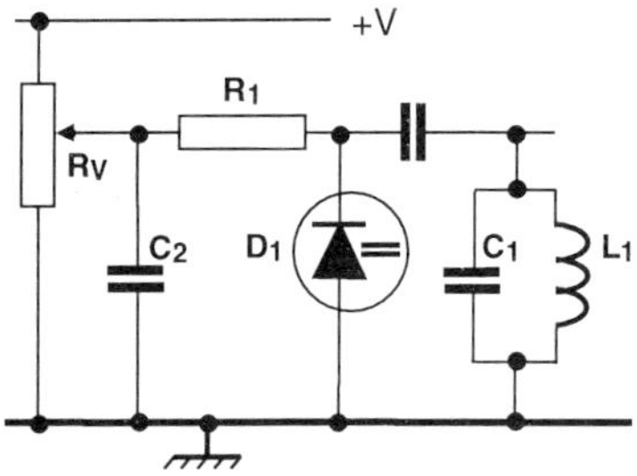

Fig.13

13. **What is the purpose of R_V in fig.13?**
   a) R_V varies the control voltage, which in turn varies the diode capacitance.
   b) It changes the power supply current in the resonant circuit.
   c) Prevents the diode being overloaded by RF from the tuned circuit.
   d) It limits the current to the diode.

Solid State Devices

14. Which one of the components listed below
    operates on the knee of the curve shown in fig.14?
    a) MOSFET mixer
    b) Junction triode.
    c) Zener diode.
    d) Varactor diode.

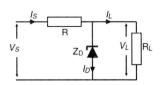

Fig.14

15. The circuit shown in fig.15 is used to-
    a) maintain a constant V_L if V_S and R_L vary.
    b) prevent parasitic oscillations in power supplies.
    c) prevent the power supply overheating.
    d) act as a 'bleeder' to discharge all capacitors in the circuit.

16. Fig.15 shows a zener diode stabilisation
    circuit, the current I_S is equal to-
    a) $I_L - I_D$
    b) $I_L + I_D$
    c) $I_D - I_L$
    d) $I_S + I_L + I_D$

Fig.15

17. Select the correct order for the four devices shown below.

1)   2)   3)   4)

a)	1 PNP	b)	1 NPN	c)	1 NPN	d)	1 NPN
	2 NPN		2 PNP		2 PNP		2 JFET
	3 JFET		3 JFET		3 MOSFET		3 MOSFET
	4 MOSFET		4 MOSFET		4 JFET		4 PNP

18. Which two of the four transistors shown above have the highest input
    resistance?
    a) NPN - PNP
    b) JFET - MOSFET
    c) PNP - MOSFET
    d) JFET - NPN

19. The semiconductor material used for the base of the
    transistor, fig.16, has a deficit of electrons, whilst the
    collector and emitter materials have an excess of
    electrons. What type of transistor is it?
    a) NPN   b) PNP
    c) GDS   d) EBC

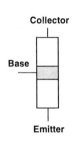

Fig.16

20. Both NPN and PNP transistors are referred to as-
    a) static sensitive devices.
    b) bipolar devices.
    c) anode-bend devices.
    d) bimagnetic devices.

21. NPN and PNP bipolar transistors are basically-
    a) voltage amplifying devices.
    b) current amplifying devices.
    c) charge completion devices.
    d) phase shift devices.

22. The d.c. current gain h_{FE} or β of the transistor shown in fig.17 is given by-

    a) $h_{FE} = \dfrac{I_C}{I_B}$

    b) $h_{FE} = \dfrac{I_B}{I_C}$

    c) $h_{FE} = I_C \times I_B$

    d) $h_{FE} = I_C - I_E$

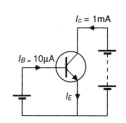

Fig.17

23. Referring to fig.17. The emitter-base junction is forward biased and the currents measured are shown. The d.c. current gain h_{FE} or β of the device is-
    a) 0.98   b) 49   c) 100   d) 200

24. Referring to fig.17, the emitter current, I_E, is given by-
    a) $I_E = I_E - I_B$
    b) $I_E = I_E + I_B$
    c) $I_E = I_C + I_B$
    d) $I_E = I_C - I_B$

25. Assume that the transistor shown in fig.17 has an h_{FE} of 100, what collector current I_C will flow when the base current I_B is increased to $20\mu A$?
    a) 1.96mA   b) 2mA   c) 98mA   d) 200mA

26. In which configuration is the amplifier of fig.18 connected?
    a) Common emitter (CE)
    b) Common base (CB)
    c) Common collector (CC).
    d) Common gate (CG)

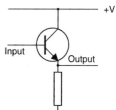

Fig.18

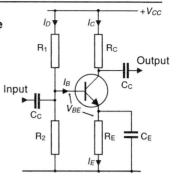

Fig.19

27. Fig.19 shows a common emitter amplifier, the base bias voltage is obtained by-
   a) the potential developed across R_C.
   b) R_L in conjunction with R_1.
   c) the potential divider R_1, R_2.
   d) the collector voltage of the previous stage.

28. Referring to fig.19, and assuming a silicon transistor, the voltage measured between base and emitter (V_{BE}) will be about-
   a) 0.2V   b) 0.7V
   c) 2.2V   d) 10V

29. If the transistor fig.19 is changed for a germanium PNP type, and the supply polarity reversed, what voltage would you expect to measure across the base-emitter junction (V_{BE})?
   a) 0.2V   b) 0.7V
   c) 2.2V   d) 10V

30. Refer to fig.19. The d.c. bias conditions are set so that the base current I_B is 20μA. What is a suitable value of bleed current, I_D, in the divider chain R_1, R_2, to ensure reasonable stability of the base bias voltage?
   a) 20μA   b) 40μA
   c) 200μA   d) 10mA

31. If the collector current increases due to the temperature or supply voltage increasing, the voltage across the emitter resistor R_E of fig.19 will-
   a) increase.   b) decrease.
   c) remain the same.   d) start to oscillate.

32. Referring to fig.19. If the voltage across R_E increases, the voltage V_{BE} will-
   a) increase.   b) decrease.
   c) remain the same.   d) reverse its polarity.

33. Referring to fig.19. If the voltage V_{BE} decreases due to an increase in voltage across the emitter resistor R_E-
   a) the bleed resistors R_1 and R_2 will overheat.
   b) electron flow will reverse due to increased supply current.
   c) there will be a reduction in I_B, which causes a reduction in I_C.
   d) the input current will increase to a point where oscillation commences.

34. **The effect of the emitter resistor R_E in fig.19 is to-**
   a) prevent collector current I_C from increasing when the leakage current increases due to temperature increase within the semiconductor.
   b) prevent heavy loading on the input stage.
   c) set the battery supply voltage.
   d) prevent excessive high frequency response in the amplifier.

35. **If the emitter resistor R_E of fig.19, is not bypassed to a.c. signals by the capacitor C_E-**
   a) negative feedback action will reduce the gain of the amplifier at the signal frequency.
   b) positive feedback will occur and cause oscillation.
   c) it will not be possible to control the thermal runaway and the transistor will be destroyed.
   d) it will become uneconomic to run the amplifier from a small battery.

36. **Referring to fig.19, what is the purpose of capacitors Cc?**
   a) They are the I/P and O/P coupling capacitors and prevent the d.c. conditions being altered by the adjoining stages, whilst allowing the a.c. signal to pass.
   b) They are the I/P and O/P decoupling capacitors which allow the bias conditions to be transferred to adjacent stages. They also increase the d.c. content of the signal.
   c) They reduce the cost of manufacture as opposed to d.c. coupling.
   d) They increase the gain by preventing free electrons escaping.

37. **Between the input signal and output signal of a common emitter amplifier there is-**
   a) no phase shift.
   b) a 90° phase shift.
   c) a 180° phase shift.
   d) a 360° phase shift.

38. **A transistor is basically a current amplifying device.**
    Which statement best describes how it produces a voltage gain?
   a) The voltage gain is produced within the power supply.
   b) The voltage gain is due to the controlling signal varying the leakage current flowing across the collector - base junction. Increasing the signal voltage.
   c) The voltage gain is the result of the signal controlled collector current I_C flowing in the collector resistor R_C, and causing the potential difference across it to vary in sympathy.
   d) It is due to the cumulative effect of the signal charge on the emitter capacitor.

39. The input impedance of a common emitter amplifier is typically-
   a) low, about 50Ω
   b) medium, about 500Ω-$5k\Omega$
   c) high, about $10k\Omega$-$50k\Omega$
   d) very high, about $1M\Omega$

40. The output impedance of a common emitter amplifier is typically-
   a) low, about 50Ω
   b) medium, about $20k\Omega$-$100k\Omega$
   c) high, about $100k\Omega$-$500k\Omega$
   d) very high, about $1M\Omega$

41. The common emitter amplifier would probably be used as a-
   a) low input impedance VHF amplifier.
   b) general purpose amplifier, low to high frequencies, AF to RF.
   c) buffer amplifier between high and low impedances.
   d) high input impedance trigger device.

42. The circuit of fig.20 shows a-
   a) tuned collector, common emitter RF amplifier.
   b) RF emitter follower.
   c) common emitter, tuned collector oscillator.
   d) negative slope oscillator.

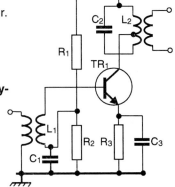

43. In fig.20, bias and stabilisation is provided by-
   a) the tap on the coil L_2.
   b) the tuned circuit $L_2 C_2$.
   c) L_1, C_1.
   d) R_1, R_2 and R_3.

44. Referring to fig.20, the capacitor C_3 should-
   a) be a very high voltage type.
   b) be a large $100,000\mu F$, 10kV working, electrolytic.
   c) have a very high reactance at the signal frequency.
   d) have a very low reactance at the signal frequency.

Fig.20

45. The tapping point on the coil L_2 in fig.20, is to-
   a) phase equalise the signal.
   b) balance the self capacitance of the coil windings.
   c) reduce the voltage before it reaches the collector.
   d) achieve a good impedance match between the medium impedance transistor and the high impedance parallel tuned circuit.

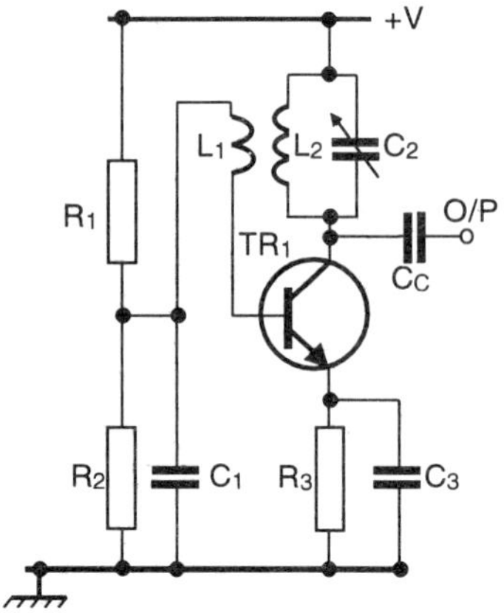

46. **Fig.21 shows the circuit of a-**
    a) tuned collector, common emitter amplifier.
    b) RF emitter follower.
    c) common emitter, tuned collector oscillator.
    d) negative feedback oscillator.

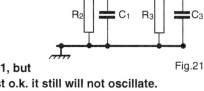

47. **Referring to fig.21. The frequency of oscillation is determined by-**
    a) R_3 and C_3.
    b) C_2 and L_1.
    c) the parallel tuned circuit L_2,C_2.
    d) the series circuit, consisting L_1,C_1.

Fig.21

48. **You have constructed the circuit fig.21, but although it and all its components test o.k. it still will not oscillate. What is the most likely cause?**
    a) The oscillator shown requires a quartz crystal to provide the negative feedback which is necessary for immediate oscillation.
    b) The feedback coil is reversed, producing negative feedback instead of positive feedback which is necessary for oscillation.
    c) A forward biased zener diode has not been fitted to stabilise the voltage.
    d) Remove capacitor C3, and don't worry, it will oscil, later!

49. **The circuit shown in fig.21 will only oscillate when-**
    a) the amplifier has enough gain to overcome the losses in the circuit.
    b) I_B is equal to I_E.
    c) there is sporadic E about.
    d) none of the above.

50. **The circuit shown in fig.22 is that of a typical-**
    a) bipolar FET oscillator.
    b) dual gate MOSFET oscillator.
    c) dual gate MOSFET RF amplifier.
    d) dual gate DIAC mixer stage.

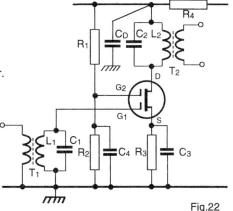

51. **Biasing and stabilisation of the circuit shown in fig.22 is provided by-**
    a) T_1 and C_1.
    b) R_1, R_2 and R_3.
    c) R_4 and C_D.
    d) C_4 and R_4.

Fig.22

52. Referring to fig.22. It has not been found necessary to tap the drain connection down the coil, this is because-
a) the high output impedance of the MOSFET is a reasonable match to the high impedance tuned circuit.
b) there is a saving in supply current to be gained.
c) the type of coil used is not manufactured with a tap.
d) the tapping point is now provided by the R_4 Cd junction.

53. Referring to fig.22. The capacitor C_D and resistor R_4-
a) decouple the power supply from RF currents.
b) provide a suitable matching point for the tuned circuit.
c) stabilise the supply voltage.
d) provide a feedback path for easy oscillation.

54. How could fig.22 be modified to enable it to be used as a mixer stage?
a) Connect the local oscillator to a centre tap on the power supply rail.
b) Insert a diode across G_1 and inject the local oscillator at T_2 secondary.
c) Short circuit the primary of T_1 and inject both signals at the battery.
d) Change the values of R_1 and R_2 to suit the MOSFET, and inject the local oscillator via a capacitor to the G_2, R_1 and R_2 junction. Tune C_2 L_2 to required mixer product.

55. The circuit shown in fig.23 is that of a typical-
a) crystal microphone amplifier.
b) crystal filter stage.
c) IF amplifier stage.
d) crystal oscillator.

56. Referring to the circuit shown in fig.23. Fine frequency adjustment is by-
a) selection of C_2 and C_3.
b) adjustment of C_1.
c) adjustment of the ratio R_1 R_2.
d) varying the crystal temperature.

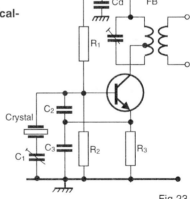

Fig.23

57. The amount of feedback applied in a crystal oscillator circuit is restricted to that just necessary to allow easy starting, this ensures that-
a) low specification crystals can be used.
b) excessive RF current does not flow in the crystal and cause it to overheat and fracture.
c) the transistor does not radiate and cause RF burns.
d) the battery power is conserved.

58. The circuit diagram shown in fig.24, is that of a-
   a) common emitter amplifier.
   b) common base amplifier.
   c) common collector amplifier.
   d) common source amplifier.

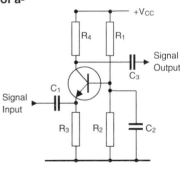

Fig.24

59. The common base circuit is useful for-
   a) providing very high voltages.
   b) suppressing mains transients.
   c) reducing distortion on sine-waves.
   d) low to high impedance matching.

60. With the configuration of fig.24, the current gain is-
   a) approximately 50.
   b) approximately 200.
   c) always less than 1.
   d) always greater than 1.

61. Referring to fig.24, it will be seen that-
   a) the base is grounded to RF currents by C_2.
   b) there is a complete reversal of supply voltage.
   c) temperature compensation is provided by C_1 and C_3.
   d) a very special type of NPN transistor has been used.

62. Referring to fig.24, the input and output signals are-
   a) in phase.
   b) 90° out of phase.
   c) 180° out of phase.
   d) 270° out of phase.

63. Referring to fig.24, the base bias potential is maintained by-
   a) resistors R_1 and R_2.
   b) resistors R_4 and R_3.
   c) resistors R_1 and R_3.
   d) capacitor C_2.

64. The input impedance of the common base amplifier is-
   a) low, 30 - 500Ω
   b) medium, 1000 - 2500Ω
   c) high, 3000 - 10,000Ω
   d) very high, 10,000 - 500,000Ω

65. The output impedance of a common base amplifier is typically-
a) low, 50 - 500Ω
b) medium, 1000 - 2500Ω
c) high, 3000 - 10,000Ω
d) very high, 200,000 - 500,000Ω

66. The circuit shown in fig.25 is that of a typical-
a) common emitter oscillator.
b) common source RF amplifier.
c) common gate RF amplifier.
d) common source RF oscillator.

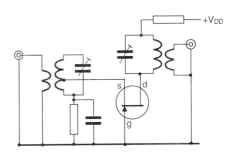

67. The circuit shown in fig.25 is often used where-
a) a radio frequency amplifier with wide bandwidth and low input impedance is required.
b) very high power gain and high current gain are required.
c) a high power oscillator is required.
d) extra low current drain is required.

Fig.25

68. What is the configuration of the amplifier circuit shown in fig.26?
a) Common collector.
b) Common emitter.
c) Common base.
d) Common source.

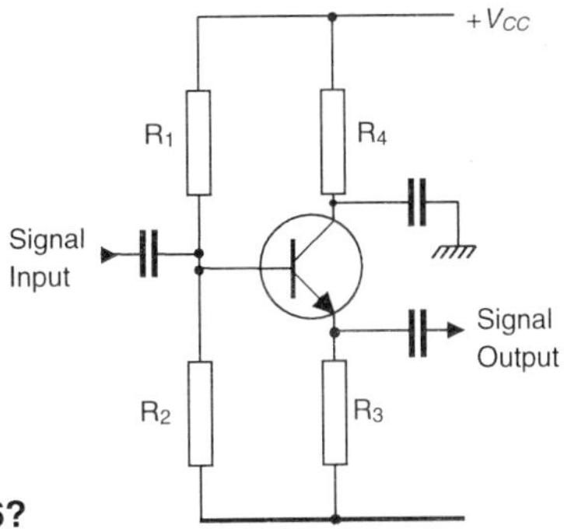

69. The circuit shown in fig.26 is referred to as -
a) a collector follower.
b) an emitter follower.
c) a base follower.
d) an emitter feeder.

70. What voltage gain would you expect from the amplifier circuit shown in fig.26?
a) Less than 1 (<1)
b) Greater than 1 (>1)
c) About 50
d) About 200

Fig.26

71. The current gain of the amplifier shown in fig.27 is-
    a) about 0.98
    b) 1
    c) usually better than 50
    d) 1000

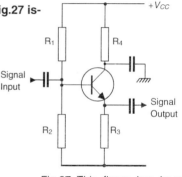

72. The circuit shown in fig.27 has-
    a) a medium power gain.
    b) a very low power gain.
    c) unity power gain.
    d) no power gain, only a loss.

Fig.27 This figure has been repeated from previous page for clarity.

73. The input impedance of the emitter follower is-
    a) high.
    b) low.
    c) equal to the source resistance.
    d) equal to R_3.

74. The output impedance of the emitter follower is-
    a) low.
    b) very high.
    c) equal to the applied load impedance.
    d) equal to $R_3 + R_4$.

75. The input and output impedances of the common collector circuit of fig.27 make it suitable for-
    a) matching high to low impedance circuits.
    b) matching low to high impedance circuits.
    c) phase shifting.
    d) earth protection circuits.

76. One very good use for the emitter follower circuit shown in fig.27 would be as a-
    a) high voltage amplifier.
    b) frequency converter.
    c) buffer amplifier for a VFO.
    d) matching device for a folded dipole.

77. Referring to fig.27, the input and output signals are-
    a) in phase.
    b) 90° out of phase.
    c) 180° out of phase.
    d) 270° out of phase.

78. Fig.28 shows the typical circuit of a-
 a) class B, complementary symmetry output stage.
 b) high speed electronic relay.
 c) device for testing NPN transistors.
 d) series power regulator.

79. Referring to fig.28. A practical circuit will require additional biasing circuitry in order to prevent-
 a) miller feedback.
 b) piezo-electric feedback.
 c) common mode signal rejection.
 d) cross-over distortion.

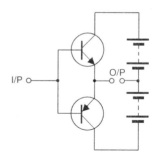

Fig.28

80. The transistor arrangement shown in fig.29 is known as a-
 a) feedback pair.
 b) base limiter.
 c) Cardington pair.
 d) Darlington pair.

81. The arrangement shown in fig.29 can be considered as a single transistor-
 a) that requires no supply current.
 b) with a negative coefficient of expansion.
 c) that has extremely low gain and low sensitivity.
 d) that has extremely high gain and high sensitivity.

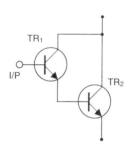

Fig.29

82. A suitable application for the configuration shown in fig.29 is as a-
 a) negative temperature stabiliser.
 b) relay or lamp driver.
 c) 5kV voltage regulator.
 d) power attenuator.

83. The symbol shown in fig.30 is a-
 a) FET switch.   b) bipolar amplifier stage.
 c) SCR (silicon controlled rectifier).   d) Zener diode.

84. A transistor used as a switch is essentially a-
 a) two state device, ON - OFF.
 b) three state device. ON - NEUTRAL - OFF.
 c) tridirectional diode.
 d) bidirectional diode.

Fig.30

85. The input/output characteristics below, show the three main classes of bias applied to transistor amplifiers, they are class A, B and C, but not in that order. Select the correct order from the list below.

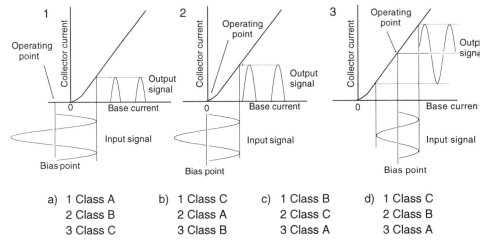

a) 1 Class A
   2 Class B
   3 Class C

b) 1 Class C
   2 Class A
   3 Class B

c) 1 Class B
   2 Class C
   3 Class A

d) 1 Class C
   2 Class B
   3 Class A

86. Class A operation is-
   a) the most efficient but least linear of the three classes.
   b) the least efficient but most linear of the three classes.
   c) no better or worse than the others for efficiency.
   d) the least efficient and least linear of the three classes.

87. Class A operation is the least efficient because-
   a) power supplies will not handle this type of operation.
   b) large input signal powers are required.
   c) there is always a collector current flowing, even with no input signal.
   d) the base current is usually zero.

88. When an amplifier is operating under class B bias conditions-
   a) collector current flows for the whole of the input cycle.
   b) collector current flows for about half of the input cycle.
   c) collector current flows for only a small part of the input cycle.
   d) there is a very high quiescent collector current.

89. With a class B amplifier the base is biased-
   a) at the point of maximum saturation.
   b) to give an I_C of 2mA.
   c) at the point where $I_B = 0.7mA$.
   d) at, or very near the point of collector current cut-off.

90. Class C operation is-
   a) the most efficient but least linear of the three classes.
   b) the most efficient and most linear of the three classes.
   c) the least linear and least efficient of the three classes.
   d) no better than any of the others for efficiency.

91. When an amplifier is operating under class C bias conditions-
   a) collector current flows for the whole of the input cycle.
   b) collector current flows for less than half of each input cycle.
   c) there is a very high quiescent collector current.
   d) there is a medium quiescent collector current.

92. Class C operation is normally used in-
   a) high quality audio amplifiers.
   b) push-pull audio amplifier stages for maximum linearity.
   c) tuned radio frequency amplifier stages.
   d) distortionless microphone amplifiers.

Answers - Solid State Devices

1	d	21	b	41	b	61	a	81	d
2	b	22	a	42	a	62	a	82	b
3	c	23	c	43	d	63	a	83	d
4	d	24	c	44	d	64	a	84	a
5	a	25	b	45	d	65	d	85	d
6	c	26	c	46	c	66	c	86	b
7	a	27	c	47	c	67	a	87	c
8	a	28	b	48	b	68	a	88	b
9	d	29	a	49	a	69	b	89	d
10	a	30	c	50	c	70	a	90	a
11	d	31	a	51	b	71	c	91	b
12	c	32	b	52	a	72	a	92	c
13	a	33	c	53	a	73	a		
14	c	34	a	54	d	74	a		
15	a	35	a	55	d	75	a		
16	b	36	a	56	b	76	c		
17	b	37	c	57	b	77	a		
18	b	38	c	58	b	78	a		
19	a	39	b	59	d	79	d		
20	b	40	b	60	c	80	d		

Answers - Solid State Devices

1. The most common material used in the manufacture of semiconductors is silicon (Si), and germanium (Ge).

2. Both silicon and germanium in their pure state are poor conductors of electricity. In order to increase the conductivity of these materials, and make them suitable for the manufacture of semiconductor devices, a small and controlled amount of impurity is introduced (a process called *doping*).

3. In N-type (negative) material there is a surplus of electrons. Electrons are the majority current carriers in N-type material.

4. In P-type (positive) material there is an excess of holes. Holes are the majority current carriers in P-type material.

5. At the junction of the P-N material there is a region depleted of holes and electrons. A barrier is thus created.

6. The diagram shows a diode, with its two terminals, referred to as the anode and cathode (as in a thermionic valve diode).

7. The diode shown is forward biased. Current will flow when the battery voltage exceeds about 0.7V for a silicon diode, and about 0.2v for a germanium diode.

8. Typical symbols encountered are: 1) Junction diode. Used in power supply units and detectors circuits. 2) Varactor, or variable capacitance diode, used in tuning and frequency modulator applications. 3) Zener diode. Used in voltage stabilisation and voltage reference circuits. 4) Thyristor. Basically a half-wave rectifier turned on by the voltage applied to the gate electrode. Used for controlling electrical power circuits, motors and lights.

9. The junction diode passes current in one direction only. It is used to change a.c. to d.c. in power supply circuits.

10. The varactor diode is operated in reverse bias, this creates a barrier at the P-N junction and the two halves of the diode are effectively isolated, and capacitance exists between them. Applying a variable reverse bias voltage varies the width of the depletion layer, hence varying the junction capacitance. An increase in reverse voltage decreases the capacitance and a decrease in reverse voltage increases the capacitance.

11. In fig.13 the reverse biased varactor diode D_1 is connected across the tuned circuit L_1 C_1. Varying the voltage across the diode with R_V will vary its capacitance and change the resonant frequency of the circuit. This tuning method is often used for oscillators and tuned RF amplifiers.

12. R_1 has a high value, about 100kΩ - 500kΩ. It prevents the d.c. control circuitry loading the oscillator. C_2 decouples any RF from the power supply.

13. R_V is the tuning control. It varies the reverse voltage across the diode. The voltage range may be restricted to ensure that the diode operates on the linear part of its capacitance/voltage curve.

14. The reverse voltage breakdown point of a diode is exploited in the Zener diode.

15,16. In fig.15 the Zener diode is used in a voltage regulator or voltage stabilisation circuit. The supply current $I_S = I_D + I_L$.

17. The devices shown are: 1) NPN transistor. 2) PNP transistor. 3) Junction field effect transistor. 4) MOSFET (Metal Oxide Semiconductor FET). The device shown has insulated gate and is referred to as an IGFET (Insulated Gate FET).

18. Field effect transistors, JFET and MOSFET have a much higher input impedance than bipolar NPN and PNP transistors.

19. Fig.16 illustrates the basic construction of an NPN transistor.

20. NPN and PNP transistors are referred to as bipolar devices because their operation depends on both positive and negative charge carriers.

21. Bipolar transistors are normally referred to as current amplifying devices.

22. The d.c. current gain h_{FE} or β (Beta). $h_{FE} = \dfrac{I_C}{I_B}$

23. $h_{FE} = \dfrac{1mA}{10\mu A} = \dfrac{1 \times 10^{-3}}{10 \times 10^{-6}} = 100$

24. The emitter current. $I_E = I_C + I_B$

25. $h_{FE} = \dfrac{I_C}{I_B}$ $\therefore$ $I_C = h_{FE}\, I_B = 100 \times 20\mu A = 2000\mu A$ or $2mA$

26. The amplifier is in the common collector configuration. It is often referred to as an emitter follower.

27. The bias voltage for the transistor is obtained from the voltage divider R1, R2.

28. In the circuit shown the base and emitter form a forward biased PN junction, the voltage V_{BE} will be approximately 0.7V for a silicon transistor.

29. For the germanium transistor voltage V_{BE} will be approximately 0.2V.

30. To ensure effective d.c. stability of the transistor the potential at the R1, R2 junction must be stable in spite of variations in base current. The current I_D in the potential divider R1, R2, should be higher than the base current, this ensures that the base is held at a reasonably constant voltage. A current in R1, R2 of $10 \times I_B$ has been chosen.

31. An increase in collector current will cause a voltage increase across the emitter resistor R_E.

32. A rise in p.d. across the emitter resistor R_E reduces the forward bias p.d., V_{BE}.

33. If the V_{BE} is reduced, I_B will decrease, reducing the collector current I_B.

34. R_E in conjunction with R_1 and R_2 provides d.c. bias and stabilisation. It reduces thermal runaway caused by any increase in leakage current I_{CBO}, this due to collector junction temperature increasing as power dissipation increases.

35. C_E is the emitter decoupling capacitor, it has a low reactance at the signal frequency and therefore bypasses the signal currents to ground, so preventing negative feedback reducing the gain of the amplifier. The d.c. bias voltage is not affected by C_E.

36. To prevent changes in the d.c. bias conditions of an amplifier stage, the stage must be isolated (from a d.c. point of view) from the adjacent stages. The a.c. signal is therefore connected to the stage via the low reactance capacitors C_C which will not pass d.c.

37. For the common emitter amplifier there is a 180° phase shift between input and output - the signal appears inverted.

38. The collector current I_C, in a correctly biased transistor varies in sympathy with the signal applied to the base. In fig.19, the varying I_C results in a varying voltage at the junction of R_C and the collector. The output signal voltage is taken between the collector and ground.

39. The input and output impedances of amplifier stages, as given, are only typical, they are dependent on circuit components and transistor gain. For a common emitter amplifier the input impedance is typically about 500Ω to $5k\Omega$.

40. The output impedance of the common emitter amplifier is typically $20k\Omega$ to $100k\Omega$.

41. The common emitter amplifier is a good general purpose amplifier, it can be used for both audio and radio frequency amplification.

42. The circuit shown is a common emitter, tuned collector amplifier.(The collector circuit is tuned by C_2, L_2.)

43. Bias and stabilisation is provided by resistors R_1, R_2 and R_3.

44. The emitter bypass capacitor C_3 should have a very low reactance X_C at the signal frequency.

45. The inductor is tapped to match the impedance of the transistor to the impedance of the parallel tuned circuit.

46. Fig.21 shows the circuit of a common emitter, tuned collector oscillator.

47. The frequency of the oscillator is determined by the resonant frequency of L_2 and C_2.

48. For oscillation to occur, the feedback voltage must be of sufficient amplitude and in the correct phase. Reversing the connections of the feedback coil L_1 may solve the problem.

49. For oscillation to occur the amplifier must overcome the losses in the circuit.

50. The circuit shown in fig.22 is a typical dual gate MOSFET RF amplifier.

51. Bias and stabilisation is provided by resistors R_1, R_2 and R_3.

52. The output impedance of the FET is a reasonable match to the parallel tuned circuit, so it isn't necessary to tap the inductor.

53. R_4 and C_D decouple the power supply from RF currents.

54. Change the frequency of the tuned circuit C_2, L_2, to required mixer product, this is usually an IF transformer in the case of a receiver, and inject the local oscillator voltage at G2. It may be necessary to change the value of resistors R_1 and R_2.

55. A crystal oscillator.

56. The frequency of the crystal may be 'pulled' over a small frequency range by capacitor C_1.

57. Excessive RF feedback may cause the crystal to overheat and fracture.

58. Fig.24 is a common base amplifier. The base is grounded to signal currents.

59. Has a low input impedance and a high output impedance. The low input impedance makes it suitable for connecting to a low impedance antenna. The common base circuit has high RF stability.

60. Current gain of the common base amplifier is always less than 1 (about 0.98).

61. The base of the transistor is grounded to signal currents, whilst retaining its d.c. bias conditions.

62. With the common base circuit the input and output signals are in phase.

63. The voltage on the base is determined by the voltage divider R_1 and R_2.

64. The input impedance of the common base amplifier is low, typically 30 - 500Ω.

65. The output impedance of the common base amplifier is high, typically 200kΩ - 500kΩ.

66. The circuit shown is that of a common gate (or grounded gate) RF amplifier employing a field effect transistor.

67. The circuit shown has low input impedance to match a typical 50 - 75Ω antenna and is suitable for wide band operation, the bandwidth determined in this case by the Q of the tuned circuits.

68. The amplifier in fig.26 is connected in the common collector configuration.

69. The common collector amplifier is often referred to as an 'emitter follower'.

70. The voltage gain of this circuit is always less than 1 (<1).

71. The current gain of the emitter follower is usually better than 50. Typical figures being between 10 and 800.

72. The emitter follower has a medium power gain. 30 - 200 is typical.

73. The input impedance of the emitter follower is high, but it depends on the shunting effect of R_1 and R_2. Typical values 20kΩ to 1MΩ.

74. The output impedance of the emitter follower is low. Typical values 20Ω - 1kΩ.

75. Due to its high input resistance and low output resistance the emitter follower is commonly used for matching (high to low resistance or impedance) and to provide isolation between stages.

76. The emitter follower is frequently used as a buffer amplifier to prevent a variable frequency oscillator from being 'pulled' or loaded by the stages that follow.

77. As with the common base amplifier, the input and output signals are in phase.

78. The circuit is a basic class B, complementary symmetry output stage. The top NPN transistor amplifies the positive half cycle of input signal, and the bottom PNP transistor amplifies the negative half cycle. In this configuration it is possible to amplify both half cycles of the input signal (with much less distortion than a single class B stage), and also retain class B operating efficiency.

79. The circuit shown will require biasing circuitry added to ensure that the amplifier is working at the correct operating point for minimum crossover distortion.

80. The configuration shown is the Darlington pair. This arrangement acts as a single transistor having a current gain equal to the product of the current gain of each individual transistor.

81. The Darlington pair has high gain and high sensitivity.

82. Typical applications are switching circuits, lamp drivers, and relay drivers.

83. Zener diode.

84. When a transistor is used as a switch it needs only two states; On and Off. In logic terms this equates to 1 and 0.

85. The three classes of operation are - 1) Class C. 2) Class B. 3) Class A.

86, 87. Class A is the least efficient of the three classes because collector current flows and power is dissipated even when no input signal is present. It will be seen from curve 3, that, provided the operating point is set to the linear part of the curve, the output signal will be an amplified replica of the input signal; this is linear amplification. Collector current will flow for the full 360° of the input cycle.

88. For class B bias, collector current flows for approximately half (180°) of the input cycle.

89. For class B operation the transistor is biased very near the point of collector current cut-off. Class B output is distorted since only half the input cycle is amplified, however, the use of two class B amplifiers connected in push-pull, where the inputs are fed 180° out of phase will result in an output signal that is a fairly faithful reproduction of the input signal. The single class B stage can be used for linear RF amplification where the original waveshape is restored by the flywheel effect of the output tuned tank circuit.

90, 91. Class C is the most efficient of the three classes of operation. Collector current flows for less than 180° of the input cycle, and the output signal is extremely distorted (non-linear) and full of harmonics; which make it suitable for use as a frequency multiplier.

92. The class C amplifier is suitable for RF amplification, and the high Q tank circuit in the output will reduce the harmonic content of the output signal.

Notes

11. Radio Receivers

In this section we will cover -
1. the superheterodyne, and the double superheterodyne receiver.
2. intermediate frequencies, adjacent channel and image frequency interference.
3. demodulation, CW, AM, FM and SSB.
4. a.g.c and other circuit features.

The Superheterodyne receiver (Superhet)

The superheterodyne receiver, since its introduction in the 1920s, has undergone various degrees of development to arrive in its present sophisticated form; offering low noise, high gain, variable selectivity, multimode operation, digitally synthesised tuning, high frequency stability, and the ability to store and scan from memory. It consumes very little power compared to its earlier valve version. It is also compact.

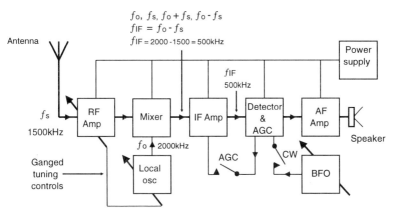

$f_0, f_s, f_0 + f_s, f_0 - f_s$
$f_{IF} = f_0 - f_s$
$f_{IF} = 2000 - 1500 = 500kHz$

Fig.1 Block diagram of the single conversion superheterodyne receiver.

The tuned RF amplifier, (or preselector) Amplifies the received signal, f_s, prior to the relatively noisy mixer stage, improving the overall signal/noise ratio. It also rejects the unwanted image signal, and prevents radiation of the local oscillator frequency. The RF stage and local oscillator are normally ganged in the tunable receiver shown in fig.1.

The local oscillator generates a signal, f_0, (f_0 is usually higher than f_s by the intermediate frequency, f_{IF}, so that $f_{IF} = f_0 - f_s$) which is applied to the mixer or frequency changer. The locally generated signal can be provided by a variable frequency oscillator, VFO, quartz crystal or frequency synthesiser. Crystal oscillators and synthesisers are more stable than variable frequency oscillators (VFOs).

11 - 1

The mixer stage translates the received signal to the intermediate frequency. It mixes f_o and f_s, producing at its output f_o, f_s, $f_o - f_s$, $f_o + f_s$, and many other frequencies. The intermediate frequency, which in fig.1 is $f_o - f_s$, is selected by the IF amplifier.

The intermediate frequency (IF) amplifier tuning is fixed, e.g. 500kHz, its purpose is to provide selectivity and reject adjacent channel signals and the unwanted mixer output frequencies. It also provides the bulk of the gain prior to the detector. In this case it is tuned to $f_o - f_s$. The IF signal is passed to the detector (or demodulator).

The detector stage in a good communication receiver should be able to demodulate CW, AM, FM, and SSB. It recovers the original modulation from the carrier. The recovered modulation is passed to the audio amplifier and then the loudspeaker.

The automatic gain control, AGC, is designed to keep the audio output level reasonably constant when the received signal level is changing.

The beat frequency oscillator (BFO) is used for the reception of CW (morse code) transmissions. Its frequency is normally variable and close to the intermediate frequency, the beat note produced is in the audible range.

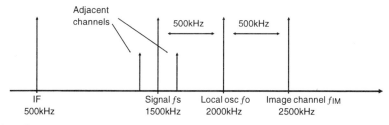

Fig.2 Frequency spectrum associated with the superheterodyne receiver in fig.1.

Adjacent channel rejection is due to the selectivity/response of the IF amplifier. Amateur communication receivers employ bandpass filters in this stage, with a passband to suit the received transmission mode. Typically - 300-500Hz for CW, 2.5-3kHz for SSB and 5 - 6kHz for AM and FM speech. As seen from fig.2 the adjacent channels are close to the wanted channel f_s.

Image channel rejection is provided by the selectivity of the RF amplifier. A high intermediate frequency is often chosen to improve image channel rejection, this has the effect of moving the image channel further from the passband of the RF amplifier.

Choice of intermediate frequency. A low intermediate frequency achieves good selectivity, since, for a given value of Q factor, the lower the centre frequency, the lower the bandwidth of the tuned circuit. A high IF provides a large frequency difference between local oscillator and signal. Therefore, the image frequency is moved further away from the signal frequency, and the selectivity characteristics of the RF stage provide greater image rejection. The double superheterodyne receiver employs a high IF for good image channel rejection and a low IF for adjacent channel rejection.

Radio Receivers

The **double superheterodyne receiver** has been designed to provide a high level of image rejection combined with a high level of adjacent channel rejection. To achieve this it has a high first IF and a low second IF. The basic block diagram is shown in fig.3.

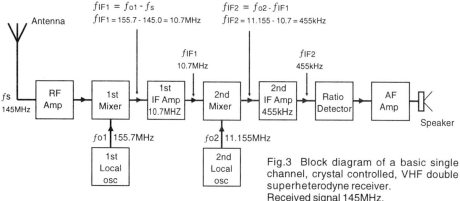

$$f_{IF1} = f_{o1} - f_s$$
$$f_{IF1} = 155.7 - 145.0 = 10.7MHz$$

$$f_{IF2} = f_{o2} - f_{IF1}$$
$$f_{IF2} = 11.155 - 10.7 = 455kHz$$

Fig.3 Block diagram of a basic single channel, crystal controlled, VHF double superheterodyne receiver. Received signal 145MHz. Showing signal frequencies at various stages. The PSU is omitted from diagram. Both oscillators are crystal controlled.

Points to note

1. Sensitivity defines a receivers ability to receive weak signals. It determines, under test conditions, the lowest signal level required to produce a given output signal/noise ratio.

2. Selectivity defines a receivers ability to receive the wanted signal and reject those on adjacent channels.

3. The bandwidth of a communication receiver is determined by the selectivity of its IF filters, which in turn are chosen to suit the mode of transmission, i.e. CW, AM, SSB, and FM.

4. A good communication receiver will have a different type of detector for each of the transmission modes it has to receive, i.e. CW, AM, SSB, and FM.

5. Image rejection. In the example shown in fig.2, the image channel is twice the IF above the signal frequency. I.e. The image frequency, $f_{IM} = f_s + 2f_{IF}$
   $= 1500kHz + (2 \times 500kHz) = 2500kHz \ or \ 2.5MHz$.
   Image rejection depends upon the ganging accuracy (where applicable), chosen IF, and selectivity of the RF stage.

6. Local oscillator 'LO' stability must be of a high order, the stability of crystal oscillators and frequency synthesisers is superior to LC oscillators.

7. The local oscillator f_o can be either above or below the signal frequency f_s.

8. The local oscillator frequency in a tunable receiver is normally chosen to be higher than the signal frequency because the minimum to maximum tuning ratio is smaller, making the tuned circuits easier to track and construct.

9. Typical IFs are 455kHz, 465kHz, 470kHz, 1.6MHz, 9MHz, 10.7MHz and 21MHz.

1. **The first function of a radio receiver is to-**
   a) detect the presence of all the signals on the antenna.
   b) absorb all signals radiated in close proximity to the antenna.
   c) select the wanted signal from the unwanted signals present at the input.
   d) act as a broad-band spectrum monitor.

2. **The selectivity of a receiver defines its ability to-**
   a) automatically select local stations.
   b) give increased audio output for decreased signal input.
   c) control the RF amplifier gain.
   d) select the wanted stations and reject the unwanted ones.

3. **The sensitivity of a receiver defines its ability to-**
   a) amplify mechanical vibrations.
   b) amplify adjacent channel signals to a level of 12dB plus.
   c) produce a useful output when receiving a weak signal.
   d) produce zero output when receiving a strong signal.

4. **Frequency stability defines a receivers ability to-**
   a) stay tuned to a wanted signal without drifting.
   b) follow the frequency of the wanted transmission if it drifts.
   c) follow the modulation of a wanted transmission with great accuracy.
   d) change frequency if required in less than $10\mu s$.

5. **In its most basic form, a radio receiver need only consist of-**
   a) a tuned circuit, diode detector and headphones.
   b) two tuned circuits, product detector, audio amplifier and headphones.
   c) a RF amplifier, an IF amplifier and a small 100mW loudspeaker.
   d) two resistors, a 1.5 volt battery and headphones.

6. **The TRF (tuned radio frequency) receiver, is known as the 'straight set' because -**
   a) it was first supplied straight from the manufacturer to the listener.
   b) it required a very long straight antenna.
   c) it was first used successfully in the 'Straits of Dover'. It should really be called a 'Dover Strait set'.
   d) the signal path is straight from the antenna and RF stages to the detector stage, with no intermediate frequency conversion.

7. **One of the problems associated with the straight set is-**
   a) that it required valves which were unobtainable when it was invented.
   b) its lack of selectivity, instability and varying gain over its tuning range.
   c) that it requires physically large tuning components, not obtainable today.
   d) that being of early 1920's design it was intended to be powered by wet Leclanche cells, not obtainable today.

Radio Receivers

8. An increase in the sensitivity of certain types of receiver is gained by including an oscillating detector stage, one such receiver is the-
   a) superheterodyne receiver.
   b) degenerative receiver.
   c) regenerative receiver.
   d) superdyne receiver.

9. The problems of the TRF receiver were overcome in the late 1920s by the-
   a) superheterodyne receiver.
   b) degenerative receiver.
   c) superlative receiver.
   d) phase-locked receiver.

10. The superheterodyne receiver is one in which-
    a) the signal frequency and the intermediate frequency are mixed to produce the audio output.
    b) the signal frequency and the local oscillator frequency are mixed to produce the intermediate frequency.
    c) the signal frequency and the intermediate frequency are mixed to produce the beat frequency.
    d) there is no selectivity in the IF stage.

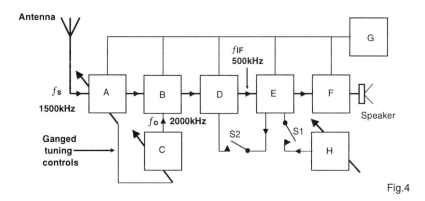

Fig.4

11. Fig.4 shows the block diagram of a basic superheterodyne receiver. What is block A?
    a) Audio amplifier. b) Tuning dial.
    c) Local oscillator. d) RF amplifier.

12. **What is the function of the RF amplifier in a superheterodyne receiver?**
    a) It matches the crystal to the mixer stage.
    b) It prevents the audio signals radiating from the antenna.
    c) It improves the IF amplifier frequency response, reduces phase distortion in the detector stage and reduces harmonic distortion in the audio stage.
    d) It improves the noise figure of the receiver, reduces image channel interference and reduces local oscillator radiation.

13. **What is block C fig.4?**
    a) Audio amplifier.   b) Power regulator.
    c) Local oscillator.   d) RF amplifier.

14. **What is block B fig.4?**
    a) Detector stage.   b) Mixer stage.
    c) Local oscillator.   d) IF amplifier.

15. **Which stage in a superheterodyne receiver provides the bulk of the gain and selectivity?**
    a) Audio amplifier.   b) Beat frequency amplifier.
    c) RF amplifier.   d) IF amplifier.

16. **Which block in fig.4 is referred to in your answer to Q15?**
    a) A   b) B
    c) C   d) D

17. **Referring to fig.4. Which block is the detector stage?**
    a) C   b) D
    c) E   d) F

18. **The detector stages in a good HF communications receiver should be capable of handling-**
    a) very large power supply changes.
    b) high voltage surges due to lightning strikes.
    c) FM, AM, SSB and CW signals.
    d) Pulse width modulation, FSTV, and wideband broadcast transmissions.

19. **What is block G fig.4?**
    a) Power supply.   b) AGC detector.
    c) Tuning control.   d) Negative feedback stage.

20. **What is block F fig.4?**
    a) Power supply.   b) Mains transformer.
    c) Detector stage.   d) Audio amplifier.

Radio Receivers

21. Referring to fig.4. What is the required frequency at the output of the mixer stage?
a) Local oscillator frequency.
b) Incoming signal frequency.
c) Intermediate frequency.
d) Audio frequency.

22. Which stage provides the adjacent channel selectivity in the superheterodyne receiver?
a) IF stage.   b) RF stage.
c) Mixer stage.   d) Beat frequency oscillator.

23. Image, or second channel rejection occurs in the-
a) IF stage.   b) RF stage.
c) Audio stage.   d) Mixer stage.

24. Which stage of a superhet reduces the level of local oscillator signal which might be fed back to the antenna?
a) IF stage.   b) RF stage.
c) Mixer stage.   d) AGC amplifier.

25. When receiving an on-off keyed morse telegraphy transmission, box H is needed. What is box H fig.4?
a) BFO.   b) Second detector.
c) Band pass filter.   d) Product detector.

26. The process known as heterodyning is-
a) not recommended, as it produces many unwanted frequencies.
b) the addition, in a linear detection device of d.c. signal currents.
c) the combination of two different high frequency currents to produce a current at a third frequency.
d) the conversion of two different RF signals into their d.c. states.

27. If two frequencies, as shown in fig.5, are applied to the input of a mixer stage that uses a single diode, which set of frequencies from the list below would you expect to be present at the output?
a) 500Hz, 10kHz and 19kHz
b) 109kHz and 209kHz
c) 9,100kHz and 9,200kHz
d) 9kHz, 1000kHz, 1009kHz and 2009kHz

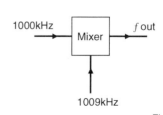

Fig.5

28. The mixer, or frequency changer stage of a superheterodyne receiver is shown in fig.6. The local oscillator frequency is usually higher than the signal frequency , by the-

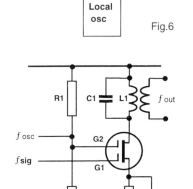

Fig.6

   a) signal frequency, $f_o = f_s + f_s$
   b) audio frequency, $f_o = f_s + 2f_o$
   c) intermediate frequency, $f_o = f_s + f_{IF}$
   d) image frequency, $f_o = f_o + f_s$

29. Fig.7 shows the circuit of a basic MOSFET mixer stage, the tuned circuit, L1, C1, should be tuned to the-

   a) RF signal frequency.
   b) intermediate frequency.
   c) oscillator frequency.
   d) image frequency.

30. Referring to fig.7. The input impedance of G1 and G2 is high, and there is good isolation between them, therefore-

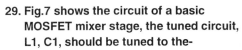

Fig.7

   a) the power supplied by the local oscillator is negligible. Oscillator pulling is minimum. There is good isolation between the local oscillator and the antenna.
   b) the local oscillator must supply at least 3 watts of RF power.
   c) the device is very inefficient.
   d) there must be a distortionless signal present.

31. Fig.8 shows the circuit of a-
   a) voltage multiplier.
   b) voltage control circuit.
   c) double balanced mixer circuit.
   d) quadro-phase mixer circuit.

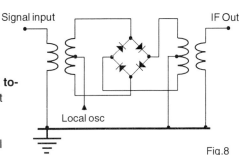

Fig.8

32. The circuit shown in fig.8 is used to-
   a) produce a high voltage output at the signal frequency.
   b) produce sum and difference frequencies by mixing the signal and local oscillator frequencies.
   c) produce the AGC voltage.
   d) multiply the input frequency by the number of diodes.

Radio Receivers

33. The type of mixer circuit shown in fig.8 requires a higher local oscillator drive level than the MOSFET mixer of fig.7. It is capable of-
   a) good intermodulation performance and good isolation between the ports.
   b) keeping the power source constant.
   c) high conversion gain.
   d) high power gain.

34. Normally transistor active mixers-
   a) are very expensive.
   b) are difficult to manufacture.
   c) exhibit a conversion gain.
   d) exhibit a conversion loss.

35. The passive diode type of mixers-
   a) are very expensive because of the diodes.
   b) are only a theoretical concept.
   c) exhibit a conversion gain.
   d) exhibit a conversion loss.

36. Fig.9 shows part of a superheterodyne receiver which tunes over the band 550 - 1500kHz. With the local oscillator frequency set above the signal frequency, what will be the minimum and maximum frequency that the oscillator will be required to tune? Note, the IF is 465kHz.
   a) 550 - 1550kHz
   b) 465 - 1465kHz
   c) 1015 - 1965kHz
   d) 3 - 30MHz

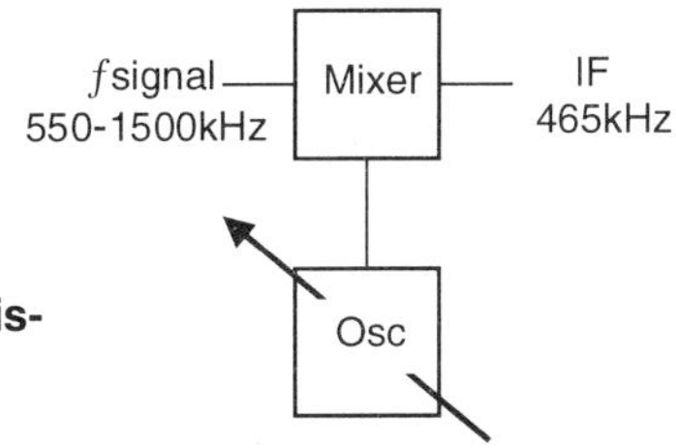

   f signal—[Mixer]— IF
   550-1500kHz   465kHz

   [Osc]

   Fig.9

37. Referring to Q 36. The oscillator tuning ratio is-
   a) 2.7:1   b) 3.15:1
   c) 1.94:1   d) 12.2:1

38. Referring to Q 36. If the local oscillator is set below the signal frequency, what minimum and maximum frequency would the oscillator be required to tune?
   a) 85 - 1035kHz   b) 3 - 30MHz
   c) 1015 - 1965kHz   d) 465 - 1465kHz

39. Referring to Q 38. The oscillator tuning ratio is-
   a) 2.7:1   b) 3.15:1
   c) 1.94:1   d) 12.2:1

40. The superheterodyne local oscillator frequency is usually higher than the signal frequency because-
  a) it has been standard practice since the 1919 Treaty of Versailles.
  b) the local oscillator voltage increases with frequency.
  c) the lower frequencies interfere with hi-fi systems.
  d) the tuned circuits are easier to design and track with a lower minimum to maximum tuning ratio.

41. Fig.10 shows the RF amplifier and local oscillator tuned circuits of super-heterodyne receiver. The trimming and padding capacitors are provided to ensure that-
  a) high voltage flashover does not occur.
  b) the resonant points of the oscillator and RF circuits are maintained at a constant frequency difference.
  c) the effects of dampness and mould on the insulators are minimised.
  d) electrical stress due to high 'Q' values is reduced.

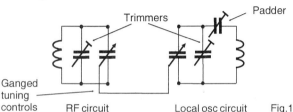

Fig.10

42. Oscillators must exhibit good frequency stability. LC oscillators should have voltage stabilised supply rails, and be mechanically rigid and stable. The tuned circuits and the other components should also-
  a) conform to BS 800.
  b) be free from temperature changes.
  c) be as large as possible.
  d) be free of soldered joints.

43. Fig.11 is the circuit of a typical-
  a) tuned collector oscillator.
  b) Hartley oscillator.
  c) Clapp oscillator.
  d) crystal oscillator.

44. The frequency of oscillation fig.11 is determined by-
  a) L1 and C1   b) R1 and R2
  c) R3 and C3   d) R3 and L2

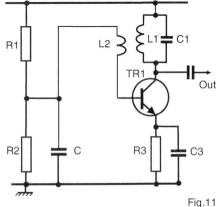

Fig.11

45. The inductor L2 in fig.11 is the-
a) feedback coil, mutually coupled to L1. It feeds part of the output back to the input in the correct phase for oscillation to occur.
b) main tuning inductor, having a very high Q factor.
c) main tuning inductor, having a very low Q factor.
d) frequency stabilising inductor, having a variable Q factor.

46. When a communications receiver is required to tune to a few spot frequencies only, with much greater frequency stability, the variable frequency oscillator can be replaced by a crystal controlled oscillator, but;-
a) the PSU is likely to overload.
b) the oscillator cavity will become parasitic.
c) a large 10 henry variable inductance will be necessary
d) a crystal for each frequency or channel will be necessary.

47. Referring to Q 46. Additional frequency stability for this type of oscillator will be achieved by-
a) selecting a FET with a high gain.
b) silver plating the cavity.
c) using gold plated wire for the inductor.
d) enclosing the crystal in a temperature controlled oven.

48. Where multi-channel operation with crystal stability is required, the local oscillator could be replaced by a-
a) moving coil oscillator.
b) frequency synthesiser.
c) harmonic generator.
d) cavity oscillator.

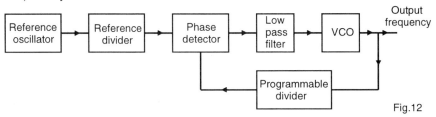

Fig.12

49. Fig.12 shows the block diagram of a frequency synthesiser. What is the VCO?
a) A variable carrier oscillator.
b) A voltage controlled oscillator.
c) A voltage coupled oscillator.
d) A versatile control oscillator.

50. The output frequency of the frequency synthesiser shown in fig12, is changed by-
   a) an external manual control on the VCO.
   b) internal switching in the low pass filter (LPF).
   c) changing the binary code on the programmable divider.
   d) internal binary switching within the VCO.

51. Selection of the frequency step size, or channel spacing of a frequency synthesiser is determined by-
   a) internal binary switching within the VCO.
   b) external switching at the low pass filter (LPF).
   c) the waveshape of the VCO output.
   d) the reference frequency at the comparator input.

52. There can be many unwanted frequencies present at the output of a mixer stage. How does the IF amplifier discriminate against them?
   a) By rejecting signals outside its passband.
   b) By passing only the audio frequencies.
   c) By exploiting the AGC circuitry.
   d) It doesn't, the rejection is in the AF amplifier.

53. The adjacent channel selectivity of the IF amplifier is determined by the-
   a) design of the IF transformers and filters.
   b) bandwidth of the RF stages.
   c) noise generated in the mixer stage.
   d) bandwidth of the beat frequency oscillator (BFO).

54. Shown below are four ideal receiver bandpass characteristics.
   Match the type of received transmission to the most suitable bandwidth.

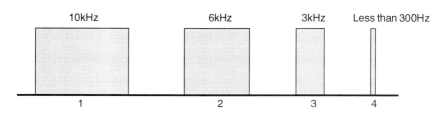

a)	1 AM b'cast.	b)	1 CW.	c)	1 SSB speech	d)	1 AM speech.
	2 AM speech		2 AM b'cast		2 CW.		2 SSB speech.
	3 SSB speech		3 AM speech.		3 AM b'cast.		3 CW.
	4 CW.		4 SSB speech.		4 AM speech.		4 AM b'cast.

Radio Receivers

55. Referring to fig.13. To where in a receiver circuit is point 'X' likely to be connected?
a) The local oscillator.
b) The AGC line.
c) The audio output.
d) The VCO.

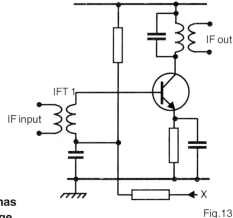

Fig.13

56. You are told that block 'X' fig.14 has been included after the mixer stage to improve the receiver selectivity. What is it?
a) A high pass filter.
b) A low pass filter.
c) An IF preamplifier.
d) An IF crystal filter.

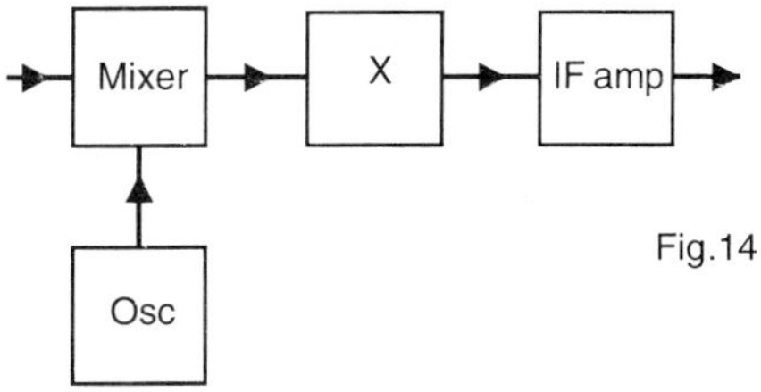

Fig.14

57. If an HF receiver has a fairly wide RF bandwidth, and a low IF, it is likely that it will suffer from-
a) image, or second channel interference.
b) severe frequency modulation distortion.
c) audio regeneration in the mixer stage.
d) severe overloading in the AGC amplifier.

58. The problem encountered in Q 57 is overcome in the double superheterodyne receiver by employing two stages of frequency conversion. The first IF is high, this improves the-
a) image, or second channel rejection.
b) audio quality.
c) receiver gain.
d) first IF rejection.

59. The second IF is lower than the first, this stage provides most of the-
a) receiver's gain and adjacent channel selectivity.
b) audio frequency gain.
c) image, or second channel rejection.
d) linearity of the audio output.

60. **Fig.15 shows the typical spectrum of various signals associated with a superhet receiver. The IF is 500kHz, the received signal is 1.5MHz. What is signal 'C' in the spectrum?**
   a) The intermediate frequency.
   b) The local oscillator.
   c) The image, or second channel.
   d) The carrier insertion oscillator.

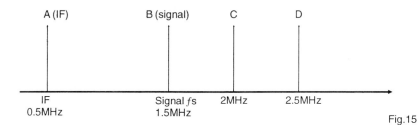

Fig.15

61. **Referring to fig.15. What is the signal 'D' in the spectrum?**
   a) The intermediate frequency.
   b) The local oscillator.
   c) The image, or second channel.
   d) The carrier insertion oscillator.

62. **Fig.16 represents the mixer stage of a superhet receiver which is tuned to receive a signal on 20MHz. The image frequency, $f_s + 2f_{IF}$ will be-**
   a) 2MHz.
   b) 23.2MHz.
   c) 3.5MHz.
   d) 4MHz.

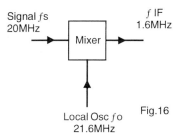

Fig.16

63. **A receiver with an IF of 10.7MHz is tuned to a wanted signal of 145.7MHz. The local oscillator frequency is 135MHz. Which one of the following frequencies is likely to cause image or second channel interference?**
   a) 124.3kHz
   b) 124.3MHz
   c) 280.7MHz
   d) 21.4MHz

64. The detector circuit shown in fig.17 is for the detection of AM signals. It is usually referred to as-
   a) an envelope detector.
   b) a product detector.
   c) a discriminator.
   d) a ratio detector.

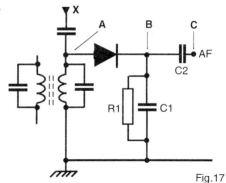

Fig.17

65. Which of the waveforms shown below would you expect to find at points A to C in the circuit shown in fig.17?

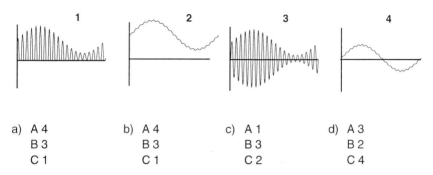

   a) A 4
      B 3
      C 1

   b) A 4
      B 3
      C 1

   c) A 1
      B 3
      C 2

   d) A 3
      B 2
      C 4

66. Referring to the detector circuit shown in fig.17. Is it possible to receive a frequency modulated signal?
   a) No.
   b) Yes, but only if it uses a silicon diode.
   c) Yes, by setting the local oscillator lower than the signal.
   d) Yes, by tuning the received signal halfway down the IF response curve (slope detection).

67. Is it possible to receive CW and SSB signals with the detector shown in fig.17?
   a) No
   b) Yes, by replacing the diode with a hot carrier diode.
   c) Yes, by injecting a BFO or a CIO at point X in fig.17.
   d) Yes, by feeding the audio output back to the RF input to produce a form of degenerative detector stage.

68. The type of detector that you would normally associate with resolving CW and SSB signals is the-
   a) envelope detector.
   b) product detector.
   c) discriminator.
   d) ratio detector.

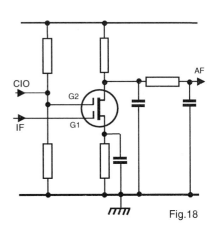

69. Fig.18 is the circuit of a typical-
   a) dual gate MOSFET CW/SSB product detector.
   b) dual gate MOSFET audio amplifier.
   c) receiver first mixer stage.
   d) CW/SSB AGC amplifier.

Fig.18

70. Part of the improvement gained by the use of an SSB system is due to-
   a) the reduced receiver bandwidth of approx: 2500Hz (2.5kHz), and a reduction in multipath propagation distortion on sky-wave transmissions.
   b) the increased receiver bandwidth of approx: 6kHz.
   c) reduced receiver bandwidth reducing the signal/noise ratio by 20dB.
   d) the noise cancelling properties of the product detector.

71. For SSB reception, the carrier insertion oscillator (CIO)-
   a) reinserts the carrier which was suppressed when the SSB signal was generated.
   b) cancels-out any residual carrier present on the received transmission.
   c) is used to hold the AGC at a constant level.
   d) is used for automatic frequency locking.

72. When receiving a CW signal, the BFO is usually adjusted by the operator to produce an audible beat note, or tone, at the detector output of about-
   a) 400 - 1000Hz
   b) 2000 - 2500kHz
   c) 500 - 2000kHz
   d) 2000 - 4500Hz

73. A suitable BFO frequency for the circuit shown in fig.19 would be-
   a) 500kHz ± 10Hz
   b) 1MHz ± 3kHz
   c) 465kHz
   d) 500kHz ± 3kHz

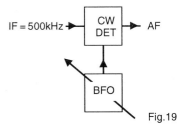

Fig.19

74. The required BFO frequency to produce a 1kHz beat note at the audio output of fig.19 is-
a) 499 or 501kHz
b) 49.9 or 50.1kHz
c) 9 or 11kHz
d) 1Hz

75. The purpose of automatic gain control (AGC), is to-
a) reduce spurious emissions from the receiver output.
b) maintain constant selectivity in the IF stages.
c) ensure a constant frequency separation between the signal and the oscillator.
d) maintain a reasonably constant audio output level when the received RF signals are varying in amplitude or fading.

76. The operation of a simple AGC system is that as the received signal level increases-
a) a feedback signal reduces the local oscillator output level.
b) the output of the AGC detector increases, and is fed back to the early stages of the receiver in such a way that it will reduce the receiver RF and/or IF gain.
c) the output of the AGC detector increases the d.c. bias in the IF coils, lowering the 'Q' and hence the gain of the IF amplifier stages.
d) the gain of the BFO decreases, reducing the audio output.

77. One of the problems of a simple AGC circuit is that-
a) it is difficult to adjust.
b) the AGC voltage will interact with the d.c. power supply voltage.
c) the AGC diodes fail when strong signals are received.
d) even weak signals cause a reduction in receiver gain and output level.

78. To overcome the problem referred to in Q 77 above-
a) the circuit is made self regulating.
b) a regulated power supply is used.
c) diodes with a higher PIV are used.
d) delayed AGC is employed.

79. Delayed AGC-
a) has a delay time of 75ms.
b) has an attack time of 1s.
c) does not start to reduce the gain of the receiver until the RF signal has reached a predetermined level.
d) must have the same time constant as the audio detector.

80. Fig.20 shows the circuit of a-
a) typical FM ratio detector.
b) wideband SSB detector.
c) narrow band CW/SSB detector.
d) linear DSB detector.

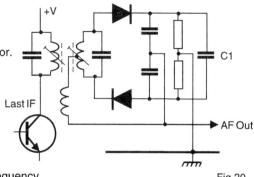

Fig.20

81. Referring to fig.20. Both tuned circuits are resonant at the-
a) signal frequency.
b) local oscillator frequency.
c) modulation frequency.
d) unmodulated intermediate frequency.

82. Some FM detectors need to be preceded by a limiter stage, however, the ratio detector is reasonably immune from amplitude variations due to-
a) an AGC circuit to reduce the level of the received signal.
b) a double balanced mixer stage.
c) the inclusion of C1.
d) a limiter stage which removes frequency variations from the received signal.

83. The term 'capture effect' is very often used when talking about FM receivers. Capture effect is-
a) a disadvantage, it captures more carrier than modulation.
b) a disadvantage, capturing any signal within 405kHz of the carrier.
c) an advantage, it locks the AGC to the incoming signal.
d) an advantage, because when two co-channel signals are present, the stronger of the two signals is captured and produces the audio output.

84. The presence of strong unwanted signals at any non-linear stage of a receiver can cause-
a) demagnetisation of the loudspeaker magnet.
b) cross-modulation, intermodulation and blocking.
c) a.c. to d.c. conversion in the BFO of the receiver.
d) a large change in the resonant frequency of the RF tuned circuits.

85. The audio stage of a communication receiver requires-
a) an audio bandwidth of 300-3000Hz, and an output power of about 1 to 2 Watts.
b) a 15kHz bandwidth, and a power output of 15 Watts.
c) a 200kHz bandwidth, and a power output of 25 Watts.
d) a flat frequency response of 30-300Hz, and a power output of 8 Watts.

1	c	16	d	31	c	46	d	61	c	76	b
2	d	17	c	32	b	47	d	62	b	77	d
3	c	18	c	33	a	48	b	63	b	78	d
4	a	19	a	34	c	49	b	64	a	79	c
5	a	20	d	35	d	50	c	65	d	80	a
6	d	21	c	36	c	51	d	66	d	81	d
7	b	22	a	37	c	52	a	67	c	82	c
8	c	23	b	38	a	53	a	68	b	83	d
9	a	24	b	39	d	54	a	69	a	84	b
10	b	25	a	40	d	55	b	70	a	85	a
11	d	26	c	41	b	56	d	71	a		
12	d	27	d	42	b	57	a	72	a		
13	c	28	c	43	a	58	a	73	d		
14	b	29	b	44	a	59	a	74	a		
15	d	30	a	45	a	60	b	75	d		

1, 2. The transmitted carrier wave places the transmission in its allocated part of the spectrum. Since the spectrum is usually overcrowded the main function of the receiver must be to select the wanted signal from the unwanted signals at its input, its ability to do this is referred to as selectivity.

3. Sensitivity defines a receivers ability to provide a useful output when receiving a weak signal. Under test conditions a signal source is connected, and the lowest RF input level noted that will produce a given output signal/noise ratio. The test could alternatively specify SINAD ratio (not discussed here) or simply output power level.

4. Frequency stability defines a receivers ability to stay tuned to the wanted signal without drifting. The local oscillator frequency must be very stable, particularly when receiving SSB and narrow band CW signals.

5. Answer a) lists the components required for a simple modern crystal set. The semiconductor diode replacing the crystal and cat's whisker of yesterday.

6. The TRF (tuned radio frequency) receiver has no frequency changing stages, the received signal is amplified and fed *straight* to the detector and audio stage.

7. The TRF receiver is likely to require several ganged stages of tuned RF amplification prior to the detector. Selectivity and sensitivity is variable from one end of the band to the other. The RF amplifiers can become unstable and start to oscillate.

8. Using the regenerative receiver for CW and SSB reception the detector is adjusted for oscillation, at a slightly different frequency from the received carrier. For AM detection the feedback is adjusted to just below the point of oscillation. The difference frequency (audio) is amplified and passed through a low pass filter.

9. The superheterodyne receiver, by converting the received signals to a common intermediate frequency (IF) is able to provide a high stable gain and defined bandwidth. This due to the fixed frequency, stable, IF amplifier.

10. In the superheterodyne receiver the required signal is mixed, or heterodyned, with a second signal, the local oscillator, to produce a third frequency, the intermediate frequency, this is amplified in the high gain, selective IF amplifier.

11, 12. Block A is the RF amplifier (sometimes called the preselector). Its selectivity is such, that when centred on the wanted signal, it rejects the image channel signal. It also amplifies the wanted signal prior to the mixer stage, resulting in improved signal/noise ratio, and reduces the possibility of local oscillator radiation from the antenna.

13. Block C, the local oscillator, in this example it is tunable. In some cases it may be a fixed frequency oscillator and use a quartz crystal for frequency stability. Also in this example its tuning is ganged to the RF amplifier tuning.

14. Block B. The mixer stage mixes or heterodynes the signal and local oscillator frequencies to produce sum and difference frequencies, one of which is the required intermediate frequency.

15, 16. From answer 14, the intermediate frequency is selected by the IF amplifier, block D, which has high gain and good selectivity.

17, 18. Block E is the detector stage. The detector stage of a communications receiver should be able to detect or demodulate FM, AM, SSB and CW signals.

19. Block G. The power supply must supply adequate power to operate the receiver. The local oscillator supply should be voltage stabilised to reduce frequency drift.

20. Block F. The audio output stage should be capable of driving a loudspeaker or headphones. In most cases an audio bandwidth of 300-3000Hz will be adequate.

21. There are many frequencies present at the output of a mixer stage, the required intermediate frequency in this case is 500kHz (0.5MHz)
$f_{IF} = f_o - f_s = 2000kHz - 1500kHz = 500kHz$.

22. Adjacent channel selectivity is provided in the IF stage.
Normally selective bandpass crystal filters will be fitted in this stage.

23. Image channel rejection is mainly due to the response of the RF stage. It selects the wanted signal and rejects signals at the image frequency.

24. The RF stage. See answer 11.

25. Box H. The beat frequency oscillator (BFO) is used for the reception of CW (on-off keyed morse telegraphy, emission class A1A) signals. It can also be used when receiving SSB (J3E) transmissions, but is not the preferred method.

26. Heterodyning is the beating or mixing of two signals to produce a third signal.

27. The output of the mixer stage produces sum and difference frequencies plus the original frequencies, i.e. 9kHz, 1000kHz, 1009kHz, and 2009kHz.
Since a mixer stage is nonlinear many other frequencies will be generated.

28. The difference between the signal frequency and the local oscillator frequency is the intermediate frequency. $f_{IF} = f_o - f_s$ and $f_o = f_s + f_{IF}$

29. There are many frequencies present at the output of a mixer stage, the output tuned circuit should be tuned to the intermediate frequency.

30. There is a high degree of isolation between the signal and the local oscillator circuits, therefore a strong signal is not likely to pull the local oscillator off tune. Since the isolation between antenna and local oscillator is high, the possibility of local oscillator energy being radiated from the antenna is minimal.

31, 32, 33. There are many types of mixer circuit in use, each type chosen for certain performance/cost characteristics. The double balanced mixer shown produces sum and difference frequencies at its output, offers good intermodulation performance, and good isolation between its ports.

34. Transistor mixers are active devices requiring a supply voltage, they exhibit a conversion gain. The converted signal being greater than the RF input signal. Typical conversion gain figures for active mixers may be 10 - 15dB.

35. Passive mixers employing diodes do not require a supply voltage, they have a conversion loss of about 6 - 8dB.

36. With an IF of 465kHz the local oscillator will be 465kHz above the signal frequency- $f_o = f_s + 465$kHz. The tuning range of the receiver is 550 to 1500kHz, therefore the oscillator will need to tune (550 + 465) to (1500 + 465) or 1015 to 1965kHz.

37. The local oscillator tuning ratio is 1965/1015 = 1.94:1.

38. With an IF of 465kHz and the local oscillator 465kHz below the signal frequency- $f_o = f_s - 465$kHz. The tuning range of the receiver is 550 to 1500kHz, therefore the oscillator will need to tune (550 − 465) to (1500 − 465) or 85 to 1035kHz.

39. The local oscillator tuning ratio is 1035/85 = 12.2:1.

40. As seen from examples 36-39, having a local oscillator above the signal frequency requires a tuning ratio of approx 2:1, whereas having the local oscillator below the signal frequency requires the oscillator tuned circuits to cope with a much larger tuning ratio, approx 12:1. The lower tuning ratio makes tuned circuit construction easier, and also allows easier tracking adjustment between the local oscillator and the RF amplifier.

41. The trimmers and padders are fitted to ensure that the local oscillator and RF amplifier tuned circuits are resonant at a constant frequency difference.

42. Temperature changes can cause component values to change. If the affected components are in the frequency determining circuits of an oscillator, the oscillator frequency will change. Oscillator design must take account of this.

43. Fig.11 shows a basic tuned collector oscillator. Oscillation is maintained by feeding back part of the output power, in the correct phase, to the input.

44. L1 and C1 determine the frequency of the oscillator. $f_o = \dfrac{1}{2\pi\sqrt{L\,C}}$.

45. Energy to maintain oscillation is fed back to the input of the transistor via the feedback coil L2, which is mutually coupled to L1. The feedback needs to be in the correct phase for oscillation to occur. If oscillation does not occur, reversing the winding connections may be necessary.

46. A crystal oscillator is very frequency stable compared with an LC oscillator, but one crystal will be needed for each channel tuned.

47. Frequency stability can be improved by enclosing the crystal in a temperature controlled oven.

48. A frequency synthesiser may be used to replace the oscillator in most modern receivers today. Its frequency stability and accuracy is derived from a quartz crystal reference oscillator. The output of the synthesiser can be made to cover a wide band of equally spaced frequencies.

49. The frequency of the VCO (voltage controlled oscillator) is changed by varying the d.c. control voltage applied to a varactor diode in its tuned circuit.

50. The output frequency of the synthesiser is determined by the division ratio of the programmable divider, this can be set by switches or a microprocessor.

51. The frequency step size, hence channel spacing, i.e. 10,12.5 and 25kHz etc; is determined by the reference frequency.

52. The IF amplifier has a preset passband, this is usually determined by the IF bandpass filters. Only signals at the intermediate frequency are passed.

53. Adjacent channel selectivity is mainly determined by the response curve of the IF stage, which in a communication receiver includes crystal filters.

54. Typical bandwidths are AM broadcast-10kHz, AM speech-6kHz, SSB-3kHz and CW-less than 300Hz.

55. Fig 13 shows a typical IF stage, automatic gain control (AGC) is applied at point X.

56. Block X is an intermediate frequency bandpass crystal filter.

57. Insufficient selectivity in the RF stage can result in image channel interference if the image channel is passed by the RF stage to the mixer.

Answers - Radio Receivers

58. The double superheterodyne overcomes the problem of image channel inter-ference by employing a high frequency first IF. The higher the IF, the further the image is separated from the signal, causing the image signal to fall outside the response curve of the RF amplifier and not reach the mixer.

59. Using a second IF stage, lower in frequency than the first, improves the adjacent channel selectivity of the superheterodyne receiver. The IF amplifier stages provide most of the receivers gain.

60. Fig.15 shows the spectrum of frequencies in a superheterodyne receiver. The IF is 500kHz, therefore, the local oscillator is 500kHz (0.5MHz) above the received signal. $f_o = f_s + f_{IF} = 1.5MHz + 0.5MHz = 2.0MHz$. Signal C on the spectrum.

61. Signal D is the image or second channel.
$f_{IM} = f_s + 2f_{IF} = 1.5MHz + (2 \times 0.5MHz) = 2.5MHz$.

62. $f_{IM} = f_s + 2f_{IF} = 20MHz + (2 \times 1.6MHz) = 23.2MHz$.

63. In this case the local oscillator is below the signal frequency, therefore the image channel is 10.7MHz below the oscillator frequency. $135 - 10.7 = 124.3MHz$.

64. The AM detector of fig.17 is referred to as an envelope detector because its purpose is to recover the modulation envelope or intelligence from the modulated wave. The diode is connected as a half wave rectifier. The time constant of C1 and R1 is important. C1 and R1 should be chosen so that the waveform across them closely follows the envelope of the modulated signal applied to the diode. C2 passes the a.c. component of the modulation and blocks the d.c. component. The output wave shape is very close to the original modulation, with little, if any, of the carrier frequency remaining. Addition of a BFO enables CW signals to be detected.

65. Looking at the waveforms we see that 3 is the amplitude modulated RF signal applied to the detector. 2 is the modulation envelope developed across C1 and R1, there is slight ripple due to the carrier wave. 4 is the original modulation with its d.c. component removed due to the action of C2.

66. The envelope detector can receive an FM signal if the receiver is slightly detuned so that the signal appears on the skirt or side of the response curve rather than at the centre of it, thus producing frequency to amplitude conversion of the modulated signal, which if fed to an AM detector restores the original modulation.

67. The envelope detector can be made to receive CW and SSB signals by injecting a signal from a BFO (beat frequency oscillator) or CIO (carrier insertion oscillator).

68, 69. The product detector is the preferred circuit for receiving SSB signals. The CIO (carrier insertion oscillator) is mixed with the IF signal to produce sum and difference frequencies. Filtering is provided at the output of the detector to ensure only the audio (difference) frequency, and no IF or BFO frequencies reach the audio stage.

70. Reduced bandwidth conserves spectrum, the space required by one DSB transmission can accommodate two SSB transmissions. With a DSB signal the USB and LSB can take different paths through the ionosphere, causing multipath distortion, whereas with SSB the second sideband is not transmitted.

71. With SSB suppressed carrier working, (J3E), the carrier is suppressed before transmission and has to be reinserted at the receiver. It must be at the same frequency as the original carrier or at least within 100Hz of it or distortion will occur.

72. For CW reception the BFO should be adjusted to give a comfortable audio tone to the listener, this may be around 500 - 800Hz.

73. To produce a suitable audio beat note, the BFO, with its centre frequency the same as the IF, should be variable, typically ±3kHz either side of the IF. In this case, for a 500kHz IF the BFO is 500kHz ±3kHz.

74. Since the IF is 500kHz, the detector will produce a 1kHz audible beat note (the difference frequency) when the BFO is set to 499kHz or 501kHz. The sum frequency will not be audible.

75, 76. Automatic gain control (AGC) enables the receiver to maintain a fairly constant output level when the received signal is fading. The received signal is fed to the AGC detector which produces the AGC voltage. The AGC voltage controls the gain of the early stages of the receiver, such that when the signal increases, the AGC voltage increases, reducing the receiver gain, and vice-versa.

77, 78, 79. The problem with the simple AGC system described above is that even weak signals can reduce the receiver gain, therefore a system of delayed AGC is employed. With delayed AGC the received signal has to reach a predetermined level before AGC action starts to take effect.

80, 81. There are several types of FM detector circuit, the ratio detector shown is probably the most common. Both tuned circuits are tuned to the unmodulated intermediate frequency.

82. FM receiver IF stages are often designed to limit amplitude variations. However, capacitor C1 renders the ratio detector fairly immune from amplitude variations.

83. An FM receiver is able to capture a strong signal in the presence of a weaker unwanted signal. This effect is particularly noticeable on wideband FM systems.

84. Strong unwanted signals present at the input of any non-linear device mix with eachother and produce intermodulation products. Strong signals present in the early stages of a receiver can also modulate other signals, causing the modulation of one signal to appear on the other, this is crossmodulation. Strong signals can cause desensitisation or blocking, the blocking signal need not be in the IF passband.

85. The audio output stage of a typical communication receiver will have a bandwidth of 300-3000Hz. An audio output power of 1 to 2 watts may be sufficient.

12. Transmitters

This section will cover-
1. oscillators and factors affecting their stability.
2. types of oscillator, L/C, crystal and frequency synthesiser.
3. transmitter stages, buffers, frequency multipliers, drivers, and valve and transistor power amplifiers.
4. principles and types of modulation. Continuous wave telegraphy (CW), Amplitude modulation (AM), Frequency modulation (FM), and Single sideband (SSB).
5. tuning and use of dummy load.

Types of transmission and class of emission
Continuous wave telegraphy CW (A1A) A continuous carrier wave is keyed on and off. Narrow transmission bandwidth of a few hundred hertz is typical.

Amplitude modulation AM (A3E) An audio frequency signal modulates the amplitude of a carrier wave. Bandwidth 6kHz for commercial quality speech. Both sidebands and carrier wave transmitted. Both sidebands carry the same intelligence.

Single sideband suppressed carrier SSB (J3E) One sideband and the carrier suppressed before transmission. Only one sideband is transmitted. Bandwidth 3kHz. Savings in transmitter power and more efficient use of the spectrum.

Frequency modulation FM (F3E) The frequency of the carrier wave is varied (deviated) about its centre frequency by the instantaneous amplitude of the modulating (speech/tone) frequency. During one half cycle of modulating wave the carrier frequency is increased, during the other half cycle the carrier frequency is decreased.

The greater the amplitude of the modulating signal (the louder you shout), the greater (or wider) the deviation. The rate at which the carrier frequency deviates is dependent upon the frequency of the modulating wave. Bandwidth of an FM transmission depends upon several factors, about 5 to 7.5kHz is typical for a deviation setting of 2.5kHz.

Amplifier class of operation
Class A. Linear. Collector or anode current flows for the full input cycle. Max efficiency 50%.

Class B. Essentially non-linear. Collector or anode current flows for half ($180°$) of the input cycle. Unsuitable for audio applications unless used in push-pull configuration, such as the audio modulator stage of an AM transmitter. Employed in linear RF power amplification, where the oscillatory energy in the output tuned circuit restores the original waveshape. Max theoretical efficiency 78.5%. Typical efficiency 66%.

Class C. Non-linear. Collector or anode current flows for less than half ($<180°$) of the input cycle. Used for RF amplification and frequency multiplication where non-linearity is essential for the production of harmonics. Typical efficiency 60%-80%.

Transmitters

The simple transmitter

The transmitter fig.1, is an RF oscillator connected to an antenna. It is on-off keyed to interrupt the carrier with a code, usually morse code.

This simple transmitter will suffer from limited output power, and the frequency will be unstable due to the loading effects of the antenna.

Instability may also arise due to the time taken for the oscillator to settle down each time the key is operated and released, this will cause a 'chirp' to be heard on a CW receiver.

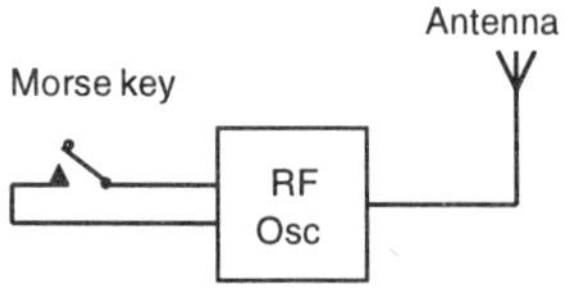

Fig.1 Showing a simple transmitter consisting of an on-off keyed oscillator connected to an antenna.

The CW, AM transmitter.

Fig.2 shows an improved transmitter. The modes will be switchable.

The oscillator must be both mechanically and electrically stable. Ideally it should not drift. It may be an L/C or crystal oscillator, or a frequency synthesiser. Its supply voltage should be stabilised.

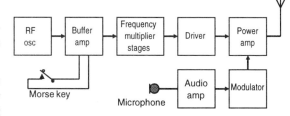

Fig.2 Showing a basic CW, and AM transmitter. The oscillator must not be keyed, and keying the PA should be avoided due to the high current causing sparks at the key contacts.

The buffer amplifier isolates the oscillator from the following stage. It will have a High input impedance to reduce oscillator loading, 'pulling,' and instability. It will most likely be operated in class A.

Frequency multiplier stages are class C (non-linear) amplifiers tuned to a harmonic of their input frequency. Multiplication factors above 5 are not normally used because the harmonic power decreases with harmonic number. In practice several stages of multiplication may be required to achieve the required final frequency.

The driver stage, tuned to the final frequency amplifies the low power RF signal from the multipliers to a power level suitable to drive the power amplifier (PA) stage. It can operate class C for maximum efficiency when used for FM, CW and AM. Basically it is, in itself, a low power PA stage. Linear operation is required for SSB.

The power amplifier (PA) stage amplifies the RF signal to the required power. Typical powers in the HF band - AM, CW, SSB - 100 to 400 watts. In the VHF band typical powers are 5 to 100 watts. Class C operation is employed for maximum efficiency when used for FM, CW and as an AM modulated stage. Linear operation is required for SSB and AM when modulation has taken place at an earlier stage.

The modulator in fig.2 is a high power audio amplifier, usually about 75W for amateur

Transmitters

service, and operating in class B push-pull. It supplies the audio frequency power to the anode (valve circuits) or the collector (transistor circuits) of the PA stage. This is high level amplitude modulation.

The audio amplifier is a low power amplifier, it drives the modulator. It may contain a low pass audio filter to remove the higher frequency components of the modulation (speech) in order to restrict the transmitted bandwidth. It will operate in a linear mode, i.e. class A. The audio frequency band is about 300-3000Hz.

Keying. It is possible to key any of the RF stages in fig.2. However, keying the oscillator is likely to cause instability and chirp, and keying a high current stage, such as the PA, will cause sparking at the key contacts, resulting in short distance or local interference.

Fast rise time of the keying waveform will cause sidebands to be generated that radiate with the signal (long distance interference), causing key clicks at the receiver and interference to adjacent channels. The key may need a suitable key-click filter.

The FM transmitter
Fig.3 shows the block diagram of an FM transmitter. The frequency multiplier, driver and PA stages are the same as previously described, and are operated in class C for greatest efficiency.

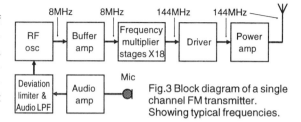

Fig.3 Block diagram of a single channel FM transmitter.
Showing typical frequencies.

FM is achieved by directly applying the modulation (speech or other intelligence) to a varactor (varicap) diode in the oscillator tuned circuit, where capacitance changes due to the modulation amplitude cause the carrier oscillator frequency to vary.

The Audio amplifier, deviation limiter and audio low pass filter condition the audio signal before it modulates the oscillator. The deviation limiter, usually a diode clipper circuit, clips the amplitude of the audio modulating signal and is adjusted to prevent over-deviation of the carrier, this is followed by a low pass filter to remove the higher frequency components and harmonics of the audio signal.

Frequency multiplying stages not only multiply the carrier frequency, but also the deviation. E.g. An oscillator running at 8MHz with a deviation of 139Hz is multiplied by x18. The output frequency is 144MHz with a deviation of approx: 2.5kHz.

The single sideband transmitter (Fig.4)
Single sideband suppressed carrier is basically an AM double sideband transmission with the carrier and one sideband eliminated, it uses only one half of the spectrum used by the AM transmission. There is also a power saving, since power is not required for the eliminated sideband or the carrier. The SSB signal is generated early in the transmitter, all amplification that follows must be linear, frequency multipliers must not be used to multiply the SSB signal. Frequency translation must be by means of mixer stages.

Transmitters

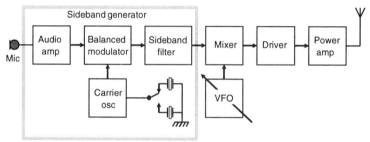

Fig.4. Block diagram of a typical SSB transmitter.

The balanced modulator mixes the audio modulating signal with the carrier oscillator to produce upper and lower sidebands. It suppresses the carrier.

The carrier oscillator in this case is crystal controlled, switching between crystals will place either the upper sideband (USB) or lower sideband (LSB) in the passband of the sideband filter.

The sideband filter, has a bandwidth of about 2.7kHz. It passes the required sideband and rejects the unwanted sideband and carrier frequency.

Mixer and VFO. The output of the sideband filter, e.g. 9MHz, must be mixed or heterodyned with another signal, supplied by the VFO in this case, to achieve the final frequency. The required mixer product is filtered and amplified by linear amplifiers.

The driver and PA stage. All amplification after the sideband has been generated must be linear. Class B RF amplification is normal.

Points to note (transmitters)

1. Radio transmitters may be rated according to their output power. E.g. Typically 1mW for local radio control devices, 1-5W for handportable use, 1-50W for mobile use, 1-400W for amateur HF band working, and up to several hundred kW for FM broadcast and TV.
2. A single transmitter may be capable of one or more of the following types of transmission;- CW, AM, SSB, FM, RTTY, Data and TV.
3. Caution! Some transmitters, particularly those types employing valves operate with high voltages.
4. Caution! The RF output power can cause severe burns. Do not work on live antennas, feeders, transmitters or power supplies.
5. Bandwidth depends on type of transmission. I.e. CW, SSB, FM, TV etc:
6. Bandwidth must be as narrow as possible for the transmission in use.
7. The carrier oscillator must be stable to reduce the possibility of frequency drift.
8. All initial tuning and adjustments should be carried out using a dummy load.
9. Tests for interference should be conducted from time to time.
10. Power supplies should be regulated.

Transmitters

1. **Fig.5 shows the diagram of a transmitter in its basic form, some of its problems are-**
   a) oscillator 'pulling' due to antenna loading.
   b) instability due to settling time when keying.
   c) very low gain transistors are not available.
   d) both a) and b) above.

2. **Some of the problems mentioned in Q1 may be overcome by-**
   a) connecting the oscillator to the antenna via a keyed buffer amplifier.
   b) using a Darlington pair transistor configuration.
   c) using a Yagi antenna.
   d) both b) and c) above.

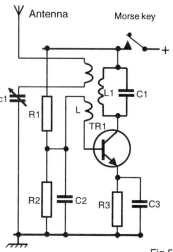

Fig.5

3. **Referring to fig.5. With the key closed, which one of the waveforms below represents the transmitter output?**

a)   b)   c)   d)

4. **The transmitter shown in fig.5 is capable of sending-**
   a) A.M. speech only (A3E).   b) F.M. speech only (F3E).
   c) C.W. telegraphy (A1A).   d) all three of the above.

5. **If the simple transmitter shown in fig.5, is used for sending CW, an additional problem is that-**
   a) the antenna will not be able to handle the power.
   b) it will not be possible to tune the antenna.
   c) the R.F. output signal will be shunted to earth.
   d) there might be a chirp on the received transmission due to the oscillator frequency stabilising each time the transmitter is keyed.

6. **One purpose of the carrier wave is to-**
   a) transfer the power from the battery to the antenna.
   b) position the transmitted signal in the RF spectrum.
   c) reduce the transmitted interference levels.
   d) prevent the PA stage overheating.

7. **How does the carrier wave convey intelligence, e.g. speech?**
   a) By its absence.
   b) By its presence.
   c) By a process called modulation.
   d) By a process called regeneration.

8. **On-off keying is a form of modulation. Select the list below which names three other forms of modulation.**

a) Heaviside	b) Reactance	c) SSB	d) Cross polar
Appleton	Resonance	Frequency	Rhombic
Rayleigh	Impedance	Amplitude	Circular

9. **Fig.6 shows the circuit of a morse key and some associated components. What are C1, R1, and L1 for?**

   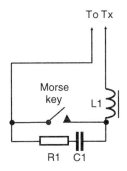

   a) To reduce collector current.
   b) To maintain frequency stability.
   c) To reduce the tuned circuit current.
   d) They form the 'key-click filter' to reduce or eliminate transmitted interference.

   Fig.6

10. **Shown below are four waveforms. Which one is typical of a CW transmitter that is not using a key-click filter?**

11. **Which one of the waveforms below is typical of the output of a CW transmitter using a key-click-filter?**

    a)   b)   c)   d)

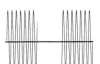 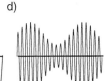

12. **The rapid transition of keying current or voltage when keying a CW transmitter is likely to result in-**
    a) a polarisation change of the CW signal.
    b) morse key fatigue.
    c) sidebands either side of the carrier wave, possibly extending up to 100kHz.
    d) many harmonics, evenly spaced 2MHz apart.

Transmitters

13. Fig.7 shows the block diagram of an amplitude modulated (AM) transmitter. It is possible to cover a number of amateur HF bands from a single VFO operating over a narrow frequency band, say 1.6 - 2.0MHz, and following it with one or more stages of box 'X'.
What is box 'X'?
a) An additional buffer amplifier to increase linearity.
b) A set of intermediate frequency amplifiers.
c) Frequency multiplier stages, or harmonic amplifiers.
d) A selective bandpass filter to prevent harmonics.

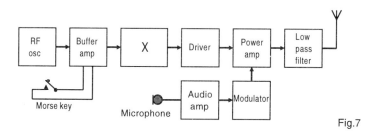

Fig.7

14. If a transmitter is required to transmit speech it will need-
a) a modulator.   b) a low pass filter.
c) a frequency synthesiser.   d) a frequency multiplier.

15. The process of modulation generates-
a) odd harmonics.   b) sub harmonics.
c) phase-locked harmonics.   d) sidebands.

16. When the modulator is connected to the power amplifier (PA) as shown in fig.7, the type of modulation is referred to as-
a) low level modulation.   b) high level modulation.
c) frequency modulation.   d) antenna modulation.

17. If the modulator shown in fig.7 is now connected to the driver stage, the type of modulation is referred to as-
a) low level modulation.   b) high level modulation.
c) frequency modulation.   d) split level modulation.

18. For amateur or commercial quality speech transmission (not broadcast), the audio speech frequency range need only be in the order of-
a) 3 - 300Hz   b) 30 - 300Hz
c) 300 - 3000Hz   d) 1200 - 3300Hz

19. A high quality music transmission requires-
a) a very narrow bandwidth.   b) a wider bandwidth than speech.
c) the whole R.F. spectrum.   d) no bandwidth at all.

20. The maximum bandwidth of an A3E (AM) transmission will be-
a) twice the carrier frequency.
b) equal to the harmonic content of the VFO.
c) twice the maximum modulating frequency.
d) the minimum modulating frequency.

21. Why should the bandwidth of a transmission be restricted to that necessary for acceptable speech quality only?
a) To ensure spectrum efficiency.
b) To save transmitter power.
c) To prevent animals being disturbed by the high frequency waves.
d) To save on receiver filter costs.

22. What precautions should be taken to restrict transmission bandwidth to the minimum necessary for the transmission of acceptable quality speech?
a) Use only the minimum power necessary for the contact.
b) Fit an audio high pass filter in the modulator stage.
c) The modulator stage should contain an audio low pass filter.
d) An electret microphone should be used.

23. A 1MHz carrier wave is amplitude modulated by an audio speech signal having frequencies in the range 300 - 3000Hz. The transmitted signal consists of-
a) a carrier wave displaced by 3000Hz.
b) two carrier waves, one at 997kHz and one at 1003kHz.
c) a carrier wave and two sidebands, total bandwidth 3kHz.
d) a carrier wave and two sidebands, total bandwidth 6kHz.

24. Fig.8 shows the R.F. spectrum of the transmission referred to in Q 23. The upper sideband (USB) is the erect sideband. Why is the lower sideband (LSB) termed the inverted sideband?
Because-
a) its frequency is below the carrier frequency.
b) it is the last sideband to be generated.
c) the carrier is above the sideband.
d) this sideband places the highest modulating frequency lowest in the R.F. spectrum.

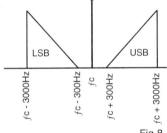

Fig.8

25. For greatest efficiency, the driver and PA stages in a CW and FM transmitter are likely to be operated in class-
    a) A   b) AB
    c) B   d) C

26. Class C amplifier stages are the most efficient, but they-
    a) do not generate harmonics.
    b) are very linear and generate harmonics.
    c) are non-linear and generate harmonics.
    d) are non-linear and do not generate harmonics.

27. Frequency multiplier stages are normally operated in class C in order to-
    a) obtain a very linear output signal.
    b) operate over the linear portion of the transfer curve.
    c) produce an output which is rich in harmonics.
    d) produce an output that is frequency stable.

28. Why, in a multiplier stage, are multiplication factors above x3, or x5 at the most, not normally used? Because the-
    a) higher order harmonics cause more interference.
    b) higher order harmonics cause excessive power drain.
    c) higher order harmonics are liable to drift independently.
    d) harmonic power reduces as the harmonic number increases.

29. In a circuit employing multiplier stages, any drift at the VFO or carrier oscillator will be-
    a) cancelled in the multiplier chain.
    b) decreased by the multiplication factor.
    c) increased by the multiplication factor.
    d) increased by 4 times the multiplication factor.

30. Why is a low pass filter normally fitted between the PA stage and the antenna of a transmitter?
    a) To prevent the transmitter receiving unwanted signals.
    b) To slow the rise time of the CW keying signal.
    c) To prevent high DC voltages reaching the antenna.
    d) To pass the carrier frequency and attenuate the harmonics.

31. Why does a buffer amplifier sometimes follow an oscillator?
    a) To prevent changes in the oscillator load pulling the oscillator off frequency.
    b) To prevent parasitic oscillations being generated in the oscillator.
    c) To prevent parasitic oscillations in the multiplier stages.
    d) To reduce the harmonic content of the oscillator output.

32. Referring to fig.9. An output frequency of 29MHz is required.
The multiplication is 4 stages of x2.
What is the frequency will the VFO?
a) 1.8125MHz   b) 3.625MHz
c) 7.25MHz   d) 9.666MHz

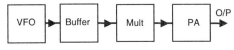

Fig.9

33. Referring to fig.9. The VFO is set
to 1.7875MHz. The multiplier chain
consists of 3 stages of x2 multiplication.
What is the output frequency?
a) 1.7875MHz   b) 3.575MHz
c) 14.3MHz   d) 28.6MHz

34. Transmitter VFOs, or carrier generation oscillators must have a high order
of frequency stability to ensure that the-
a) multiplier stages do not detune.
b) multiplier stages do not generate 7th order harmonics.
c) amplitude of the output signal does not vary.
d) transmitted signal does not drift outside the allocated frequency band.

35. How is it possible to communicate with half the transmitted bandwidth and
save transmitter power?
a) By suppressing the carrier wave and one of the sidebands.
b) By suppressing the sidebands and transmitting only the carrier wave.
c) By suppressing both sidebands.
a) By shifting the carrier frequency 1kHz high.

36. Fig.10 shows the block diagram of a typical-
a) single sideband transmitter.
b) carrier wave generator.
c) NBFM modulator.
d) reactance modulator.

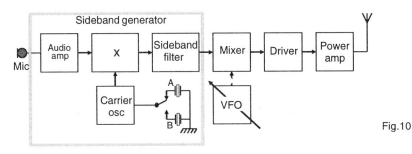

Fig.10

Transmitters

37. What is box X fig.10?
a) The pre-mixer stage.
b) The oscillator voltage stabiliser.
c) The frequency multiplier stage.
d) The balanced modulator.

38. The output of a balanced modulator consists of-
a) a carrier wave and two sidebands.
b) a carrier wave and one sideband.
c) a carrier wave only. (With both sidebands suppressed.)
d) two sidebands only. (The carrier is suppressed.)

39. The frequency spectrum diagrams shown below represent the signals at various points in the SSB generator section of the transmitter shown in fig.10. Where would you expect to find spectrum a)?
a) The output of the carrier oscillator.
b) The audio input to the balanced modulator.
c) The output of the balanced modulator.
d) The output of the sideband filter.

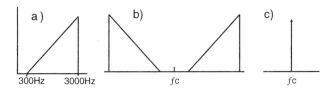

40. Where would you expect to find spectrum b) in the SSB generator of fig.10?
a) The input to the audio amplifier.
b) The input to the balanced modulator.
c) The output of the balanced modulator.
d) The output of the sideband filter.

41. Referring to fig.10. Spectrum diagram c), above, will represent the-
a) output of the carrier oscillator.
b) audio input to the balanced modulator.
c) output of the balanced modulator.
d) output of the sideband filter.

42. Where would you expect to find spectrum d) in the SSB generator of fig.10?
a) The input to the audio amplifier.
b) The input to the balanced modulator.
c) The output of the balanced modulator.
d) The output of the sideband filter.

43. The filter at the output of the balanced modulator in fig.10 should-
   a) have a bandwidth of approx 2.7 to 3kHz (the speech bandwidth).
   b) have a bandwidth at least five times the speech bandwidth.
   c) attenuate the wanted sideband by at least 60dB.
   d) be able to pass the frequency of the carrier oscillator.

44. The SSB output from the sideband filter in fig.10 must be-
   a) amplified in a frequency multiplier chain.
   b) amplified by linear stages only.
   c) mixed or heterodyned with other frequencies to reach its output frequency.
   d) both b and c above are correct answers.

45. Referring to fig.10. The method used to change from upper sideband to lower sideband is by-
   a) switching the oscillator frequency .
   b) switching the sideband filter.
   c) reversing the spectrum of the modulating signal.
   d) phase-shifting the modulating signal.

46. A radio frequency power meter is connected in the antenna feeder of a single sideband suppressed carrier transmitter. With no audio input to the transmitter, what will the power meter register?
   a) Nothing.
   b) Full scale deflection.
   c) Half scale deflection.
   d) A pulsed deflection.

47. The overall power gain of a single sideband suppressed carrier radio system, compared with a DSB AM system is about-
   a) 1dB
   b) 3dB
   c) 9dB
   d) 27dB

48. The power output of an SSB transmitter is rated in-
   a) Peak Envelope Power (PEP).
   b) Peak Drive Power (PDP).
   c) Peak Antenna Power (PAP).
   d) Peak Input Power (PIP).

49. An SSB transmitter is connected to a dummy load, and the output signal monitored on an oscilloscope connected across the load.
Which waveshape, from those shown below, would you expect when a single audio tone is applied to the input?

a)   b)   c)   d)

50. Which of the waveforms, shown above, would you expect when a two tone audio signal (both tones of equal amplitude) is applied to the microphone input of the transmitter connected as in Q49?

51. With the drive level of the PA stage too high, the waveform, under two tone test conditions, may 'flat-top' and become distorted, and differ from waveform d) above. This is likely to result in-
a) a great reduction in supply voltage.
b) serious 'splatter' in adjacent channels.
c) oscillator instability.
d) ionisation at the tip of the antenna.

52. What does the spectrum diagram of Fig.11 represent?
a) A J3E transmission working on upper sideband.
b) A J3E transmission working on lower sideband.
c) A DSB full carrier transmission.
d) A wideband FM transmission.

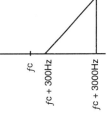

Fig.11

53. The deviation of the carrier frequency, of a frequency modulated wave, is proportional to the-
a) frequency of the modulating wave.
b) amplitude of the modulating wave divided by four.
c) instantaneous amplitude of the modulating wave.
d) cost of the microphone used.

54. In the case of frequency modulation (FM), the carrier frequency change due to the modulating signal is termed-
a) modulation factor.
b) modulation index.
c) deviation.
d) bandwidth.

55. Fig.12 shows the block diagram of a typical VHF FM transmitter.
The required output frequency is 145MHz.
What is the frequency of the oscillator crystal?
a) 8.055kHz   b) 8.0555MHz
c) 10.7MHz   d) 27MHz

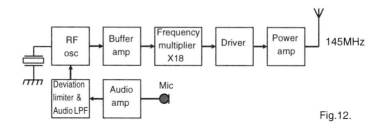

Fig.12.

56. **Why is it desirable to limit the peak amplitude of the audio signal applied to the frequency modulator?**
a) To ensure that harmonics are transmitted.
b) To save 6dB of carrier power.
c) To ensure that single sidebands are not generated.
d) To maintain the carrier deviation within its specified limits.

57. **A simple limiter stage consisting of an audio clipper is likely to generate harmonics of the audio signal, therefore;-**
a) an audio low pass filter with a cut off frequency of 2.5kHz to 3kHz is required at the limiter output.
b) a 'key-click filter' must be fitted across the microphone.
c) at least three multiplier stages must follow.
d) a 12.5kHz band stop filter must be fitted after the limiter.

58. **Referring to fig.12. The output frequency of the transmitter is required to have a frequency deviation of 2.5kHz (2500Hz), what will be the deviation at the output of the oscillator/modulator?**
a) 138.888Hz   b) 138.888kHz
c) 138.888MHz   d) 9MHz

59. **For the FM transmitter. All RF amplifiers and multipliers can be operated in-**
a) class A, for maximum linearity.
b) class AB, for improved linearity.
c) class C, for maximum efficiency.
d) parallel for higher frequency amplification.

60. **Fig.13 shows a typical circuit for direct frequency modulation. Why is the bias required?**
    a) To maintain a high standing current through the varicap.
    b) To power feed the microphone.
    c) To bias the varactor diode D1 to operate over the linear part of its characteristic.
    d) To bias the transistor to the linear portion of its characteristic.

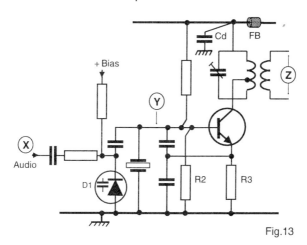

Fig.13

61. **Refer to fig.13. Which one of the waveforms shown below would you expect at point 'X' when an audio frequency tone is applied to the input?**

a)   b)   c)   d)

62. **Referring to fig.13. Which one of the waveforms shown above might you expect at point 'Y' with no audio input present?**

63. **Referring to fig.13. Which one of the waveforms shown above might you expect at point 'Z' when an audio signal is applied to the input?**

64. **What are the two components Cd and FB on the supply rail of fig.13?**
    a) Discharge capacitor and field interference blanker.
    b) Discharge capacitor and fixed battery.
    c) Supply decoupling capacitor and a ferrite bead.
    d) Earth coupling capacitor and a fine break in the wire.

Transmitters

65. **The carrier frequency power of a frequency modulated wave diminishes during modulation. Where does it go?**
   a) Into the power supply unit.
   b) Into the side frequencies to be transmitted.
   c) It is dissipated as heat in the crystal.
   d) It is dissipated as heat in the power transistors.

66. **Amateur FM voice transmission (F3E) is known as -**
   a) NBFM (narrow band frequency modulation).
   b) WBFM (wide band frequency modulation).
   c) ECFM (extinct carrier frequency modulation)
   d) ZCFM (zero carrier frequency modulation).

67. **Fig.14 shows the circuit of a-**
   a) frequency modulated PA stage.
   b) phase modulated transmitter PA stage.
   c) linear mixer stage.
   d) frequency multiplier stage.

68. **The L C circuit in the collector of TR1 fig.14 is tuned to the-**
   a) input frequency.
   b) third harmonic of the input frequency.
   c) ripple frequency.
   d) parasitic frequency.

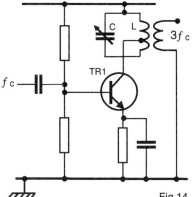

Fig.14

69. **Once frequency modulation has taken place, all subsequent amplifier stages can be operated for maximum efficiency in-**
   a) class A   b) class AB   c) class B   d) class C

70. **Fig.15 is the circuit of a typical-**
   a) phase modulated PA stage.
   b) high power carrier oscillator.
   c) plate modulated PA stage.
   d) low power (5-20W) PA stage.

71. **Capacitors Cd and FT fig.15 are to-**
   a) decouple the supply rail and the collector of TR1.
   b) keep the output amplitude constant.
   c) keep the output frequency constant.
   d) maintain constant deviation.

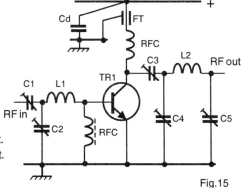

Fig.15

Transmitters

72. Components C1 and C2 in fig.15 assist in-
a) matching the source impedance to the low input impedance of TR1.
b) removing the carrier frequency from the transmission after modulation.
c) removing the carrier frequency from the transmission before modulation.
d) reducing collector current drain.

73. See fig.15. What is the function of components C3, C4, C5 and L2?
a) matching the source impedance to the low input impedance of TR1.
b) matching the low output impedance of TR1 to the antenna and reducing harmonic radiation.
c) reducing collector current drain.
d) removing the carrier frequency before transmission.

74. Fig.16 represents a PA stage connected to a 50 ohm dummy load. All voltage and current measurements are shown. Calculate the DC input power.
a) 1W   b) 5W
c) 10W   d) 50W

75. Referring to fig.16 and Q74. Calculate the power in the load and the efficiency of the stage.
a) 30W/60%   b) 30W/166%
c) 50W/60%   d) 38.75W/77.5%

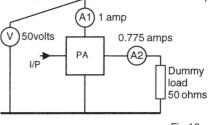

Fig.16

Note:- The C&G syllabus current at the time of publication requires some attention to be given to valves used in power amplifier stages. Little use is made of the valve in the modern amateur transmitter, and transistors will be used in most cases.

However; valves are likely to be encountered in high power linear amplifiers. Extra caution (☠)should be exercised when working with valve circuitry, since supply voltages may be as high as 5000 volts in the case of the linear amplifier.

Valve circuit and transistor circuit configurations are to some extent similar. Class A,B and C bias is used. The configurations are compared below.

Common cathode — — (Common emitter)
Common grid — — — (Common base)
Common anode — — (Common collector)

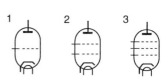

76. Name the three types of valve shown above.

a)	1. Pentode.	b)	1. Tetrode	c)	1. Hexode	d)	1. Triode
	2. Tetrode		2. Pentode		2. Diode		2. Tetrode
	3. Triode		3. Triode		3. Pentode		3. Pentode

Transmitters

77. Fig.17 below, shows a pentode valve.
Name the electrodes.

a)		b)		c)		d)	
1	Control grid	1	Heater	1	Cathode	1	Anode
2	Screen grid	2	Control grid	2	Heater	2	Cathode
3	Suppressor grid	3	Focusing grid	3	Control grid	3	Heater
4	Anode	4	Suppressor grid	4	Accelerator grid	4	Control grid
5	Cathode	5	Anode	5	Suppressor grid	5	Screen grid
6	Heater	6	Cathode	6	Anode	6	Extractor grid

78. Valves are used in high power RF amplifier stages because-

a) they are made of glass.
b) they can operate in class A.
c) the heater current loads the PSU.
d) they are able to handle high voltages.

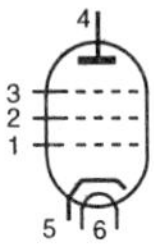

Fig.17

79. The circuit shown in fig.18 is typical
of a PA stage using a tetrode valve.
Negative bias is applied to the control
grid via RFC1 and L1 to-
a) neutralise the valve.
b) cancel the miller effect.
c) reduce harmonics to zero.
d) operate the stage in class
B or C bias as required.

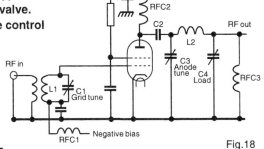

Fig.18

80. Capacitor C2 and RFC3 fig.18-
a) will prevent RF voltages appearing on the antenna.
b) will prevent lethal DC voltages appearing on the antenna.
c) enable the DC input power of the stage to be measured.
d) prevent secondary emission from the anode.

81. Referring to fig.18. What is the purpose of components L2, C3 and C4?
a) They prevent lethal DC voltages appearing on the antenna.
b) They prevent secondary emission from the anode.
c) They form a high pass filter to reduce harmonics.
d) To reduce harmonics, and match the PA impedance to the antenna impedance.

82. Referring to fig.18. To reduce the possibility of self oscillation-
a) double the anode voltage.
b) remove the capacitor Cd.
c) screen the input circuitry from the output circuitry as much as possible.
d) provide some inductive coupling between input and output.

Answers - Transmitters

1	d	16	b	31	a	46	a	61	a	76	d
2	a	17	a	32	a	47	c	62	c	77	a
3	c	18	c	33	c	48	a	63	b	78	d
4	c	19	b	34	d	49	c	64	c	79	d
5	d	20	c	35	a	50	d	65	b	80	b
6	b	21	a	36	a	51	b	66	a	81	d
7	c	22	c	37	d	52	a	67	d	82	c
8	c	23	d	38	d	53	c	68	b		
9	d	24	d	39	b	54	c	69	d		
10	a	25	d	40	c	55	b	70	d		
11	b	26	c	41	a	56	d	71	a		
12	c	27	c	42	d	57	a	72	a		
13	c	28	d	43	a	58	a	73	b		
14	a	29	c	44	d	59	c	74	d		
15	d	30	d	45	a	60	c	75	a		

1. The transmitter shown is simply an oscillator coupled to an antenna. The loading caused by the antenna may pull the oscillator off frequency. When the oscillator is keyed on and off the frequency may change slightly before it stabilises.

2. The problems mentioned above may be avoided if a keyed buffer amplifier is connected between the oscillator and the antenna.

3. When the key is closed the output of the transmitter will be a continuous carrier wave of constant amplitude, as shown in waveform c).

4. The transmitter shown in fig.5 is only suitable for transmitting an on-off keyed carrier wave. Emission class A1A. The keying can be morse code.

5. Since the received CW signal is heterodyned in the receiver using a beat frequency oscillator (BFO), frequency changes due to the transmitter carrier oscillator stabilising may be heard as a chirp on the received signal.

6. If audio speech signals were transmitted simultaneously they would interfere with eachother, and be unintelligible because there would be no frequency separation. They would only propagate for short distances. By modulating separate radio frequency carrier waves with the audio signals (i.e. intelligence) each transmission can be given an allocated position in the spectrum, determined to some extent by the propagation conditions and the frequency band in use.

7. A continuous carrier wave on its own carries no intelligence, intelligence has to be implanted on it by process called modulation.

8. The four most common types of modulation are - A1A, on-off keying of a carrier wave. A3E, Amplitude modulation. J3E, single sideband suppressed carrier, and F3E, frequency modulation.

9. C1, R1 and L1 are the components of the key click filter. L1 slows the rise of the keying waveform and C1, R1 slow the decay.

10. Waveform a) is the result of not using a key click filter. It is characterised by the sharp rise and decay of the morse code elements.

11. Waveform b) results when a key-click filter is used. This is characterised by the slow rise and decay of the code elements.

12. Rapid transition of keying current or voltage results in fast rise and decay of the leading and trailing edge of the code elements transmitted, resulting in more side frequencies being generated either side of the carrier, and causing key clicks on the received signal and in adjacent channels. This is long distance interference, since it is radiated from the antenna. This problem is largely overcome in the design of modern transmitters. A key click filter may be necessary.

13. Box X is a frequency multiplier stage. It is usually a class C non-linear amplifier with its output tuned to a harmonic of the input frequency. High multiplication factors are possible by using several frequency multiplier stages in series.

14. A carrier wave on its own carries no intelligence, intelligence has to be implanted on it by process called modulation. This requires a modulator.

15. The process of modulation causes two sidebands to be generated, an upper and lower sideband in the case of AM (A3E).

16. In the case of high level modulation, the modulating audio signal amplitude modulates the carrier wave in the final RF amplifier stage when the carrier has reached its final power level.

17. In the case of low level modulation, modulation takes place prior to the final amplifier, the modulated wave is then amplified by the final stage or stages. In this case the PA stage should be operated in class B for linear operation.

18. For intelligible audio speech quality (commercial quality speech), only audio frequencies in the range 300 - 3000Hz need to be transmitted.

19. The transmission of music requires a wider bandwidth than speech, since frequencies in the range 30 - 15000Hz may need to be transmitted.

20. The maximum bandwidth of an A3E (AM) transmission is twice the maximum modulating frequency because the process of modulation produces two sidebands.

21. The bandwidth of a transmission should be such as to ensure the most efficient utilisation of the spectrum. Since, for speech, bandwidth is dependent upon modulating frequency, it is a waste of valuable frequency spectrum to allow signals to be transmitted with modulating frequencies above 3000Hz.

22. An audio low pass filter should be included somewhere in the modulation amplifier or microphone circuit to cut off at 2700 to 3000Hz.

23. The 1MHz carrier, amplitude modulated by an audio band of frequencies in the range 300 to 3000Hz will produce, at the output of the modulated stage, a 1MHz carrier wave and two sidebands, having a total bandwidth of 6kHz. See fig.8.

24. Inspection of the lower sideband (LSB) in fig.8 will show that, due to the process of modulation, the highest modulating frequency has become the lowest frequency in the RF spectrum.

25. For the greatest efficiency, stages used only for the amplification of an RF carrier wave should be operated in class C. In class C operation the collector or anode current flows for less than $180°$ of the input cycle, as a result the waveform suffers distortion. Amplifiers operating in class C are not suitable for linear amplification, such as the amplification of amplitude modulated or SSB signals. They are suitable for amplifying CW and frequency modulated signals.

26,27. The class C amplifier is non-linear and generates harmonics, making it suitable for frequency multiplication purposes.

28. The collector circuit of a multiplier stage is tuned to the frequency of the harmonic required, however; the harmonic power decreases as the harmonic number increases. Multiplications above x3 to x5 are normally achieved by more than one stage of multiplication.

29. When an oscillator is followed by multiplier stages to achieve the final frequency, it should be remembered that any drift in the oscillator will be multiplied by the multiplication factor of the multiplier stages.

30. The output signal of a transmitter, due to non-linearities in the RF amplifiers, particularly the output stage, will contain harmonics of the carrier frequency. A low pass filter should be fitted between the transmitter and the antenna to reduce the harmonic content to an acceptable level. Note:- VHF/UHF transmitters often employ band pass filters in the output.

31. Use of a buffer amplifier will prevent impedance changes in the stages following the oscillator from 'pulling' it off tune. Usually operates in class A.

32. The oscillator is multiplied by 4 stages of x2. (i.e. 2 x 2 x 2 x 2 = x16). Dividing the final frequency by 16. $\dfrac{29MHz}{16} = 1.8125MHz.$

33. The oscillator frequency is multiplied by 3 stages of x2. (i.e. 2 x 2 x 2 = x8). The final frequency is therefore, $1.7875MHz \times 8 = 14.3MHz.$

34. All operation must take place within a specified frequency band. Oscillator instability and drift may result in signals being transmitted outside the allocated band. Oscillators should be as stable as possible. It is advisable not to operate near a band edge if drift is suspected.

35. Single sideband suppressed carrier (SSB), Emission class J3E, requires only half the spectrum used by an AM (A3E) transmission, this is due to the fact that since both sidebands carry the same information only one need be transmitted, saving both power and spectrum. Suppressing the carrier will also save on transmitter power, hence, only one sideband is transmitted, either upper or lower.

36. Fig.10 shows a basic SSB transmitter. The sideband generator is shown boxed.

37,38. Box X is a balanced modulator, in which the carrier oscillator is mixed with the audio modulation to produce an upper and lower sideband. The carrier wave will not appear at the output due to cancellation within the modulator.

39. Frequency spectrum a) is the audio frequency band at the audio input to the balanced modulator.

40. Frequency spectrum b) shows both upper and lower sidebands as seen at the output of the balanced modulator and the input of the sideband filter.

41. Frequency spectrum c) is the output of the crystal controlled carrier oscillator.

42. Frequency spectrum d) is the selected sideband output from the sideband filter. in this case it is the upper sideband (USB).

43. The bandwidth of the sideband filter should be about 2.7kHz wide.

44. The modulated output of the sideband filter must be raised to the required power level for transmission. The RF amplification stages should be linear (usually operated in class B) or severe distortion will result. Frequency translation to the final frequency should be by mixing or heterodyning. Multiplier stages should not be used for an amplitude modulated or SSB signal.

45. Switching the carrier frequency oscillator will place either the upper or lower sideband in the passband range of the sideband filter.

46. With the balanced modulator correctly balanced, and a selective sideband filter, there should be no carrier leakage. Only the chosen sideband will be present when modulation is actually taking place. As a result there will be no RF power output when there is no modulation.

47. Power savings in an SSB system result mainly from not having to transmit a carrier wave and one of the sidebands. Up to 9dB is normally quoted.

48. Peak envelope power (PEP) is the average power supplied to the antenna by a transmitter during one radio frequency cycle at the crest of the modulation envelope taken under normal conditions.

49. With a single audio frequency tone applied to the input, the output will be a single radio frequency, constant amplitude wave, as shown in c).

50. The waveform shown in d) will result when two audio frequency tones of equal amplitude are applied to the input. The waveform will have twice the amplitude of that produced by a single tone.

51. Overdriving the PA stage is likely to result in splatter interference in adjacent channels, the production of harmonics of the carrier wave, and distortion.

52. Fig.11 represents the upper sideband of an SSB transmission.

53,54. In an FM system, the deviation of the carrier wave is proportional to the instantaneous amplitude of the modulating wave.

55. Fig.12 shows that the oscillator frequency is multiplied by x18 before it is fed to the antenna. The final frequency is therefore 18 times the crystal frequency.

Therefore;- $f_{osc} = \dfrac{Final\ frequency\ (MHz)}{18} = \dfrac{145}{18} = 8.0555 MHz.$

56. The peak amplitude of the audio signal is limited to prevent over-deviation of the carrier wave. This would result in adjacent channel interference.

57. A simple peak limiter stage clips the peak amplitude of the modulating signal, the resulting modulating signal is flat topped, in the worst case it will look like a square wave. This form of distortion results in harmonics of the modulating wave being produced. An audio low pass filter will reduce the harmonic content.

58. The deviation as well as the carrier frequency is multiplied by the multiplication factor of the multiplier stages. In this case the final deviation required is 2.5kHz. Therefore the deviation at the oscillator/modulator output will be;-

$\dfrac{2.5kHz}{18} = \dfrac{2500}{18} = 138.888 Hz.$

59. Since there are no amplitude changes in an FM signal, all RF amplifier stages, except the buffer amplifier, can be operated in class C for maximum efficiency.

60. The bias voltage is adjusted so that operation is over the linear part of the diode characteristic. The capacitance change of the diode will then be proportional to the modulating voltage, thus eliminating a possible cause of distortion.

61. Waveform a) represents an audio tone at the input to the FM modulator.

62. A point Y, waveform c) will be observed when no audio signal is present. This is the basic crystal oscillator frequency.

63. Waveform b) shows the frequency modulated waveform to be expected at the output of the modulator, point Z.

64. The two components are a decoupling capacitor and a ferrite bead. They form a simple, but effective, low pass filter to remove or decouple RF oscillator voltages and currents from the supply rail.

65. A power meter in the antenna feeder of an FM transmitter will always read a constant power level, even when modulated. Observing the FM wave on a spectrum analyser will show that at certain modulating frequencies the carrier decreases, and even disappears (carrier extinction), although the power meter reading remains unchanged. The carrier power goes into the side frequencies.

66. Frequency modulated amateur voice transmission (emission class F3E) is known as narrow band frequency modulation (NBFM).

67,68. Fig.14 is a frequency multiplier stage. The clue to look for on the diagram shown is that the input frequency is fc and the output frequency is $3fc$. Indicating a multiplication of x3. L and C are tuned to the third harmonic of the input frequency.

69. Since there are no amplitude changes in an FM signal, all RF amplifier stages, except the buffer amplifier, can be operated in class C for maximum efficiency.

70. Fig.15 shows a typical common emitter VHF RF power amplifier stage.

71. Both the feedthrough capacitor, FT, and capacitor, Cd, are decoupling capacitors, they pass any RF currents appearing on the supply rail to ground.

72. Adjustment of C1 and C2 will match the drive circuit output impedance to the input impedance of the transistor.

73. Tuning C3,C4,C5 and L2 enable the low output impedance of the transistor to be matched to the 50 ohm antenna. They also provide RF filtering.

74. DC input power = $V_{supply} \times I_{PA}$ = 50×1 = $50W$.

75. Power in load = $I_{Load}^2 \times R_{Load}$ = $0.775^2 \times 50$ = $30W$.

   Efficiency = $\dfrac{RF\ output\ power}{DC\ input\ power} \times 100$ = $\dfrac{P_{out}}{P_{in}} \times 100$ = $\dfrac{30}{50} \times 100$ = 60%.

76. 1) Triode, 2) Tetrode, and 3) Pentode.

77. The pentode valve is shown in fig.17. The heater is required to heat the cathode to such a temperature that it readily emits electrons.

78. Valves are used because of their of their ability to handle high voltages, particularly the peak voltages occurring during AM and SSB modulation.

79. The bias voltage sets the operating class. Class B for linear RF amplification of AM and SSB signals, and Class C for RF amplification of FM and CW signals.

80. C2 prevents high DC voltages appearing on the antenna. RFC3 will ground the transmitter output to DC if C2 fails and most likely blow the PA fuse.

81. L2,C3 and C4, form a pi (π) tank circuit for matching and filtering.

82. The input circuit, e.g. L1,C1, must be screened as much as possible from the pi tank and other output circuitry. Placing input and output circuits on opposite sides of the chassis and RF screening must be considered.

Notes

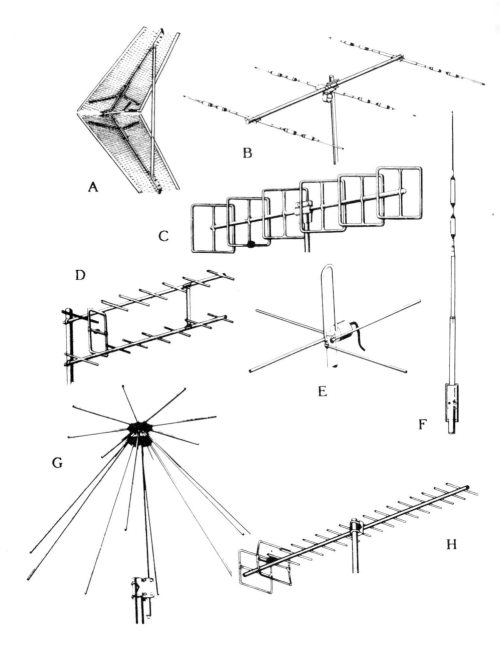

Typical amateur antennas, by Jaybeam Ltd.
A. Corner reflector for 23cm. B. Triband yagi for HF bands, showing traps. C. 2 metre quad antenna. D. 70cm 8 over 8 slot yagi array. E. 2 metre omnidirectional ground plane antenna. F. Triband vertical antenna for 10-15-20 metres. G. Wide band Discone antenna, covering 100-470MHz. H. 70cm, 18 element slot yagi.

13. Antennas and Feeders

This section will cover-
1. transmission lines and feeder cables.
2. the dipole, vertical ground-plane, yagi, trap dipole, and long wire antennas.
3. radiation patterns and polar diagrams.
4. antenna coupling and matching circuits.
5. standing waves, VSWR and field strength.

The Transmission Line
The purpose of the transmission line (or feeder) is to transfer the RF power from the source to the load, or in our case from the transmitter to the antenna. A good transmission line will have very little attenuation per unit length, so that most of the power delivered by the source will arrive at the load. A feeder should not cause power loss or radiate, as interference might result.

The twin transmission line shown fig.1 is referred to as a balanced line, or feeder, because both conductors are at equal potential to earth. There will be only a small amount of radiation if the two wires are closely spaced, since the electromagnetic fields due to currents I_1 and I_2 flowing in opposite directions cancel.

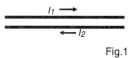

Fig.1

A coaxial cable, shown in fig.2 is referred to as an unbalanced feeder because the outer conductor, or screen, is earthed. The current flows on the outside of the inner conductor and on the inside of the outer conductor. A perfect coaxial cable will have no external radiation because the currents and the resultant electromagnetic fields are contained within the cable.

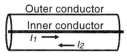

Fig.2

The velocity factor of a feeder is the ratio of the speed of travel of the RF signal in the feeder cable relative to its speed of travel in free space. Typical velocity factors are 0.66 for solid dielectric coaxial cables, up to 0.85 for foam dielectric coaxial cables, and 0.9 for air dielectric coaxial cables. The velocity factor of parallel conductor twin feeder may vary between 0.7 and 0.9.

The Characteristic Impedance 'Z_0' of a transmission line is the impedance measured at the input to a line of infinite length. A finite length of line, say 100 or 200 meters long, when terminated by a resistive load equal to the characteristic impedance of the transmission line, will appear to the source as a line of infinite length.

Antennas and Feeders

The characteristic impedance, 'Z_0', of a twin feeder is dependent upon the diameter and spacing of the conductors. Typical values of Z_0 for balanced feeders are 75, 300, and 600 ohms. The 'Z_0' of a coaxial cable is dependent upon the inside diameter of the outer and the outside diameter of the inner conductor. Typical values of Z_0 for coaxial cables are 50 and 75 ohms.

The Half-Wave Dipole

Antenna questions in basic examinations may require the length of $\lambda/2$, $\lambda/4$, and trapped antennas to be calculated. When velocity factor and diameter of the elements, plus end-effects, which shorten the antenna length are considered, a multiplying factor is given, e.g. VF (or 'K') = 0.95.

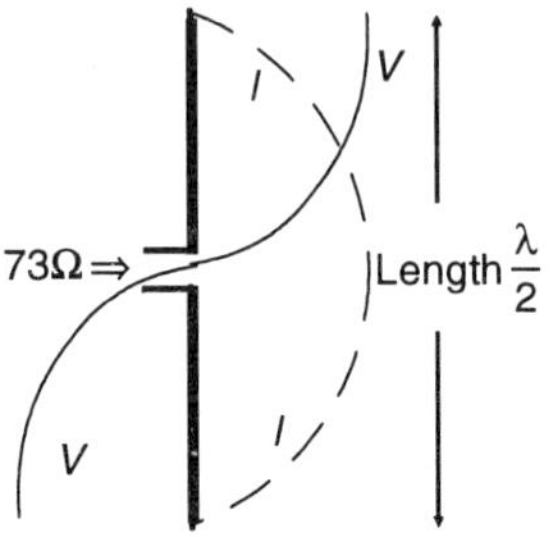

Fig.3 shows the basic centre-fed, half-wave dipole. At the tuned frequency the input impedance is approximately 73 ohms resistive. This resistance is due mainly to: a) the resistance of the antenna elements which is very low, and b), another resistance, referred to as the radiation resistance.

Fig.3 The half-wave, centre-fed antenna. Showing voltage and current standing waves. Current is maximum at centre and voltage maximum at ends.

The radiation resistance is not a physical resistance, it is a resistance, which when substituted in place of the antenna dissipates the same power as the antenna would radiate into space. For the half-wave centre-fed dipole the radiation resistance is considered to be about 73 ohms, the input impedance. The physical length of the antenna is about 4 - 5% less than the electrical length due to a) the velocity of the radio waves in the wire being less than in free space, b) the 'end effect' capacitance, and c) the wire diameter.

The $\lambda/4$ vertical antenna

Fig.4 shows a vertical $\lambda/4$ (quarter-wave), ground-plane antenna. The input impedance is about 36Ω resistive. By the correct choice of dimensions, it can be made to operate at any frequency. As mentioned above, the velocity factor has to be considered when calculating the length of a practical antenna.

A good ground-plane is required for satisfactory operation, good impedance match, and low angle radiation. In practice a number of wires, see fig.4, connected to a central ground point should prove satisfactory. This type of antenna is suitable for both HF and mobile operation at VHF and UHF, where the steel vehicle roof will provide the ground plane.

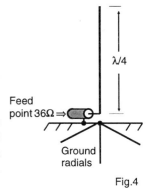

Fig.4

Polarisation

A radio wave consists of two components, the electric (E), and the magnetic (H) field at right angles to each other. When the E field is vertical, the wave is said to be vertically polarised, and when the E field is horizontal the wave is said to be horizontally polarised. E.g. A vertical dipole radiates a vertically polarised wave. A horizontal dipole radiates a horizontally polarised wave.

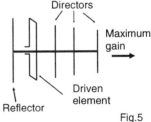

Fig.5

The Yagi Antenna

This antenna, shown in fig.5, consists of a driven element, a reflector and a number of directors. Its gain, in the direction of maximum radiation is usually specified relative to a half-wave dipole. The reflector is slightly longer than the driven element, while the directors are progressively shorter toward the front. The driven element is normally a folded λ/2 dipole, having an input impedance of 300Ω when operated on its own, but, when operated close to the parasitic elements its impedance falls to about 75Ω to provide a reasonable impedance match to a coaxial cable. Since the folded dipole is a balanced antenna, and the feeder is normally an unbalanced 50Ω coaxial cable, a *balun* (**bal**ance to **un**balance) transformer should be used, this can also provide an impedance match, i.e. 50/75Ω. The gain and directional characteristics are determined by the spacing and number of the elements. Typical gain figures relative to a dipole are between 3 and 12dB.

The Trap Dipole

The *trap dipole* is a multiband antenna. The example shown in fig.6 will operate on two bands, e.g. 14MHz and 21MHz. When operating on the highest frequency, the traps (due to their high impedance at resonance) isolate the section between the traps, from the section beyond the traps. When operating at the lower frequency, the traps are no longer resonant and the full length of the antenna is used. The full length of the antenna will be somewhat shorter than normal due to the loading effect of the traps.

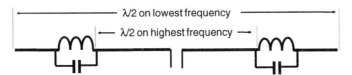

Fig.6 The trap dipole. This example shows a two band trap dipole for operation on 21MHz and 14MHz. The traps are parallel tuned circuits, resonant at the highest frequency of operation (21MHz).

The long wire end-fed (harmonic) antenna.

The long wire antenna is normally half wavelength at its lowest frequency of operation, end-fed, and connected to the transmitter via an antenna tuning unit. It has the disadvantage that the end of the antenna is a high RF voltage point, which; in close proximity to the house, may cause interference to radio, TV, and other electronic equipment. A very good earthing system will also be required.

The long wire antenna will be resonant when it is whole number of half wavelengths long, and will operate on harmonics of its fundamental. For instance; a 40 metre long wire will have one half wavelength on it at 3.5MHz (the fundamental), two half wavelengths on it at 7MHz (the 2nd harmonic), and eight half wave lengths at 28MHz (the 8th harmonic).

a) Length =λ/2   b) Length = λ   c) Length = 1.5λ   d) Length = 2λ

Fig.7. Radiation patterns of resonant wire antennas remote from ground. The patterns should be imagined as cross sections of figures of revolution about the axis of the wire.

Voltage Standing Wave Ratio (VSWR)

To obtain maximum power transfer from a transmission line to a load (or from a feeder to an antenna), the impedance of the load or antenna should match the characteristic impedance 'Z_0' of the feeder. A correct match will result in all the incident (forward) power being absorbed by the load. (VSWR is often abbreviated SWR.)

If there is a mismatch, i.e. the antenna impedance does not match the characteristic impedance of the feeder, some of the incident power will be reflected by the antenna. The reflected waves interact with the incident waves and set up *standing waves* on the line.

Standing waves do not travel, they are stationary. In an antenna system, the *standing wave ratio* is an indication of the amount of mismatch between antenna and feeder.

The ratio of maximum voltage (or current) to the minimum voltage (or current) on a feeder defines the voltage or current standing wave ratio.

$$SWR = \frac{V_{max}}{V_{min}} = \frac{I_{max}}{I_{min}}$$

Also:- $$SWR = \frac{Z_o}{R_L} \ or \ \frac{R_L}{Z_o}$$

⇑

Use whichever gives a quantity greater than 1.

Where:-
V_{max} = Maximum voltage on line.
V_{min} = Minimum voltage on line.
I_{max} = Maximum current on line.
I_{min} = Minimum current on line.
Z_o = Characteristic impedance of transmission line.
R_L = Load resistance.

Radio frequency SWR measurements may be made with a fairly simple reflectometer type instrument, employing a directional coupler and calibrated to read SWR directly.

However, some reflectometer type instruments, usually referred to as directional RF wattmeters, are calibrated to measure forward and reflected power, which by means of a chart, or the formula below, can readily be converted to SWR. This type of measurement should be made as near to the load (or antenna) as possible or else feeder loss may need to be included in the calculations.

A low SWR, e.g. 1.2 : 1 is good, and a high SWR, e.g. 10 : 1 is bad.

$$SWR = \frac{1 + \sqrt{\frac{P_{Ref}}{P_{Fwd}}}}{1 - \sqrt{\frac{P_{Ref}}{P_{Fwd}}}}$$

Where:-
P_{Fwd} = Forward power on line.
P_{Ref} = Reflected power on line.

Antennas and Feeders

Field Strength

Field strength is the strength of an electromagnetic wave measured at a particular location. Field strength is measured in units of volts/metre (V/m), millivolts/metre (mV/m), or microvolts/metre (µV/m).

Practical field strength measurements are affected by any signal-reflecting, and/or signal-absorbing objects near to the signal path between the transmitter and receiver. Antenna height, terrain and weather also affect measurements.

When dealing with interference and EMC problems it is often necessary to make an approximate calculation of field strength at a particular distance from a transmitter. The following formula can be used, it is derived from the free-space field strength formula, modified to allow for the effective gain of the transmitting antenna relative to a half-wave dipole:-

a) $$e = \frac{7.02\sqrt{ERP}}{d}$$

b) $$d = \frac{7.02\sqrt{ERP}}{e}$$

c) $$ERP = \left(\frac{e\,d}{7.02}\right)^2$$

Where:-
e = Field strength (volts/metre).
d = Distance from transmitter (metres).
ERP = Effective radiated power (watts).

Note:-
Formulas b) and c) are derived from the basic formula a) by transposition.

Points to note.

1. Accurately cut lengths $\lambda/4$ or $\lambda/2$ of feeder can be used as matching devices or wave traps. (allow for the velocity factor of the feeder.)
2. A close spaced twin transmission line will have very little external radiation field.
3. A good quality coaxial feeder will have no external radiation field.
4. Twin feeder is balanced. Coaxial feeder is unbalanced.
5. For maximum power transfer the generator impedance must match the load impedance.
6. Radiation resistance is normally taken as 73Ω for $\lambda/2$ dipoles in free space.
7. A wave is said to be vertically polarised when its E field (electric field) is vertical, this is produced by a vertical antenna.
8. A wave is said to be horizontally polarised when its E field (electric field) is horizontal, this is produced by a horizontal antenna.
9. The physical length of a dipole is slightly less than the electrical length.
10. Adding parasitic elements, i.e. directors and reflectors, increases the forward gain and changes the directional radiation pattern of an antenna.
11. An increase in forward gain is at the expense of power radiated in other directions.
12. Adding parasitic elements, in front of, or behind the driven element reduces the input impedance, therefore matching is required. A folded dipole is usually employed as the driven element in a yagi antenna to achieve matching.
13. End-fed antennas usually require matching by means of an antenna tuning unit.
14. End-fed antennas can cause interference problems.

1. A single wire can be used as a transmission line to connect a transmitter to an antenna, but two disadvantages are that-
   a) it will radiate and needs a good earth return.
   b) it will not withstand high currents or high voltages.
   c) its skin resistance is high and power dissipation is low.
   d) it is expensive and must be operated in a vacuum.

2. A transmission line, or feeder, consisting of two parallel wires moulded into a polythene ribbon is shown in fig.8. Does it radiate energy?
   a) Yes, but only a small amount when properly terminated.
   b) Yes, when passing zero current.
   c) Yes, if operated in a copper screen
   d) No.

Fig.8

3. The type of feeder cable shown in fig.9 is-
   a) coaxial.   b) triaxial.
   c) balanced.   d) Litz.

Fig.9

4. A good quality coaxial cable of the type shown in fig.9 should have no external radiation, but if it has, it could be due to-
   a) a poor quality screen or outer conductor (the braid).
   b) the conductive material used for the dielectric.
   c) the plastic outer not being thick enough.
   d) the inner conductor being highly conductive.

5. The characteristic impedance (Z_0) of a transmission line is the-
   a) d.c. loop resistance.
   b) impedance of a 1 metre length of open-circuit line.
   c) impedance of a 1 metre length of short-circuit line.
   d) input impedance of a uniform line of infinite length.

6. The Z_0 of a transmission line as shown in fig.8 is mainly dependent upon-
   a) line temperature.
   b) spacing between, and diameter of the wires.
   c) the terminating resistance of the line.
   d) the current carrying capacity of the feeder.

7. The attenuation of a transmission line-
   a) decreases with frequency.
   b) increases with frequency and length.
   c) is independent of frequency and length.
   d) increases as the power dissipated decreases.

Antennas and Feeders

8. The characteristic impedance (Z_0) of a transmission line of finite length can be calculated from impedance measurements of the line, with the distant end short-circuited ($Z_{s/c}$) and then open-circuited ($Z_{o/c}$), and applying the formula-
   a) $Z_0 = \sqrt{Z_{o/c} \times Z_{s/c}}$
   b) $Z_0 = Z_{o/c} \times Z_{s/c}$
   c) $Z_0 = 2(Z_{o/c} \times Z_{s/c})$
   d) $Z_0 = 2\sqrt{Z_{o/c} \times Z_{s/c}}$

9. The velocity of a wave travelling in a length of feeder is-
   a) lower than its velocity in free space.
   b) higher than its velocity in free space.
   c) the same as its velocity in free space.
   d) equal to the speed of light.

10. What is the typical velocity factor of a polythene dielectric coaxial feeder?
    a) 0.5   b) 0.65   c) 0.85   d) 0.96

11. What is the typical velocity factor of a polythene insulated balanced twin feeder?
    a) 0.5   b) 0.65   c) 0.85   d) 0.96

12. A typical air-spaced twin feeder might have a velocity factor of about-
    a) 0.65   b) 0.85   c) 0.95   d) 1.25

13. If a finite length of 50 ohm feeder is correctly terminated in a non-inductive load resistor of 50 ohms-
    a) 1/50th of the incident power will be returned to the feeder.
    b) no power is dissipated in the load.
    c) all the power will be absorbed by the generator.
    d) no power will be returned from the load to the feeder.

14. Referring to fig.10. Maximum power will be transferred from the generator to the load when-
    a) $Z_L = 300\Omega$
    b) $Z_L = 100\Omega$
    c) $Z_L = 50\Omega$
    d) $Z_L = 25\Omega$

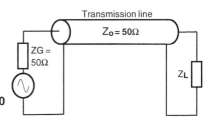

15. If the transmission line shown in fig.10 is not terminated in its characteristic impedance of 50Ω-

Fig.10

   a) all the reflected power will be absorbed by the load.
   b) a mismatch will occur, and no power will reach the load.
   c) all the incident power will be absorbed by the load.
   d) a mismatch will occur, and power will be reflected back to the generator.

16. **When the end of a feeder is short-circuited-**
    a) all the incident power is dissipated by the short-circuit.
    b) all the incident power is reflected by the short-circuit.
    c) all the generator power is dissipated by the short-circuit.
    d) no power will leave the generator.

17. **An antenna is connected to a transmitter by a feeder cable having an impedance that does not match the antenna, therefore-**
    a) the polarisation of the antenna will reverse.
    b) it will never be possible to radiate more than 1.414 Watts.
    c) the antenna will overheat and melt.
    d) standing waves will appear on the feeder.

18. **What is the impedance of the quarter-wave, short-circuit transmission line shown in fig.11, measured at point A?**
    a) Very low
    b) Very high
    c) 50Ω
    d) 300Ω

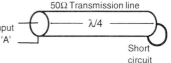

Fig.11

19. **What is the impedance of the quarter-wave, open-circuit transmission line shown in fig.12, measured at point A?**
    a) Very low
    b) Very high
    c) 50Ω
    d) 75Ω

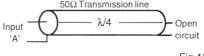

Fig.12

20. **What is the impedance of the half-wave, short-circuit transmission line shown in fig.13, measured at point A?**
    a) Very low
    b) Very high
    c) 50Ω
    d) 300Ω

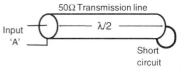

Fig.13

21. **What is the impedance of the half-wave, open-circuit transmission line shown in fig.14, measured at point A?**
    a) Very low
    b) Very high
    c) 50Ω
    d) 600Ω

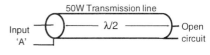

Fig.14

22. A quarter-wave stub, for operation at 30MHz is constructed from a piece of coaxial cable having a velocity factor of 0.66. What is the physical length?
    a) 1.65 metres   b) 7.5 metres
    c) 19.8 metres   d) 30 metres

23. A coaxial cable is specified as having an attenuation of 1dB per 10 metre length. What is the attenuation or loss of a 30 metre length of the cable?
    a) 3dB   b) 10dB   c) 30dB   d) 100dB

24. What is the loss in dB, of the length of coaxial cable shown in fig.15, when the power sent at 'A' is 100 watts and the power received at 'B' is 50 watts?
    a) 0.5dB
    b) 3dB
    c) 6dB
    d) 20dB

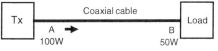

Fig.15

25. A balanced feeder is one in which-
    a) there is a central balancing point.
    b) full optimisation has been carried out.
    c) each conductor has equal impedance to earth.
    d) several baluns have been fitted.

26. A typical unbalanced feeder is-
    a) screened twin.
    b) balanced twin.
    c) a twisted pair.
    d) coaxial cable.

27. An unbalanced feeder is one in which-
    a) there is no central balancing point.
    b) full optimisation has not been carried out.
    c) each conductor has an unequal impedance to earth.
    d) several matching sections have been fitted.

28. What is an isotropic radiator?
    a) A radio active device used on modern lightning conductors.
    b) A device that radiates a narrow beam of light.
    c) A hypothetical antenna which radiates energy uniformly in all directions.
    d) An antenna that radiates only a narrow beam of energy.

29. An isotropic radiator is mainly used as a-
   a) device to ionise the atmosphere.
   b) device for measuring the speed of a radio wave in a cable.
   c) reference with which the gain of a practical antenna is compared.
   d) reference to boost the gain figure of a CB antenna by 10dB.

30. What is the effective gain of a λ/2 dipole using an isotropic radiator as the reference?
   a) 0dB   b) 1.5dB
   c) 2.15dB   d) 6dB

31. Radio waves in free space travel at a speed of-
   a) 3×10^8 m/s   b) 3×10^6 m/s
   c) 2×10^8 m/s   d) 1.414×10^8 m/s

32. Where λ = wavelength in metres, and f = frequency in Hertz, the wavelength of a radio wave is given by the formula-
   a) $\lambda = \dfrac{f}{3 \times 10^8}$ b) $\lambda = \dfrac{f}{300 \times 10^6}$

   c) $\lambda = \dfrac{3 \times 10^6}{f}$ d) $\lambda = \dfrac{3 \times 10^8}{f}$

33. Fig.16 shows a half-wave dipole. Calculate its length at a frequency of 150MHz.
   a) 0.5m   b) 1m
   c) 1.5m   d) 2m

Fig.16

34. See Fig.16. What is the electrical length of the half-wave dipole, operating at 21MHz?
   a) 110m   b) 30m
   c) 7.14m   d) 2.08m

35. The actual, or physical length of a resonant half-wave dipole is about 5% less than its calculated electrical length, this is due to the-
   a) high dielectric constant of free space.
   b) insulation resistance of the antenna feed-point.
   c) oxygen content of the atmosphere.
   d) velocity of propagation on the wire being slower than it is in free space.

36. The practical or physical length of the half-wave dipole shown in fig.16, operating at 21MHz, and assuming a velocity factor of 0.95, is about-
   a) 100m   b) 28.5m
   c) 6.78m   d) 1.99m

Antennas and Feeders

37. What is the feed-point impedance of the dipole shown in fig.16 when operating at its resonant frequency?
   a) 36Ω resistive.   b) 72Ω resistive.
   c) 300Ω inductive.   d) 600Ω capacitive.

38. If the length of the dipole shown in fig.16 is 5m (λ/2 = 5m), what is the approximate frequency to which it is cut?
   a) 30MHz   b) 15MHz
   c) 20MHz   d) 7MHz

39. The physical length of a λ/2 centre-fed dipole for operation at 432MHz will be approximately-
   a) 33cm   b) 43.2cm
   c) 70cm   d) 100cm

40. Fig.17 shows a quarter-wave, ground-plane antenna designed for operation at 14MHz. The velocity factor of the wire is 0.95. What is the length of the antenna?
   a) 1.4m   b) 5.09m
   c) 14m   d) 28m

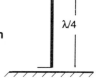

Fig.17

41. What is the feed-point impedance of the antenna shown in fig.17 when operating at its resonant frequency?
   a) 36Ω resistive.   b) 72Ω resistive.
   c) 300Ω inductive.   d) 600Ω capacitive.

42. The physical length of a λ/4 ground-plane antenna for mobile use at 145MHz will be approximately-
   a) 0.49m   b) 0.98m
   c) 1.96m   d) 14.5m

43. The gain of an antenna is quoted in 'dBd' - this means that-
   a) the gain is referenced against a diabolic radiator.
   b) the gain is referenced against a λ/2 dipole.
   c) an isotropic antenna has been used as a reference.
   d) the gain figures apply to dipoles only.

44. Refer to fig.18. The advancing electromagnetic wavefront has been produced by a-
   a) horizontal antenna.
   b) vertical antenna.
   c) slanting antenna.
   d) radial antenna. (Radius = 2πλ)

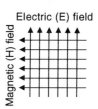

Electric (E) field

Fig.18

45. Which one of the diagrams shown below represents the voltage and current distribution on a resonant, centre-fed, half-wave dipole?

a)   b)   c)  d)

46. The centre-fed dipole is-
   a) an unbalanced antenna.
   b) a balanced antenna.
   c) a concentric antenna.
   d) an isotropic antenna.

47. A balanced antenna is one in which-
   a) both sides have the weight evenly balanced.
   b) the SWR is higher than 2 to 1.
   c) the standing waves on the elements are nulled.
   d) both elements have equal impedance to earth at all points.

48. The outer ends of a resonant, half-wave, centre-fed dipole are-
   a) high current points and require grounding.
   b) low resistance points and need to be well insulated.
   c) low voltage points and require a good earth connection.
   d) high voltage points and require good insulators.

49. Which one of the diagrams shown below represents the voltage and current distribution on a resonant, half-wave, end-fed antenna?

a)   b) c) d)

50. Referring to Q 49. It may be deduced that the resonant, half-wave, end-fed antenna has a feed-point impedance that is-
   a) low.   b) high.
   c) zero.   d) 50Ω.

51. Which one of the vertical plane patterns shown below is characteristic of a vertical, quarter-wave, ground-plane antenna?

a) b) c) d)

52. Which polar diagram shown below represents the radiation pattern, in the horizontal plane, of a vertical, quarter-wave, ground-plane antenna?

a) b) c) d)

   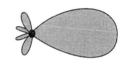

53. An ideal ground-plane for a vertical antenna system would be-
a) an infinitely large copper sheet.
b) several acres of dry rock.
c) a large damp plastic sheet.
d) radial wires, $\lambda/2$ long, buried about 30 feet below the surface of the earth.

54. Referring to Q 53. Which answer would be a more practical solution to the ground-plane problem?
a) An infinitely large copper sheet.
b) Several acres of dry sandstone.
c) A large dry plastic sheet.
d) Radial wires, $\lambda/2$ long, buried just below the surface of the earth.

55. What type of polarisation gives the strongest ground waves?
a) Horizontal. b) Vertical.
c) Circular. d) Slant.

56. A horizontal antenna is said to radiate a-
a) vertically polarised wave.
b) horizontally polarised wave.
c) radially polarised wave.
d) circularly polarised wave.

Antennas and Feeders

57. In order to obtain the maximum signal at the receiver-
   a) the receive and transmit antennas must have the same polarisation.
   b) the receive and transmit antennas must have opposite polarisation.
   c) a quarter-wave dipole must be used at the receiver.
   d) both antennas must be constructed of copper wire.

58. What is the impedance of a centre-fed, half-wave folded dipole, as shown in fig.19?
   a) 50Ω   b) 75Ω
   c) 300Ω   d) 600Ω

Fig.19

59. A suitable feeder cable for connecting the antenna shown in fig.19 will be-
   a) 50Ω coaxial.   b) 75Ω coaxial.
   c) 300Ω twin feeder. d) 600Ω twin feeder.

60. What type of antenna uses additional elements, referred to as directors and reflectors, to give an increase in directional gain?
   a) End-fed dipole.   b) Collinear.
   c) Yagi.   d) Isotropic.

61. Placing elements in front of, or behind a dipole will-
   a) reduce the wind resistance.
   b) improve the mechanical stability.
   c) increase the gain by a minimum of 20dB.
   d) reduce the impedance of the driven element.

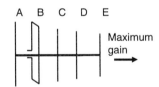

62. A Yagi antenna is shown in fig.20. The effect of using a folded λ/2 driven element will-
   a) ensure vertical polarisation.
   b) restore the feed-point impedance to about 75Ω.
   c) reject horizontally polarised signals.
   d) reduce the wind resistance.

Fig.20

63. Referring to the yagi antenna of fig.20. Elements C D and E are the-
   a) driven elements. b) reflectors.
   c) radials   d) directors.

64. Referring to the yagi antenna of fig.20. Element A is the-
   a) driven element.   b) reflector.
   c) radial element   d) director.

65. Referring to the yagi antenna of fig.20. Element B is the-
   a) driven element.   b) reflector.
   c) collector.   d) director.

Antennas and Feeders

66. A yagi antenna has the advantage over a dipole antenna when-
   a) output power has to be attenuated.
   b) accurate time schedules must be adhered to.
   c) easy matching is required.
   d) an increase in forward gain, and a high front-to-back ratio is required.

67. Which one of the polar diagrams, shown below, is typical of the radiation pattern of a yagi antenna in the horizontal plane?
   a)   b)   c)   d)

68. What type of antenna is shown in fig.21?
   a) Rhombic.   b) Unipole.
   c) Quadropole.   d) Trap dipole.

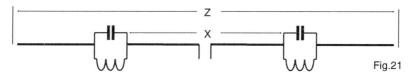

Fig.21

69. The centre section 'X' of the antenna shown in fig.21 is required to operate as a λ/2 dipole at 7MHz. What is the approximate length 'X'?
   a) 42m   b) 20.35m   c) 10.5m   d) 5.25m

70. When the centre section 'X' of the antenna shown in fig.21 is cut for operation at 7MHz, the two tuned circuits should resonate at-
   a) 28MHz   b) 21MHz   c) 14MHz   d) 7MHz

71. Referring to fig.21. The centre length 'X' forms-
   a) a λ/2 dipole resonant at the highest frequency of operation.
   b) a λ/2 dipole resonant at the lowest frequency of operation.
   c) the matching section for the antenna system.
   d) the anti-interference trap.

72. Referring to fig.21. The full length of the antenna 'Z', forms-
   a) a λ/2 dipole resonant at the lowest frequency of operation.
   b) a λ/2 dipole resonant at the highest frequency of operation.
   c) the matching device for the traps.
   d) the anti-interference trap.

73. The lowest operating frequency of the antenna, fig.21, is in the 80 metre band. Why is its overall length 'Z' shorter than might have been calculated?
   a) Because of the added inductance of the traps.
   b) Because of the added capacitance of the traps.
   c) Because of the propagation time of the feeder at lower frequencies.
   d) Because of the coupling effect of the atmosphere.

74. Referring to fig.21, and ignoring the effect of the traps. Calculate the approximate physical length of Z for $\lambda/2$ operation at 3.5MHz.
   a) 20.35m   b) 40.71m
   c) 61.21m   d) 81.42m

75. In addition to operation at 7MHz and 3.5MHz, the trap dipole shown in fig.21 will operate on-
   a) harmonic frequencies, 14, 21 and 28MHz.
   b) sub-harmonic frequencies, 1.8MHz, 900kHz and 450kHz.
   c) 10 and 20MHz only.
   d) all of the VHF and UHF bands.

76. Fig.22 shows a three band trapped vertical antenna for operation at 10,15 and 20 metres. In which frequency band does the shortest length 'X' operate as a ground plane $\lambda/4$ antenna?
   a) 7-7.1MHz   b) 14-14.350MHz
   c) 21-21.450MHz   d) 28-29.7MHz

77. What is the approximate resonant frequency of trap 'B' fig.22?
   a) 7MHz   b) 14MHz
   c) 21MHz   d) 28MHz

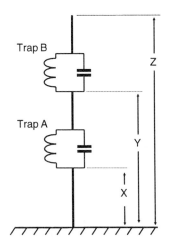

78. The full length 'Z' of the antenna, fig.22, will operate as a resonant $\lambda/4$ ground-plane antenna at a frequency of about-
   a) 7MHz   b) 14MHz
   c) 21MHz   d) 28MHz

79. What is the approximate resonant frequency of trap 'A' fig.22?
   a) 7MHz   b) 14MHz
   c) 21MHz   d) 28MHz

Fig.22

80. For long distance (Dx) communication in the HF band, the antenna must be capable of-
   a) high angle radiation.
   b) low angle radiation.
   c) ground attenuated radiation.
   d) causing gyro-resonance in the D layer.

81. For short distance sky wave communication (100-500 miles), the antenna must be capable of-
   a) high angle radiation.
   b) low angle radiation.
   c) ground attenuated radiation.
   d) causing gyro-resonance in the E layer.

82. Why is the height above ground of an HF antenna an important factor? Because-
   a) wind loading becomes a problem.
   b) the weight of the antenna increases in direct proportion to the height.
   c) TVI will increase from the traps as the air gets thinner.
   d) the radiation pattern varies with height.

83. The polar diagrams below show the vertical plane radiation patterns of a horizontal λ/2 antenna at various heights above ground. Which polar diagram represents the antenna erected at a height of λ/4 above ground?

   a)   b)

   c)   d)

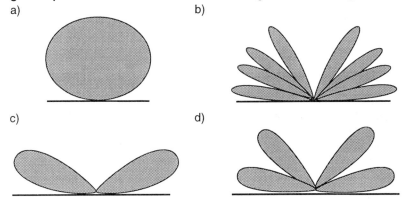

These diagrams are in a plane at right angles to the wire.
All patterns are above perfectly conducting ground.

84. Which one of the above polar diagrams is typical of a λ/2 horizontal antenna at a height of λ/2 above ground?

85. Which one of the polar diagrams on the previous page is typical of a λ/2 horizontal antenna at a height of 1λ above ground?

86. Which one of the polar diagrams on the previous page is typical of a λ/2 horizontal antenna at a height of 2λ above ground?

87. The polar diagrams below show the vertical plane radiation patterns of a typical vertical λ/2 antenna at various heights above ground. Which polar diagram is representative of a λ/2 vertical antenna with its centre at a height of λ/4 above ground?

a)   b)

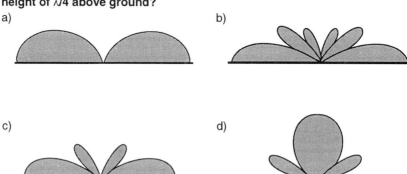

c)   d)

All patterns shown are above perfectly conducting ground.

88. Which one of the above polar diagrams is typical of a λ/2 vertical antenna with its centre at a height of λ/2 above ground?

89. Which one of the above polar diagrams is typical of a λ/2 vertical antenna with its centre at a height of 1λ above ground?

90. Fig.23 shows an end-fed antenna suitable for harmonic operation, with its associated tuner unit to bring the system to resonance.
At which frequency will the antenna operate as a λ/4 antenna?
a) 1.875MHz   b) 3.5MHz   c) 21MHz   d) 28MHz

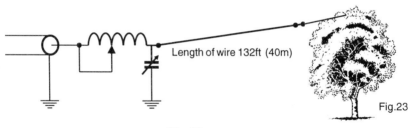

Length of wire 132ft (40m)

Fig.23

91. The antenna shown in fig.23 can be operated as a λ/2 end-fed antenna at a frequency of-
   a) 1.8MHz.   b) 3.75MHz.
   c) 21MHz.   d) 28MHz.

92. How many wavelengths long is the antenna shown in fig.23 at a frequency of 14MHz?
   a) 1   b) 2
   c) 3   d) 4

93. How many wavelengths is the antenna shown in fig.23 at a frequency of 28MHz?
   a) 1   b) 2
   c) 3   d) 4

94. Fig.24 shows a 5/8λ vertical ground-plane antenna.
   What advantage has it over a λ/4 ground-plane antenna?
   a) 5/8λ is an optimum length that gives a gain of about 3dB over a λ/4 vertical antenna.
   b) Economy, eight of them can be cut from a standard five wavelength length of steel wire.
   c) The tip will glow when transmitting and give a good indication of the output power.
   d) It gives excellent high angle radiation.

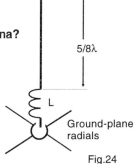

Fig.24

95. See fig.24. What is the purpose of loading coil 'L'?
   a) It is tuned to reject lightning strikes.
   b) It assists the high angle radiation pattern.
   c) It can be used to tune the 5/8 wave whip to 3/4 wave resonance.
   d) It absorbs mechanical shock when the whip hits overhead obstructions.

96. The impedance of a λ/2 antenna is-
   a) high at each end and low in the centre.
   b) high in the centre and low at each end.
   c) high at the transmit end, low at the far end.
   d) low at the transmit end, high at the far end.

97. Fig.25 shows an antenna tuning unit suitable for tuning a high impedance long wire antenna. The length of the antenna 'X' should be-
   a) 0.25λ   b) 0.5λ
   c) 0.75λ   d) 1.75λ

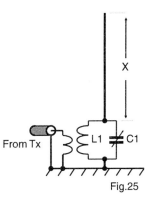

Fig.25

98. Referring to fig.25. The tuned circuit L1,C1 should be tuned to the-
    a) second harmonic frequency.
    b) third harmonic frequency.
    c) image channel.
    d) transmit frequency.

99. Fig.26 shows an antenna tuning unit suitable for tuning a marconi antenna. The length of the antenna 'X' should be-
    a) 0.25λ   b) 0.5λ
    c) 1λ   d) 2λ

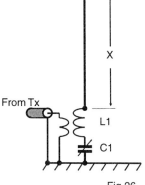

Fig.26

100. Referring to fig.26. When the tuned circuit L1, C1 is resonant at 3.5MHz, the length of the antenna will be about-
    a) 20m   b) 40m
    c) 35m   d) 80m

101. Fig.27 shows a ferrite rod receiving aerial, L1 and C1 are tuned to the signal frequency. L2 is a link coupling to the receiver.
Which is the direction of maximum response?
    a) A - A   b) B - B   c) C   d) D

102. Referring to fig.27. Which is the direction of minimum response?
    a) A - A   b) B - B   c) C   d) D

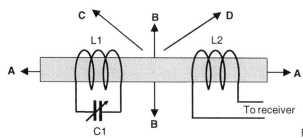

Fig.27

103. When the VSWR on an antenna and feeder system is very high-
    a) there could be a complete mismatch or faulty feeder.
    b) the antenna and feeder are correctly matched.
    c) the antenna has been replaced by a dummy load equal to the Z of the feeder cable.
    d) the transmitter output stage is faulty.

104. When the VSWR on an antenna feeder is unity-
a) there is a complete mismatch between antenna and feeder.
b) there is a perfect match between antenna and feeder.
c) it is likely that the antenna has been disconnected.
d) the antenna has been replaced by a short-circuit.

105. What can be done at the transmitter to remove standing waves?
a) Change to the FM mode of transmission.
b) Retune the Pi-tank circuit of the transmitter.
c) Fit a narrow band BPF at the transmitter output.
d) Nothing, because standing waves are generated at the distant end.

106. Which two devices listed below are suitable for VSWR measurements?
a) 'Q' meter and LCR bridge.
b) Moving coil meter and calibrated plumb-line.
c) Moving iron meter and hydrometer.
d) Reflectometer and slotted line.

107. Using one of the devices from the pair that you selected in Q 106 above, you are able to measure the maximum and minimum value of the standing wave by means of a sliding probe. What is this device called?
a) A reflectometer.
b) A slotted line.
c) A calibrated plumb-line.
d) An LCR bridge.

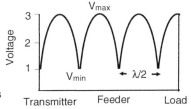

**108. The maximum and minimum standing wave voltage on a transmission line is shown in fig.28.
What is the VSWR?**
a) 2:1   b) 5:1
c) 3:1   d) 300:1

Fig.28

**109. A VSWR of 10:1 is measured on an antenna system.
You would most likely regard this as-**
a) very good   b) very bad
c) reasonable   d) just acceptable

**110. An antenna is specified as having a VSWR of 1.1:1.
you will probably regard this as-**
a) very good   b) bad
c) very bad   d) just acceptable

111. Effective Radiated Power (ERP) may be calculated by multiplying the input power to the antenna by its gain in the direction of maximum radiation. A yagi antenna has power gain of 4, and an input power of 400W. What is the ERP?
    a) 400W   b) 800W
    c) 1200W   d) 1600W

112. A transmitter has an ERP (Effective Radiated Power) of 400 watts, fig.29. What is the field strength at a distance of 30 metres?
    a) 4.68V/m
    b) 400V/m
    c) 30V/m
    d) 12,000V/m

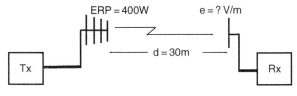

Fig.29

113. Referring to the set-up in fig.29. What is the field strength at a distance of 10m when the ERP is 100W?
    a) 7.02V/m   b) 70.2V/m
    c) 100V/m   d) 702V/m

114. Referring to the set-up in fig.29. What is the field strength at a distance of 200m when the ERP is 400W?
    a) 0.702V/m   b) 7.02V/m
    c) 100V/m   d) 702V/m

115. For the layout shown in fig.29. What is the ERP required to give a field-strength of approximately 2V/m at the side of a house 15m away?
    a) 4.27W   b) 18.26W
    c) 30W   d) 70.2W

116. It has been calculated that in order to avoid interference to a sensitive receiving installation at a point 100m from a transmitting antenna, the field strength at that point should not exceed 1V/m. What is the maximum ERP, in that direction, that should not be exceeded?
    a) 14.02W   b) 100W
    c) 203W   d) 702W

117. At what distance from a transmitting antenna, in the direction of maximum radiation, is the field strength 3V/m? The ERP is 400W.
    a) 46.8m   b) 140.4m
    c) 11.85m   d) 1200m

Answers - Antennas and Feeders

1	a	21	b	41	a	61	d	81	a	101	b
2	a	22	a	42	a	62	b	82	d	102	a
3	a	23	a	43	b	63	d	83	a	103	a
4	a	24	b	44	b	64	b	84	c	104	b
5	d	25	c	45	a	65	a	85	d	105	d
6	b	26	d	46	b	66	d	86	b	106	d
7	b	27	c	47	d	67	c	87	a	107	b
8	a	28	c	48	d	68	d	88	c	108	c
9	a	29	c	49	a	69	b	89	b	109	b
10	b	30	c	50	b	70	d	90	a	110	a
11	c	31	a	51	a	71	a	91	b	111	d
12	c	32	d	52	a	72	a	92	b	112	a
13	d	33	b	53	a	73	a	93	d	113	a
14	c	34	c	54	d	74	b	94	a	114	a
15	d	35	d	55	b	75	a	95	c	115	b
16	b	36	c	56	b	76	d	96	a	116	c
17	d	37	b	57	a	77	c	97	b	117	a
18	b	38	a	58	c	78	b	98	d		
19	a	39	a	59	c	79	d	99	a		
20	a	40	b	60	c	80	b	100	a		

1. A single wire carrying a high frequency current will radiate.

2. A twin feeder will radiate energy, but only a small amount if the two wires are relatively closely spaced so that the electromagnetic fields cancel.

3,4. A coaxial cable is shown. Due to 'skin effect', RF currents flow on the outer surface of the inner conductor and the inner surface of the outer conductor, or screen, which may be a copper tube or braid. The RF currents should not penetrate the screen to sufficient depth to reach the outside surface.

5. The characteristic impedance, 'Z_0', of a transmission line is the impedance measured at the input of a line of infinite length. Terminating a short length of the line in an impedance equal to its characteristic impedance will make the line appear to be of infinite length.

6. The Z_0 of a twin feeder depends upon the diameter and spacing of the wires.

7. The attenuation or loss in a feeder increases with frequency. A given length may have a loss of 1dB at 100MHz and approximately 2dB at 400MHz.

8. Use the formula $Z_0 = \sqrt{Z_{o/c} \times Z_{s/c}}$

9. Energy in a transmission line travels slower than the speed of light. The ratio of the velocity of a wave travelling in a transmission line, to its velocity in space is the velocity ratio or velocity factor VF.

Answers - Antennas and Feeders

10. A typical polythene dielectric coaxial feeder will have a VF of about 0.65.

11. A polythene insulated twin feeder may have a VF of about 0.85.

12. An air spaced twin feeder is likely to have a VF of about 0.95.

13,14. When a power source is connected to a given load, i.e. a transmitter to an antenna or an antenna to a receiver, maximum efficiency, hence maximum power transfer occurs when both source and load are correctly matched. All incident power will be absorbed by the load. When the load is connected via a feeder, the characteristic impedance of the feeder must match the load impedance for maximum power to be transferred from the source to the load.

15. If the load impedance Z_L does not match the feeder impedance some of the incident power will be reflected from the load, and set up standing waves on the feeder.

16. When the end of a feeder is either open circuit or short circuit, all the incident power will be reflected. Standing waves will result.

17. A mismatch will cause power to be reflected from the load. Standing waves will result when the incident waves react with the reflected waves.

18,19. The impedance condition at the input of the $\lambda/4$ length of transmission line will be opposite that of the terminating end. The $\lambda/4$ with the short circuit end will have a high Z and the $\lambda/4$ with the open circuit end will have a low Z.

20,21. The impedance condition at the input of the $\lambda/2$ length of transmission line will be the same as that at the terminating end. The $\lambda/2$ with the short circuit end will have a low Z and the $\lambda/2$ with the open circuit end will have a high Z.

22. A $\lambda/4$ stub is required for operation at 30MHz. VF of coaxial cable is 0.66. First calculate the wavelength-

$$\lambda = \frac{3 \times 10^8}{f} = \frac{3 \times 10^8}{30 \times 10^6} = \frac{300 \times 10^6}{30 \times 10^6} = \frac{300}{30} = 10 \ metres.$$

Now we need a to calculate a quarter of a wavelength and multiply it by the velocity factor of the coaxial cable; $\frac{\lambda}{4} \times 0.66 = \frac{10}{4} \times 0.66 = 1.65 \ metres$

23. Feeder loss is 1dB for every 10 metres. Therefore the loss of 30 metres is 3dB.

24. Using formula-

$$dB = 10 \ Log_{10} \frac{P_{out}}{P_{in}} = 10 \ Log_{10} \frac{50}{100} = 10 \ Log_{10} \ 0.5 = 10 \times -0.3 = -3dB$$

Note. Use the *Log* key on your calculator. The minus sign indicates a loss. This is obvious since the power out of the feeder is less than the power in.

25. In a balanced feeder each conductor has equal impedance to earth at any point.

Answers - Antennas and Feeders

26,27. Coaxial cable is unbalanced with respect to earth. The outer conductor, or screen, is normally earthed.

28,29. An isotropic radiator has no directional characteristic and radiates energy uniformly in all directions. The gain of a practical antenna may be assessed by using the isotropic antenna as a reference.

30. A half-wave dipole has a gain of 2.15dBi (dBi - Decibels relative to isotropic).

31. The velocity of radio waves in free space is 3×10^8 metres per second.

32. $\lambda = \dfrac{3 \times 10^8}{f}$ and by transposition $f = \dfrac{3 \times 10^8}{\lambda}$

33. First calculate the full wavelength λ at 150MHz and divide by 2 to get a half wavelength.

$$\lambda = \frac{3 \times 10^8}{f} = \frac{3 \times 10^8}{150 \times 10^6} = \frac{300 \times 10^6}{150 \times 10^6} = \frac{300}{150} = 2 \text{ metres.}$$

Therefore length of $\lambda/2$ dipole is 1 metre.

34. $\lambda = \dfrac{3 \times 10^8}{f} = \dfrac{3 \times 10^8}{21 \times 10^6} = \dfrac{300 \times 10^6}{21 \times 10^6} = \dfrac{300}{21} = 14.29 \text{ metres.}$

Therefore length of $\lambda/2$ dipole is 7.14 metres.

35. The actual or physical length of the radiator is about 5% less than the electrical length due to the velocity of the wave in the wire being slower than in free space.

36. The electrical length for the $\lambda/2$ dipole at 21MHz is 7.14m, as calculated in A34. Multiplying this by 0.95 will give the practical length.

$7.14 \times 0.95 = 6.78 \text{ metres.}$

37. A centre-fed $\lambda/2$ dipole will have an input impedance of approximately 72Ω resistive.

38. Since 5m is half wavelength, a full wavelength will be 10m.
Calculate the frequency based on the full wavelength;

$$f = \frac{3 \times 10^8}{\lambda} = \frac{3 \times 10^8}{10} = \frac{300 \times 10^6}{10} = 30 \times 10^6 \text{ Hz or 30MHz.}$$

39. $\lambda = \dfrac{3 \times 10^8}{f} = \dfrac{3 \times 10^8}{432 \times 10^6} = \dfrac{300 \times 10^6}{432 \times 10^6} = \dfrac{300}{432} = 0.69 \text{ metres (69cm).}$

Therefore physical length of $\lambda/2$ dipole, using 0.95 as the velocity factor is;

$$\frac{\lambda}{2} \times 0.95 = \frac{0.69}{2} \times 0.95 = 0.345 \times 0.95 = 0.33 \text{ metres (33cm).}$$

40. $\lambda = \dfrac{3 \times 10^8}{f} = \dfrac{3 \times 10^8}{14 \times 10^6} = \dfrac{300 \times 10^6}{14 \times 10^6} = \dfrac{300}{14} = 21.43$ *metres.*

Therefore physical length of λ/4 antenna is;

$\dfrac{\lambda}{4} \times 0.95 = \dfrac{21.43}{4} \times 0.95 = 5.36 \times 0.95 = 5.09$ *metres*

41. Approximately 36Ω resistive.

42. $\lambda = \dfrac{3 \times 10^8}{f} = \dfrac{3 \times 10^8}{145 \times 10^6} = \dfrac{300 \times 10^6}{145 \times 10^6} = \dfrac{300}{145} = 2.069$ *metres.*

Therefore physical length of λ/4 antenna is;

$\dfrac{\lambda}{4} \times 0.95 = \dfrac{2.069}{4} \times 0.95 = 0.52 \times 0.95 = 0.49$ *metres.*

43. To determine the gain of an antenna in the direction of maximum radiation it is compared with a reference antenna, usually a half-wave dipole. The antenna gain is then expressed in decibels relative to a dipole, abbreviated dBd.

44. The electric (E) field in the diagram is vertical, with an associated, and inseparable magnetic (H) field at right angles to it. The electric and magnetic fields are in phase and reverse direction every half cycle of the transmitted carrier frequency.
The polarization of a wave is determined by the direction of the E field.
The wavefront shown is vertically polarised by a vertical antenna.

45. Diagram a) represents the voltage and current standing wave pattern on a resonant λ/2 dipole. Maximum voltage is developed at the high impedance ends of the antenna.

46,47. The centre-fed dipole is a balanced antenna. In free space, both elements have equal capacitance and impedance to earth.

48. The ends of the dipole are high voltage points and require good insulators.

49,50. The half-wave end-fed antenna will have high voltage points at each end, consequently the input impedance is high.

51. Diagram a) assumes a good ground plane. This may require buried radials or use of a metal vehicle roof for VHF/UHF.

52. Diagram a) The ground plane λ/4 antenna has an omnidirectional radiation pattern in the horizontal plane.

53,54,55. The vertical ground-plane antenna diagrams assume a perfectly conducting ground, e.g. an infinitely large copper sheet. Wires (called radials)radiating from a point below the end of the antenna, and buried just below the surface of the earth are often used as a ground-plane for vertical HF antennas. A vertical antenna gives the strongest ground-wave propagation.

Answers - Antennas and Feeders

56. A horizontal antenna radiates a horizontally polarised wave.

57. For line-of-sight paths both receive and transmit antennas must have the same polarisation or severe signal loss will occur.

58,59. A folded dipole is a balanced antenna and has an input impedance of 300Ω resistive. It may be fed by 300Ω twin feeder.

60. The yagi antenna uses parasitic elements (the reflector and directors) to increase the gain in a certain direction.

61. Placing parasitic elements close to a dipole will reduce its impedance.

62. A folded dipole has an input impedance of 300Ω. Placing a reflector behind, and a director in front of it (to make a yagi) will reduce the impedance to about 75Ω.

63,64,65. CDE are directors. A is the reflector. B is the driven element.

66. Compared to a dipole, at a given point, say 1km distant, a yagi will give greater signal strength in its direction of maximum radiation. There should be only a very small signal off the back of the yagi. Measurement of the forward signal and the signal off the back will give the front-to-back ratio.

67. Diagram c). There is a main lobe and often some smaller lobes at the back.

68. This antenna is a trap dipole. It may have several pairs of traps.

69. Calculate the full wavelength λ at 7MHz and divide by 2 to get a half wavelength.

$$\lambda = \frac{3 \times 10^8}{f} = \frac{3 \times 10^8}{7 \times 10^6} = \frac{300 \times 10^6}{7 \times 10^6} = \frac{300}{7} = 42.86 \; metres.$$

Therefore physical length of λ/2 antenna is;

$$\frac{\lambda}{2} \times 0.95 = \frac{42.86}{2} \times 0.95 = 21.43 \times 0.95 = 20.35 \; metres \; (\text{Approx:})$$

70,71. 7MHz. When the traps are resonant at 7MHz their impedance is very high and they isolate the inner section X, from the outer section Z. The centre section, being shortest in length operates at the highest frequency, i.e. 7MHz.

72. The full length of the antenna will determine the lowest operating frequency.

73. With the antenna required for operation on the 80m band, one would expect the antenna to be about 40m long. However; due to the inductance of the traps, the overall length of the antenna can be considerably shorter than calculated.

Answers - Antennas and Feeders

74. Calculate the full wavelength λ at 3.5MHz and divide by 2 to get a half wavelength.

$$\lambda = \frac{3 \times 10^8}{f} = \frac{3 \times 10^8}{3.5 \times 10^6} = \frac{300 \times 10^6}{3.5 \times 10^6} = \frac{300}{3.5} = 85.7 \ metres$$

Therefore physical length of λ/2 antenna is;

$$\frac{\lambda}{2} \times 0.95 = \frac{85.7}{2} \times 0.95 = 42.86 \times 0.95 = 40.71 \ metres \ \text{(Approx:)}$$

75. The dipole shown is suitable for operation on harmonic frequencies.

76. Length X is the shortest length, it therefore operates at the highest frequency. The highest frequency relates to the shortest wavelength, i.e.10m. Converting 10m to frequency;

$$f = \frac{3 \times 10^8}{\lambda} = \frac{3 \times 10^8}{10} = \frac{300 \times 10^6}{10} = 30 \times 10^6 \ Hz \ or \ 30MHz$$

The nearest frequency band listed is 28 - 29.7MHz.

Note. The waveband in metres does not always convert to the frequencies scheduled for that waveband, this is not faulty maths, but convention. E.g. The 10m band; converting 10m to frequency gives 30MHz. This is correct; however; the related amateur frequency band is 28 - 29.7MHz.

77. Trap B is the 15m trap. Converting 15m to frequency;

$$f = \frac{3 \times 10^8}{\lambda} = \frac{3 \times 10^8}{15} = \frac{300 \times 10^6}{15} = 20 \times 10^6 \ Hz \ or \ 20MHz$$

The nearest frequency listed is 21MHz.

78. The full length of the antenna will operate in the 20m band.

$$f = \frac{3 \times 10^8}{\lambda} = \frac{3 \times 10^8}{20} = \frac{300 \times 10^6}{20} = 15 \times 10^6 \ Hz \ or \ 15MHz$$

The nearest frequency listed is 14MHz.

79. 28MHz. It isolates the 28MHz (10m) section from the lower frequency sections.

80. The greatest single hop distances are achieved by signals radiated at a low take-off angle and reflected from the highest possible ionised layer (F2 layer).

81. Short distance sky-wave communication requires a fairly high take-off angle.

82. The radiation pattern and the number of lobes is a function of the antenna height above ground. Knowledge of the radiation pattern can be used to advantage when directivity is required.

83 - 86. These diagrams show how the radiation pattern changes with height.

87 - 89. These diagrams show how the radiation pattern changes with height.

90. The length of the antenna is 40m. Since it is operating as a $\lambda/4$, the full wavelength is 160m.

$$f = \frac{3 \times 10^8}{\lambda} = \frac{3 \times 10^8}{160} = \frac{300 \times 10^6}{160} = 1.875 \times 10^6 \; Hz \;\; or \;\; 1.875MHz.$$

91. The length of the antenna is 40m. Since it is operating as a $\lambda/2$, the full wavelength is 80m.

$$f = \frac{3 \times 10^8}{\lambda} = \frac{3 \times 10^8}{80} = \frac{300 \times 10^6}{80} = 3.75 \times 10^6 \; Hz \;\; or \;\; 3.75MHz.$$

92. At 14MHz (20 metre band) the antenna will be two wavelengths (approx:). See note on previous page between A76 and A77.

93. At 28MHz (10 metre band) the antenna will be four wavelengths (approx:) See note on previous page between A76 and A77.

94,95. The $5/8\lambda$ vertical has about a 3dB gain over a $\lambda/4$ vertical. The loading coil L is used to match the antenna and bring it to $3/4\lambda$ resonance.

96. The impedance of a half-wave antenna is high at each end and low at the centre.

97,98. The tuning unit - a parallel tuned circuit - is high impedance at resonance, it is therefore suitable for tuning a half-wave, end-fed antenna. In this case 0.5λ ($\lambda/2$). The tuned circuit, including the antenna, is resonant at the transmit frequency.

99,100. A marconi antenna is a $\lambda/4$ vertical used at HF. It may be shorter and top loaded. As it is basically $\lambda/4$ the feed point Z will be low. The series tuned circuit has a low Z and is suitable for matching this antenna. When the tuned circuit is resonant at 3.5MHz ($\lambda = 80m$), the transmit frequency, the antenna will be approximately 20m.

101,102. Maximum response is broadside to the rod B-B. Minimum response is A-A.

103. A very high VSWR; say 6:1 or 10:1, indicates there may be a faulty feeder, a broken cable, poorly terminated connection, or broken antenna element.

104. A unity VSWR (1:1) is very good. Everything is perfectly matched.

105. Nothing; standing waves are due to antenna or load mismatch or faulty feeder.

106,107. The reflectometer and slotted line are used for VSWR measurements. The slotted line uses a probe, sliding in a narrow slot to detect maximum and minimum voltage on a coaxial line.

108. $VSWR = \dfrac{V_{max}}{V_{min}} = \dfrac{3}{1} = 3:1$

109. A VSWR of 10:1 is very bad. Retune the antenna or look for a fault.

110. A VSWR of 1.1:1 is very good. Can't get much better than this.

111. $ERP = Input\ power \times Power\ gain = 400 \times 4 = 1600\,W.$

112. $e = \dfrac{7.02\,\sqrt{ERP}}{d} = \dfrac{7.02\,\sqrt{400}}{30} = \dfrac{7.02 \times 20}{30} = \dfrac{140.4}{30} = 4.68\,V/m.$

113. $e = \dfrac{7.02\,\sqrt{ERP}}{d} = \dfrac{7.02\,\sqrt{100}}{10} = \dfrac{7.02 \times 10}{10} = \dfrac{70.2}{10} = 7.02\,V/m.$

114. $e = \dfrac{7.02\,\sqrt{ERP}}{d} = \dfrac{7.02\,\sqrt{400}}{200} = \dfrac{7.02 \times 20}{200} = \dfrac{140.4}{200} = 0.7\,V/m\ (Approx.).$

115. $ERP = \left(\dfrac{ed}{7.02}\right)^2 = \left(\dfrac{2 \times 15}{7.02}\right)^2 = \left(\dfrac{30}{7.02}\right)^2 = 4.27^2 = 18.26\,W\ (ERP).$

116. $ERP = \left(\dfrac{ed}{7.02}\right)^2 = \left(\dfrac{1 \times 100}{7.02}\right)^2 = 14.25^2 = 203\,W\,(ERP).$

117. $d = \dfrac{7.02\,\sqrt{ERP}}{e} = \dfrac{7.02\,\sqrt{400}}{3} = \dfrac{7.02 \times 20}{3} = \dfrac{140.4}{3} = 46.8\,m.$

14. Propagation

In this section we will cover :-
1. the ionosphere and heights of the ionised layers.
2. refraction and reflection of radio waves by the ionosphere.
3. HF, VHF and UHF propagation.

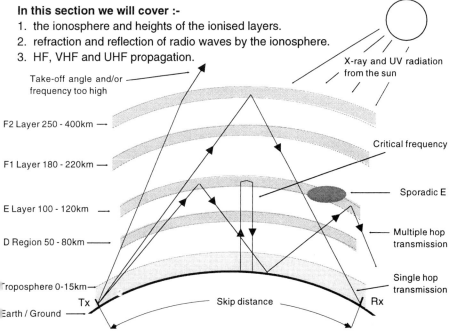

Fig.1 Showing possible HF transmission paths via the ionosphere. The skip distance is the minimum distance from the transmitter at which a sky reflected wave of given frequency is returned to earth by the ionosphere. Maximum single hop distances are 2000km via E layer and 4000km via F2 layer.

Propagation in the HF band (3 - 30MHz).

Due to the action of UV and X radiation from the sun, the rarefied atmosphere 50 - 400km above the surface of the earth becomes ionised in layers, as shown in fig.1.

The ionisation density varies with the time of day, month and season. There is also a periodic eleven year variation corresponding to the eleven year sunspot cycle maxima. When the sun is highest, around mid day, the layers are most densely ionised.

The ionised layers refract or bend electromagnetic waves entering them. If the frequency and angle of incidence of a wave is suitable it will be refracted and returned to earth. If the frequency is increased, or the angle of arrival (angle of incidence) is too near the vertical, the wave will pass through that layer to the next, where again, it will either be returned to earth or pass through to the next layer, or into space and lost. The approximate heights of the layers are shown in fig.1.

At night the situation changes, the F2 and F1 layers combine to form a single F layer, and the D and E layers, for most practical purposes disappear.

14 - 1

Propagation

Points to note (HF Propagation)

1. D layer. Height 50 - 80km. Highly absorptive of LF and MF signals (including the 1.8MHz and 3.5MHz amateur bands) during daylight hours when sun is highest. Disappears at night.
2. E layer. Height about 100 - 120km. Maximum ionisation intensity at noon. Single hop E layer communication distance can be up to 2000km. For most practical purposes the E layer disappears at night.
3. Sporadic E. Irregular cloud-like regions of high ionisation in the E layer, very reflective. Signals between 28 and 146MHz, which would normally pass through the E layer are reflected. Extended distances of up to 2000km are possible.
4. F1 layer. Height about 180 - 220km. Exists mainly in daylight hours.
5. F1 and F2 combine at night to form a single F layer.
6. F2 layer. Height about 250 - 400km. Single hop distances up to 4000km possible. Principal reflecting layer for long distance HF communication.
7. The height and ionisation density of the layers depends on the position of the sun, the sunspot cycle, time and season.
8. The critical frequency, see fig.1, is the highest frequency that is returned to earth by a particular layer for a signal transmitted at vertical incidence.
9. The maximum usable frequency (MUF) for a transmission path is the highest frequency with which it is possible to maintain communication with a given point.
10. MUFs for long distance radio paths are usually 2 to 3.5 times the critical frequency.
11. Transmissions above the MUF will penetrate the layer and may be lost in space.
12. For the longest transmission paths, the transmitted signal should have a low take-off angle to the horizon so that it grazes the F2 layer and is returned to earth.
13. Multiple hop propagation will cover long distances. The signal being reflected between the ionosphere and the earth a number of times, see fig.1.
14. Normally, at night, it is necessary to change frequency (QSY) to a lower frequency to maintain communication over a given path, this due to the ionised layers becoming less densely ionised and not refracting the higher frequency signals sufficiently to bend them back to earth.
15. The ground-wave attenuation increases with increase in frequency, and may extend to only a few kilometres at frequencies of 10 - 20MHz.

Propagation above 30MHz.

In the VHF/UHF bands the main mode of propagation is line-of-sight, and normally between elevated antennas. In practice the radio horizon is slightly beyond the the visible horizon due to refraction of the signal in the lower atmosphere. It is possible to calculate the radio horizon by assuming straight line propagation and increasing the radius of the earth by a factor of 4/3 (1.33). Typical distances between VHF/UHF stations may be 20-120km, this depends on terrain, antenna height, antenna gain, transmitted power, and weather. Under abnormal conditions, such as sporadic E and tropospheric ducting, distances may be considerably extended, particularly in the lower VHF band, and

Propagation

maximum distances of 1000-1500km may be possible for short periods of time.

Obstacles in the signal path, such as tall buildings, hilly terrain and mountains, have the effect of reducing the signal level or blocking it completely. High gain directional antennas and high sites are necessary for maximum distances.

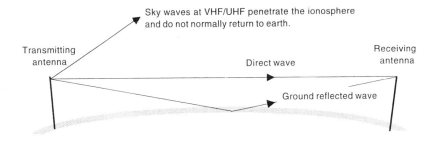

Fig.2. Showing propagation at VHF/UHF between elevated antennas.

Points to note (VHF/UHF Propagation)

1. VHF/UHF propagation is basically line-of-sight. If the transmit antenna can see the receive antenna, communication is possible.

2. In practice the radio horizon is greater than the visible horizon. This is due to refraction or bending of the wave in the earth's atmosphere.

3. The received signal strength will depend on transmitter power, gain and height of both receiving and transmitting antennas, and path length and route.

4. Mountains, hills, tall buildings, forests, and other obstacles in the signal path will affect the received signal.

5. Typical range for VHF/UHF signals under normal conditions, i.e. fairly flat terrain, low gain antenna at 30m a.g.l, and transmitter power 25 watts, may be 20-60km. A sea path may increase the usable range, while a cross city path will have an adverse effect on the range.

6. Sporadic E and tropospheric ducting can extend the range of VHF operation up to 1000-2000km for short periods of time.

7. Fig.2 shows the received signal consisting of a direct wave and a ground reflected wave. When the two waves reach the receiver out of phase, they cancel (no reception), when they arrive in-phase, they reinforce (double the signal strength), this assumes equal path attenuation of both signals.

8. In practice the receive antenna may receive a signal via several paths due to reflection and scattering from obstacles in or near the signal path. This can cause distortion of the wanted signal, the amount of distortion depending on the relative levels and phases of the signals present at the receiver input.

9. High gain directional antennas are smaller and more practical at VHF/UHF than at HF.

1. **The ionosphere is a-**
   a) ball of ionised gasses which form during thunderstorms.
   b) region of ionised gasses surrounding the earth.
   c) region of ionised gasses surrounding the sun.
   d) big sphere of iron, capable of reflecting radio waves.

2. **The ionosphere-**
   a) extends from about 50km to about 400km above the surface of the earth.
   b) extends from the earths surface to about 10km above it.
   c) surrounds the sun at a distance of exactly 30,000 metres.
   d) travels at a speed of 300,000 m/s (metres/second).

3. **What is the velocity of radio waves in free space?**
   a) 470m/s   b) 625m/s
   c) 3×10^6m/s   d) 3×10^8m/s

4. **Ionisation of the gas molecules in the earths upper atmosphere is due to-**
   a) U.V. radiation from the sun.
   b) small particles of moon dust, more dense in winter.
   c) evaporation of the oceans.
   d) gasses emitted from aerosol spray cans.

5. **The height of the F1 layer above the earths surface is approximately-**
   a) 50km   b) 200km
   c) 10km   d) 6km

6. **The height of the F2 layer is variable, but generally during the winter months it-**
   a) is higher than the F1 layer.
   b) is lower than the F1 layer.
   c) is lower than the E layer.
   d) drops below the D layer.

7. **What is the height of the F2 layer?**
   a) Exactly 100km above sea level.
   b) 35,000km above sea level.
   c) 22,000km above sea level.
   d) Variable between about 250km and 400km above the surface of the earth.

8. **How many F layers exist during daytime?**
   a) 1   b) 2   c) 3   d) 4

9. **How many F layers exist at night?**
   a) 1   b) 2   c) 3   d) 4

10. Which two of the ionised layers merge at night to form a single ionised layer?
    a) D - E
    b) E - F1
    c) F1 - F2
    d) D - F1

11. At night the level of ionisation of the layers-
    a) increases.
    b) decreases.
    c) decreases to zero.
    d) remains the same as daytime.

12. The principal mode of propagation for long distance (Dx) communication in the HF band is by-
    a) ground-wave.
    b) reflection from the ionosphere.
    c) direct-wave.
    d) tropospheric reflection.

13. In which frequency band is sky-wave the principal mode of propagation?
    a) LF
    b) MF
    c) HF
    d) VHF

14. The principal mode of propagation for long distance (Dx) communication in the LF band is by-
    a) ground-wave.
    b) reflection from the ionosphere.
    c) direct-wave.
    d) tropospheric reflection.

15. The height of the E layer above the earths surface is approximately-
    a) 250 - 400km
    b) 200 - 250km
    c) 100 - 120km
    d) 50 - 80km

16. What happens to the E layer at night?
    a) It disappears.
    b) It remains, but rather weakly ionised.
    c) It remains, but with increased density.
    d) It drops below the horizon.

17. The maximum reflecting properties of the E layer occur around-
    a) midday.
    b) midnight.
    c) early morning.
    d) early evening.

18. In winter the height of the E layer -
    a) increases.
    b) decreases.
    c) is 20km.
    d) is about the same as in summer.

19. The D layer is ionised-
    a) during the hours of darkness.
    b) during daylight hours.
    c) at all times.
    d) in summer only.

20. **What happens to the D layer at night?**
    a) It becomes heavily ionised.
    b) It de-ionises and disappears.
    c) It remains the same as in daytime.
    d) It drops below the troposphere.

21. **What is the approximate height of the D layer?**
    a) 250 - 400km   b) 200 - 250km
    c) 100 - 140km   d) 50 - 80km

22. **In which one of the following frequency bands is sky-wave propagation the accepted mode?**
    a) 30 - 300kHz   b) 300 - 3000kHz
    c) 3 - 30MHz   d) 300 - 3000MHz

23. **The frequencies used for transcontinental transmission at night are-**
    a) generally higher than those used during the day.
    b) generally lower than those used during the day.
    c) very much higher than those used during the day.
    d) normally the same as those used during the day.

24. **To maintain long distance sky-wave transmission at night, it is necessary to-**
    a) increase the working frequency.
    b) decrease the working frequency.
    c) decrease the transmitter power.
    d) switch to frequency modulation.

25. **To achieve the greatest skip distances-**
    a) the sun must shine.
    b) it must be noon at Greenwich.
    c) the take-off angle of the radio wave must be low.
    d) it should be winter below the point of reflection.

26. **You are in contact with a few Russian stations during the day on a frequency of 21MHz, but when night falls you find that you have to change frequency to 14MHz or 7MHz to maintain contact. What is the reason?**
    a) There is no reason other than that it has become accepted practice.
    b) Tidal variations causing signal take-off angles to vary.
    c) The ionised layers are less densely ionised at night and the higher frequencies are not reflected but pass through into space.
    d) Severe absorption and attenuation in the actual 'Iron Curtain'.

27. What are the designated frequencies for the following bands?
   a) MF___   b) HF___
   c) VHF___   d) UHF___

28. Eruptions on the surface of the sun are often referred to as-
   a) volcanoes.   b) black holes.
   c) blemishes.   d) solar flares.

29. One cause of weak signal strengths on a sky wave transmission path is-
   a) ionospheric storms.
   b) thunderstorms along the skip route.
   c) heavy rain along the skip route.
   d) the political climate of the country over which the radio waves pass.

30. Regular variations occur in the ionosphere, daily, seasonally, and also-
   a) in phase with the equatorial thunderstorm season.
   b) at civil airline flight peak busy hours.
   c) with the 11 year sunspot cycle.
   d) with the mean noon temperature maxima.

31. The 'critical frequency' is the-
   a) lowest frequency returned from the horizon.
   b) optimum traffic frequency for a given propagation path.
   c) most stable frequency for day and night use.
   d) highest frequency that will be reflected when a wave strikes an ionised layer at vertical incidence.

32. What happens to radio waves entering a layer at vertical incidence when their frequency is above the critical frequency for that layer?
   a) They get trapped between the ionised layers and are attenuated.
   b) They are attracted to the sun and are reradiated as heat.
   c) They pass through that layer to the next layer, where they are either reflected or pass through into space.
   d) They are reflected back to earth some distance from the transmitter.

33. High absorption of MF and HF waves takes place during the day in the-
   a) D layer.   b) E layer.
   c) F1 layer.   d) F2 layer.

34. For daytime communication in the HF band over distances of 1000 miles (1600km), reflection is most likely to be from the-
   a) D layer.   b) E layer.
   c) F1 layer.   d) F2 layer.

35. Sometimes greatly increased propagation distances are obtained, particularly in the VHF band, this is due to a phenomenon called-
   a) Sporadic E.   b) Dynamic D.
   c) Refractive F.   d) Filtered F.

36. When the condition referred to in Q 35 occurs, it is due to-
   a) natural oscillations in the F2 layer.
   b) irregular, and highly ionised cloud-like areas in the E layer causing reflection of the radio wave.
   c) rain clouds beyond the blue horizon.
   d) secondary emission of the signal by sea water.

37. When the condition referred to in Q 35 occurs, transmission path distances in the band from 28-150MHz may be extended by typically up to-
   a) 38km.   b) 75km.
   c) 1000km.   d) 6000km.

38. The 'maximum usable frequency' (MUF)-
   a) refers to the upper band edge at 29.7MHz.
   b) specifies the highest output frequency of a transmitter.
   c) is the highest frequency that will be reflected when a wave strikes a layer at vertical incidence.
   d) is the highest frequency for a given communication path.

39. MUFs are highest-
   a) at or near midnight or early morning.
   b) at or near noon or early afternoon, and during periods of high sunspot activity.
   c) during early evening when tropo ducting might occur.
   d) as a general rule of thumb, whenever there is an R in the month.

40. The optimum traffic frequency, or optimum frequency for communication, is-
   a) chosen to be 10MHz above the MUF.
   b) chosen to be 2MHz below the MUF.
   c) chosen to be lower than the MUF by a safety margin of about 15% to allow for changes in the ionosphere.
   d) normally 15% lower than the critical frequency.

41. A radio wave will travel through the ionosphere and out into space without being reflected or refracted back to earth if-
   a) its frequency is above 470kHz.
   b) there is a harsh frost followed by a full moon.
   c) its frequency is below the critical frequency.
   d) its frequency is much greater than the MUF.

42. A typical F2 layer, single hop skip distance is about-
- a) 10 - 50km.
- b) 50 - 100km.
- c) 24,000km.
- d) 800 - 4000km.

43. The distance covered by the ground wave-
- a) increases with frequency.
- b) decreases with frequency.
- c) is independent of frequency.
- d) is dependent on the height of the F2 layer.

44. In the Low Frequency LF band-
- a) long distance ground-wave communication is possible.
- b) the ground-wave is only suitable for short distance communication.
- c) very small antennas are used for transmission.
- d) the influence of the moon affects the signal strength.

45. A vertical antenna is said to be-
- a) horizontally polarised.
- b) vertically polarised.
- c) circularly polarised.
- d) cross polarised.

46. F Layer signal reflection may be possible at 50MHz (6 metres) when-
- a) the radio waves are cross polarised.
- b) there is unusually high solar activity, i.e. the peak of the sunspot cycle.
- c) solar activity is very low and the F layer has deionised.
- d) a layer of snow causes secondary reflection from the ground.

47. Which of the ionised layers gives the longest single hop path length?
- a) D layer
- b) E layer
- c) F1 layer
- d) F2 layer

48. The troposphere extends to approximately-
- a) 1000km above the earths surface.
- b) 2000km above the earths surface.
- c) 10 - 15km above the earths surface.
- d) 1.25km above the earths surface.

49. A radio wave transmitted in the HF band could have its range extended to 8000km or more by means of-
- a) a large metal reflector in front of the antenna.
- b) a large metal reflector behind the antenna.
- c) increasing the speed of propagation to 30,000m/s.
- d) multiple hop propagation.

50. **Fading over sky-wave paths may be caused by-**
    a) the received signal arriving at the receiver via different paths and cancelling.
    b) obstructions in the skip zone.
    c) variations in temperature of the earths core.
    d) the operators keying technique.

51. **Selective fading of a DSB transmission can cause severe distortion due to-**
    a) black holes in the F2 layer.
    b) gyro-resonance in the E layer.
    c) using an unsuitable receive IF filter.
    d) the different frequency components in the sidebands of the received signal fading independently.

52. **Selective fading referred to in Q 51 may be reduced by-**
    a) waiting for the black holes to ionise.
    b) increasing the frequency to 4 times the critical frequency.
    c) removing the harmonics of the carrier wave before transmission.
    d) the use of single-sideband (SSB) transmission and reception.

53. **Complete fade-out of a signal transmitted via the ionosphere may be due to-**
    a) changes in sea temperature and tidal variations.
    b) lunar flares and ionospheric storms on the circumference of the moon.
    c) ozone discharge from industrial areas.
    d) solar flares and ionospheric storms.

54. **The skip zone is the-**
    a) distance between the two antennas.
    b) the distance from the point of reflection to the receiver.
    c) dead zone, from the end of the ground-wave, to the start of the area illuminated by the sky reflected wave.
    d) diameter of the area illuminated by the sky reflected wave.

55. **Propagation in the VHF/UHF bands is normally-**
    a) moon bounce.   b) line-of-sight.
    c) sky-wave.   d) D layer reflection.

56. **To achieve the greatest distances on the VHF/UHF bands during normal propagation conditions-**
    a) there has to be a sunspot minima.
    b) there has to be a sunspot maxima.
    c) all tall buildings outside the signal path must be below sea level.
    d) antennas and sites should be as high as possible and clear of obstructions.

57. The normal range of a VHF transmission is-
a) about 250km in summer and 400km in winter.
b) line-of-sight, extended by a factor equivalent to increasing the earths radius by $4/3^{rds}$.
c) approximately double the E layer distance.
d) fairly constant at 6.284km.

58. It is sometimes possible to achieve short term, long distance communication in the VHF band when certain natural phenomena occur, one of which is sporadic E, another is-
a) auroral storms.
b) the hertzian dipole effect.
c) helmholtz resonance.
d) earthquake activity.

59. Another well-known form of short term, long distance propagation occurs at VHF due to-
a) the insulating properties of the troposphere.
b) ducting in the troposphere.
c) the ionospheric vacuum effect.
d) changes in ground conductivity.

60. The range of VHF signals may also be increased by means of -
a) tropospheric scatter.
b) sun bounce.
c) terrestrial F.
d) sonic scatter.

61. You have set up a line of sight VHF path over flat, good conductivity ground, but the received signal is much weaker than expected, a possible cause is-
a) absorption in the D layer.
b) gyro-resonance in the E layer.
c) the transmitted signal being reflected from the F2 layer.
d) the direct wave and the ground reflected wave arriving at the receive antenna out of phase.

62. How might you be able to overcome the problem encountered in Q 61?
a) Wait until the D layer deionises.
b) Wait until the E layer returns to normal.
c) Reduce power.
d) Gradually increase or decrease the height of one of the antennas until the signal increases.

63. It is possible for VHF signals to be received at the opposite side of a mountain or ridge when-
    a) the signals are below 146MHz.
    b) knife-edge diffraction occurs.
    c) the signal wavelength does not exceed 2 metres.
    d) the top of the ridge is covered with sandy soil.

64. A 144MHz VHF signal entering the F2 layer would-
    a) remain trapped in that layer.
    b) be returned to earth at a distance of 1600km.
    c) be returned to earth at a distance of 2400km.
    d) pass through and not normally be returned to earth.

65. When might a 144MHz signal, passing through the ionosphere as in Q 64 above, be used for communication?
    a) When it is bounced off the moon or used to communicate with a satellite.
    b) When it is raining in the ionosphere.
    c) During an eclipse of the sun.
    d) During an eclipse of the moon.

66. When operating a VHF transmitter from a poor location, such as in a valley or near sea level and surrounded by hills, it may be possible to improve coverage and propagation path distances by using a-
    a) loss reducer.
    b) signal attenuator.
    c) beacon station.
    d) repeater.

67. A radio operator regularly works a VHF station to his north. This is usually interfered with by a strong transmission to his south.
    How might he overcome this problem?
    a) Use the F1 layer for signal reflection.
    b) Change the phase of the signal.
    c) Call QRM and QRN before each period of transmission.
    d) Use a directional (Yagi) antenna.

68. Which one of the following is the UHF band?
    a) 3 - 30MHz.
    b) 30 - 300MHz.
    c) 300 - 3000MHz.
    d) 3000 - 30000MHz.

Answers - Propagation

1	b	13	c	25	c	37	c	48	c	60	a
2	a	14	a	26	c	38	d	49	d	61	d
3	d	15	c	27	*(See P14-14)*			50	a	62	d
4	a	16	b	28	d	39	b	51	d	63	b
5	b	17	a	29	a	40	c	52	d	64	d
6	a	18	d	30	c	41	d	53	d	65	a
7	d	19	b	31	d	42	d	54	c	66	d
8	b	20	b	32	c	43	b	55	b	67	d
9	a	21	d	33	a	44	a	56	d	68	c
10	c	22	c	34	b	45	b	57	b		
11	b	23	b	35	a	46	b	58	a		
12	b	24	b	36	b	47	d	59	b		

1,2. The ionosphere is a region between about 50-400km above the earth's surface where ionisation of the rarefied atmosphere occurs. The 4 main layers of ionisation affecting radio transmission are shown in fig.1.

3. In free space radio waves travel at the speed of light. 3×10^8 metres/second.

4. Ionisation occurs when the gas molecules comprising the rarefied atmosphere are split into free electrons and ions, this being due mainly to X and UV radiation from the sun. The free electrons and ions recombine after sunset.

5. The height of the F1 layer is about 220km above the earth's surface.

6,7,8,9,10. The F2 layer varies between 250 and 400km above the earth's surface. It is always above the F1 layer. Both F1 and F2 layers exist during daylight hours but combine to form a single F layer at night.

11. Due to recombination of the free electrons and ions after sunset, the layers are less densely ionised, reducing the refractive and reflecting properties of the ionosphere.

12,13. Long distance communication in the HF band relies on signals being reflected or refracted (bent) back to earth from the ionosphere.

14. Reliable VLF and LF communication can be established by ground waves. The waves follow the curvature of the earth.

15,16,17,18. The Height of the E layer is about 120km above the surface of the earth. At night its ionisation level decreases to a point where it plays no significant part in HF propagation, although it does not disappear completely.
The E layer has maximum ionisation and reflecting properties around midday. Its Height is fairly constant all year through.

Answers - Propagation

19,20,21. The D layer is ionised during daylight hours only, and rapidly de-ionises and disappears at sunset. The D layer is highly absorptive of RF signals. It has an attenuating effect on signals in the 1.8MHz band and below during daytime. The height of the D layer varies between 50 and 90km.

22. The 3-30MHz HF band is normally used for sky wave transmission.

23,24. The maximum usable daytime frequencies will penetrate the ionised layers when they become less densely ionised (and less reflective) at night. It is therefore necessary to decrease the working frequency to maintain communication.

25. To achieve the greatest skip distances the angle at which the transmitted wave departs from the transmit antenna must be low. Ideally it will just graze the horizon. This can be seen from the geometry of the reflected wave shown in fig.1.

26. See answer 23,24.

27. a) 300-3000kHz   b) 3-30MHz   c) 30-300MHz   d) 300-3000MHz

28. Solar flares erupting on the surface of the sun give rise to an increase in the ionisation level of the D layer, increasing its attenuation to radio signals. As a result, complete fade-outs can occur in the HF band (Dellinger fade-out). This may last from a few minutes to a few hours. Often referred to as a Sudden Ionospheric Disturbance (SID). SIDs affect radio propagation about 10 minutes after the solar event.

29. Ionospheric storms can disrupt HF communications some period of time after an SID due to slower moving particles arriving from the eruption on the sun. They tend to last longer than an SID, from a few hours to several days; hence they are more disruptive.

30. Sunspot activity reaches a maximum approximately every 11 years. This is referred to as the eleven year sunspot cycle. The intensity of the radiation varies during the cycle, and each cycle has a different level of activity. During sunspot maxima; maximum usable frequencies may be very high and readily allow long distance communication on the 28 and 50MHz bands.

31,32. The critical frequency is the highest frequency, of a wave directed vertically into a layer, that will be returned to earth by that layer before passing through it. When the frequency of the wave is increased above the critical frequency, it passes through the layer, to be reflected from the next layer or pass through into space.

33. The D layer is highly absorptive in the daytime.

34. For short distance sky-wave working the E layer can be used for ranges up to 1000km. Frequency has to be correct for the geometry of the path.

35,36,37. Sporadic E. Highly reflective, irregular clouds of ionisation in the E layer, making propagation over distances of up to 2000km possible from about 28-150MHz.

Answers - Propagation

38,39. The MUF is the maximum usable frequency for a given communication path. MUFs are highest at and around noon and during periods of high sunspot activity.

40. When using the MUF, small changes in the height or electron density of the ionised layer can result in signal loss. Working about 10-15% below the MUF makes for a more stable path.

41. Frequencies greater than the MUF for the layer in use will pass through that layer to the next, where if not reflected will be lost in space.

42. Typical F2 skip distances are between 800-4000km. (4000km is maximum).

43,44. The distance covered by the ground-wave decreases with increase in frequency. At 100kHz ground-wave coverage might extend to 2000km and be very reliable, but at 20MHz extend only a few kilometres.

45. A vertical antenna radiates a vertically polarised wave.

46. During periods of very high sunspot activity, the electron density of the F2 layer may be sufficiently high to refract or reflect signals of up to 50MHz back to earth.

47. Longest distance propagation paths are by reflection from the highest ionised layer - the F2 layer. 4000km is possible.

48. The troposphere is the lowest level of the earth's atmosphere. It extends from the ground to a height of approximately 10 - 15km.

49. In the HF band multiple hop transmission can extend the range of a transmission above that expected for a single hop transmission. The signal, returned to earth by refraction in the ionosphere is reflected from the earth's surface back to the ionosphere, where it is again refracted and returned to earth. This process may repeat itself for several hops.

50. A transmission may arrive at the receiver via different paths, the resulting phase differences at the receive end will cause the signal strength to increase or decrease. Fading and distortion will be observed. This is multipath interference.

51. When the different frequency components in the sidebands of an amplitude-modulated, double-sideband transmission, fade independently, distortion may occur. This is selective fading.

52. Selective fading may be reduced by the use of SSB suppressed carrier.

53. See answer 28 and 29.

54. The skip zone is the dead zone between the end of the ground-wave and the point where the sky-wave returned from the ionosphere becomes usable.

55,56,57. Propagation in the VHF/UHF bands is line-of-site, extended by a factor equivalent to increasing the earth's radius by 1.33 (4/3R). For maximum

Answers - Propagation

distances the transmit and receive antennas should be as high as possible, and the path should be free of obstructions such as tall buildings and mountains. The typical range of a VHF/UHF path under normal conditions is about 20-60km.

58. The aurora, (northern or southern lights), caused by charged particles from the sun, are highly absorptive of HF signals passing the auroral region, resulting in fading and flutter. Reflection of VHF/UHF signals can occur from the aurora, although this is likely to be subject to rapid fading and distortion.

59. Tropospheric ducting, due to changes in refractive index with height can extend VHF/UHF signal propagation up to about 2000km or more. Ducting can occur in the lower atmosphere due to temperature inversion conditions, when cool air near the surface of the earth is overrun by a layer of warm air. The signal follows the duct until the refractive index changes sufficiently to return it to earth.

60. Tropospheric scatter propagation can occur when a signal meets irregular changes in refractive index in the troposphere. High power and high gain antennas are normally required.

61,62. When the direct wave and the ground reflected wave, see fig.2, arrive at the receive antenna out of phase, they cancel. Increasing or decreasing the height of the receive antenna will bring the signals into phase, resulting in an increase in signal strength. Signal paths over tidal waters can be subject to fading due to the ground reflected wave path length changing with the state of the tide. System design using spaced antenna diversity will overcome this problem.

63. VHF signals passing over a mountain ridge can undergo knife-edge diffraction. The signal is diffracted at the ridge and can sometimes be received the other side of the mountain where signals would not normally be considered possible.

64,65. Under normal propagation conditions all VHF signals will pass through the ionosphere. Earth-moon-earth (EME) transmission (moon bounce) and satellite communication are possible.

66. The use of suitably positioned amateur repeaters makes communication possible between mobiles and base stations in mountainous and hilly terrain.

67. Assuming a non-directional antenna was used in the first instance. Switching to a yagi antenna, and exploiting its directional characteristics will increase the received and transmitted signal level in the required direction, and reduce the unwanted received and transmitted signal levels from the rear of the antenna. The ratio of forward power in the direction of maximum radiation, to the unwanted radiated power at the rear of the antenna, is termed the front-to-back ratio and expressed in decibels.

68. The UHF band is 300 - 3000MHz (0.3 - 3GHz).

15. Measurement

This section will cover :-

1. instruments used for the measurement of d.c., a.c. and r.f. voltages, currents, and powers. Including analogue and digital multimeters and oscilloscopes.
2. measurement of d.c. input power and r.f. output power of power amplifiers, and current at radio frequencies.
3. digital frequency meters, absorption wavemeters, crystal calibrators, standing wave ratio meters and the dummy load.
4. the decibel and the dBW.

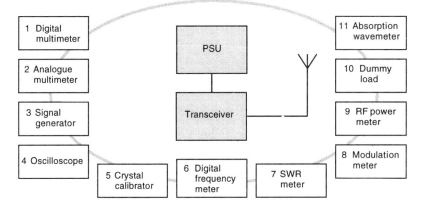

Fig.1. Showing a radio transceiver surrounded by typical instrumentation available for test and measurement at a radio station. (See list below)

The test instruments

1. **The digital multimeter.** A very accurate instrument with a digital display. It has a high input resistance. Typical instruments measure alternating and direct voltage and current, also resistance. Not suitable when tuning for peaks and dips.

2. **The analogue multimeter.** Uses a moving coil microammeter. A good general purpose testmeter. Input resistance depends on range selected and sensitivity of the meter movement. It will measure alternating and direct voltage and current, also resistance. It is suitable for tuning peaks and dips.

3. **The signal generator** will provide a variable a.f. or r.f. signal of high frequency stability. It will be possible to amplitude modulate and frequency modulate the r.f. output. The signal level will be variable from about 0.1µV to 2V.

4. **The oscilloscope** is a general purpose instrument for measuring and observing

waveforms. The display (usually green) is on a small cathode ray tube.

The horizontal 'X' deflection is controlled by a variable speed time base, and the vertical deflection by the 'Y' amplifier and the signal being observed.

5. **The crystal calibrator** is a device that produces harmonics from a very accurate and stable crystal oscillator. The crystal frequencies may be 100kHz, 500kHz, 1MHz, 5MHz, or 10MHz. Receiver tuning can be checked and calibrated against the crystal harmonics. Some receivers have a built-in crystal calibrator.

6. **The digital frequency meter** (frequency counter) counts the number of cycles of a waveform over an accurately measured period of time, it then displays the count on a digital display. The overall accuracy of the instrument is determined by the stability of the crystal in the clock, and the resolution is determined by the number of digits of the display. It will only measure the fundamental, It will not measure harmonic frequencies that may be present on a transmission.

7. **The SWR meter** (reflectometer or through-line power meter) measures the performance and matching of a transmission line and antenna system. It uses a moving coil milliammeter to indicate forward and reflected power. It may be calibrated in both VSWR and r.f. power (watts).

8. **The modulation meter** is to ensure the correct level of modulation for a system. It gives a direct read-out of percentage modulation in a.m. systems, and frequency deviation in f.m. systems. Badly adjusted modulation levels can result in distortion and interference to other radio channels.

9. **The r.f. power meter** measures the power in watts at the output of a transmitter, it sometimes incorporates a non-reactive dummy load, usually 50 or 75Ω.

10. **The dummy load** is used when carrying out transmitter adjustments prior to transmitting. It must be non-reactive i.e. purely resistive. It must also be able to dissipate the full output power of the source transmitter.

11. **The absorption wavemeter,** the most basic of all the test instruments. It consists of an L C circuit which absorbs maximum r.f. power when it is tuned to the frequency of a nearby radiating source, i.e. an antenna or an energised tuned circuit.

The instrument will only indicate the order of frequency to within 5-10% accuracy. It is not suitable for accurate frequency measurement but is suitable for checking that transmitters employing crystal control are in the correct frequency band.

The moving coil meter movement
The basic moving coil meter movement is the basis of practically all analogue measuring instruments. The movement itself will only measure direct current, but with additional circuitry added, it is capable of measuring resistance and alternating voltage and current up to r.f. Resistors called *multipliers* are used in series with the basic movement to extend the d.c. voltage range, and low value resistors called *shunts* are

Measurement

connected in parallel with the movement to extend the d.c. current ranges. A.c. ranges require an instrument rectifier, and when a.c. current is to be measured, a current transformer. A thermocouple element may be used for r.f. power measurements.

Typical moving coil instruments require a current of between 20μA and 10mA for *full scale deflection* (f.s.d.), and have resistances in the order of 2000Ω to 5Ω.

An instrument having an f.s.d. of 20μA is more sensitive, but less robust than the 10mA f.s.d. instrument. Both f.s.d. and meter resistance are usually written on the instrument scale.

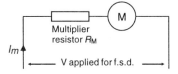

The moving coil d.c. voltmeter.
Fig.2 shows a d.c. voltmeter. The sensitivity is expressed in *'Ohms per volt'* (Ω/V).

E.g. A $1000\Omega/V$ meter - when switched to the 10 volt range - has a resistance of $10 \times 1000\Omega = 10,000\Omega$. The Ω/V rating for a d.c. voltmeter is given by the formula :-

Fig.2. Showing a basic meter movement M converted to a d.c. voltmeter. The multiplier resistance R_M is chosen to drop the difference in potential between the maximum voltage to be measured and the small p.d. across the meter movement for f.s.d.

$$\Omega/V = \frac{1 \ volt}{current \ \text{for} \ f.s.d.}$$

The multiplier resistance is given by :-

$$R_M = \frac{V}{I_m} - R_m.$$ In practice it may be

possible to neglect R_m and the formula

simplified to :- $R_M = \frac{V}{I_m}$

> **Where :-**
> R_M = Resistance of multiplier.
> R_m = Resistance of meter movement.
> I_m = Meter current for f.s.d.
> V = The required voltage for f.s.d.

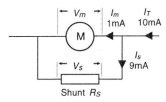

The moving coil d.c. ammeter.
Fig.3 shows a meter movement employing a shunt resistance to provide a higher current range. The shunt, R_s, diverts a known proportion of the external circuit current I_T. The remainder flows in the meter coil. A meter movement, with an

Fig.3. Shows a 1mA meter movement shunted to make the instrument indicate 10mA f.s.d.

f.s.d. of 1mA, is required to have a 10mA range. In this case, of the 10mA flowing in the external circuit, 1mA will flow in the meter, and 9mA in the shunt. The p.d. across the shunt, V_s, is the same as the p.d. V_m across the meter, since both are in parallel :-

$$V_m = V_s = I_m \times R_m$$

The current in the shunt :-

$$I_s = I_T - I_m$$

Resistance of shunt, from Ohm's Law :-

$$R_s = \frac{V_m}{I_s} = \frac{I_m \times R_m}{I_T - I_m}$$

> **Where :-**
> R_s = Resistance of the shunt.
> R_m = Resistance of meter movement.
> I_m = Meter current for f.s.d.
> I_T = The required range current.
> I_s = Current in shunt for f.s.d.
> V_m = P.d. across the meter for f.s.d.
> V_s = P.d. across the shunt for f.s.d.

Measurement

The moving coil meter movement configurations shown below are typical of the various analogue measuring instruments using this device.

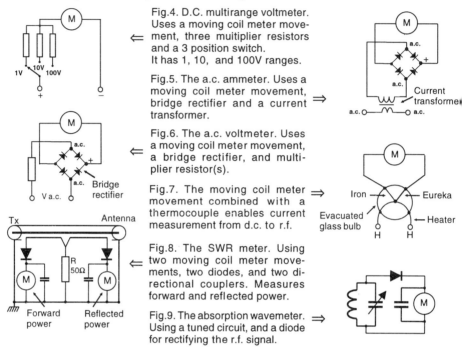

Fig.4. D.C. multirange voltmeter. Uses a moving coil meter movement, three muitiplier resistors and a 3 position switch. It has 1, 10, and 100V ranges. ⇐

Fig.5. The a.c. ammeter. Uses a moving coil meter movement, bridge rectifier and a current transformer. ⇒

Fig.6. The a.c. voltmeter. Uses a moving coil meter movement, a bridge rectifier, and multiplier resistor(s). ⇐

Fig.7. The moving coil meter movement combined with a thermocouple enables current measurement from d.c. to r.f. ⇒

Fig.8. The SWR meter. Using two moving coil meter movements, two diodes, and two directional couplers. Measures forward and reflected power. ⇐

Fig.9. The absorption wavemeter. Using a tuned circuit, and a diode for rectifying the r.f. signal. ⇒

Points to note

1. Ohm's Law may be applied to shunt and multiplier calculations.
2. Voltmeters should be connected across the circuit they are measuring.
3. The lower the current for f.s.d. the higher the Ω/V rating.
4. The higher the Ω/V rating, the less will be the loading on the circuit.
5. Meter resistance can affect the circuit under test and cause false readings.
6. A good moving coil voltmeter may have a sensitivity of 20,000 - 50,000Ω/V.
7. When calculating a voltmeter multiplier resistance, the meter resistance can be ignored if it is small compared with the multiplier resistance.
8. Ammeters should have very low resistance to minimise voltage drop.
9. Ammeters should be connected in series with the circuit under test.
10. Damage may result if an ammeter is connected directly across a power source.
11. The basic moving coil meter movement will only measure direct currents.
12. RF voltage measurements may be made with an electronic voltmeter employing a diode detector circuit.
13. Current, D.C. to RF, may be measured using a thermocouple meter.
14. The accuracy of a frequency measuring instrument must be considered, particularly when working near to a band edge.

Measurement

The Decibel (dB)

The decibel (dB) is a unit based on common logarithms, and is extensively used in radio and communication engineering to provide a measure of gain or loss in a system. The following system elements have their gain or loss measured in dB:- antennas, antenna feeders, amplifiers (audio and r.f.), receivers, transmission lines, attenuators, and filters. Field strength is also measured in dB.

Basically the dB is a unit of power ratio, and not absolute power, however, if some standard power level is used as a reference, then any absolute power level can be expressed in dB above or below the reference power. Common reference levels are the watt, abbreviated dBW, the milliwatt, abbreviated dBm, and the volt, millivolt, and microvolt; abbreviated dBV, dBmV, and dBµV respectively.

When the ratio of two powers, see fig.10, is expressed in decibels, the number of decibels, N_{dB}, is given by :-

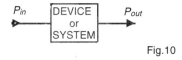

$$N_{dB} = 10 \, Log_{10} \frac{P_{out}}{P_{in}}$$

Fig.10

When the ratio of two voltages or currents is expressed in decibels, the number of decibels, N_{dB}, is given by :-

$$N_{dB} = 20 \, Log_{10} \frac{V_{out}}{V_{in}}$$

$$N_{dB} = 20 \, Log_{10} \frac{I_{out}}{I_{in}}$$

← **Note.** Assumes voltages and currents are developed across same value of input and output resistance or impedance. (Not always adhered to.)

Note. When the ratio $\frac{P_{out}}{P_{in}}$, $\frac{V_{out}}{V_{in}}$, $\frac{I_{out}}{I_{in}}$ is less than unity it is normal to invert the fraction and express the result as a dB loss. This avoids complicated negative logarithms. However, the scientific calculator has no problem in this respect.

Power (dBW)

The amateur radio licence currently specifies the maximum radio frequency power supplied to the antenna in dBW (decibels relative to 1 watt). It is often necessary to convert dBW to watts when taking measurements, and convert the measured watts to dBW when checking that the power level complies with the regulations.

The two useful formulae are :-

1) To convert *Actual Power* to *dBW* :-

$$Power\,(dBW) = 10 \, Log_{10} \frac{Actual\ power}{Reference\ power} = 10 \, Log_{10} \, Actual\ power\,(watts)$$

2) To convert *Power in dBW* to *Actual Power* in watts:-

$$Power\,(watts) = Antilog \frac{dBW}{10}$$

Measurement

1. The basic moving coil instrument is suitable for the measurement of-
   a) direct current (DC) only.
   b) alternating current (AC) only.
   c) either AC or DC.
   d) resistance only.

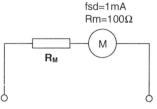

fsd=1mA
Rm=100Ω

2. Fig.11 shows a basic moving coil meter. 'R_M' is fitted to enable the meter to measure higher values of d.c. voltage. It is known as a-
   a) shunt.   b) multiplier.
   c) voltage dropper.   d) voltage divider.

Fig.11

3. The meter in fig.11 has an fsd of 1mA and an internal resistance of 100Ω. What is the value of the multiplier, 'R_M' if the meter is to read 10V fsd?
   a) 99Ω   b) 10,100Ω
   c) 9,900Ω   d) 1,010Ω

4. The sensitivity of a voltmeter is usually expressed in terms of-
   a) Volt Amps (VA)   b) Volt Watts (VW)
   c) kilohms (kΩ)   d) Ohms per Volt (Ω/V)

5. The basic moving coil meter shown in fig.12 has a full scale deflection (FSD) of 1mA, and an internal resistance 'R_m' of 100Ω. What value of shunt resistance 'R_s' is required to extend the range of the meter to read 100mA FSD?
   a) 0.101Ω   b) 1.010Ω
   c) 10.10Ω   d) 101Ω

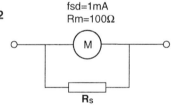

fsd=1mA
Rm=100Ω

Fig.12

6. A basic moving coil meter has an fsd of 100μA and a resistance of 500Ω. What shunt resistance will be required to give the meter a 1mA fsd range?
   a) 55.55Ω   b) 111.11Ω
   c) 500Ω   d) 5000Ω

7. When a basic moving coil meter is connected as shown in fig.13, it is suitable for the measurement of-
   a) current.   b) resistance.
   c) voltage.   d) power.

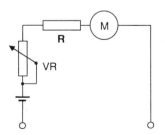

Fig.13

Measurement

8. Various voltmeter sensitivities are given below, which one will have the minimum loading effect on the circuit being measured?
   a) 100Ω/V
   b) 1000Ω/V
   c) 10,000Ω/V
   d) 1MΩ/V

9. The moving coil instrument circuit shown in fig.14 is suitable for the measurement of-
   a) alternating voltages.
   b) alternating currents.
   c) resistance.
   d) RMS power.

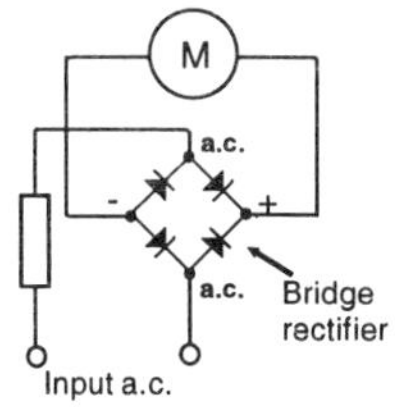

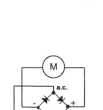

Fig.14

10. The scale of a moving coil a.c. instrument is normally calibrated to read the-
    a) average value of a sinewave.
    b) RMS value of a sinewave.
    c) peak value of a sinewave.
    d) RMS value of any waveform.

11. The instrument shown in fig.15 has been designed for the measurement of-
    a) alternating voltages.
    b) alternating currents.
    c) inductance and capacitance.
    d) wattless power.

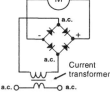

Fig.15

12. Fig.16 shows the moving coil instrument used in conjunction with device 'X' to enable it to measure RF currents. What is device 'X'?
    a) A magnetic coupler.
    b) A cold cathode.
    c) A bridge sensor.
    d) A thermocouple element.

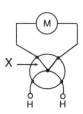

13. The instrument shown in fig.16 is capable of:-
    a) harmonic measurement.
    b) measuring VSWR on the PSU.
    c) measuring oscillator frequency and averaging the drift.
    d) RMS current measurement from d.c. to above 500MHz.

Fig.16

Measurement

14. What type of instrument depends for its deflection upon the expansion of a wire heated by the current flowing in it?
    a) Iron-alloy ammeter.
    b) Thermal-sag meter.
    c) Heated element voltmeter.
    d) Hot wire ammeter.

15. The type of meter that depends for its deflection upon the attraction or repulsion of a piece of iron under the influence of a magnetic field, is known as a-
    a) moving iron ammeter.
    b) magnetically coupled ammeter.
    c) magnetron.
    d) gyro-magnetic ammeter.

16. Fig.17 shows the circuit of a basic-
    a) RF voltmeter.
    b) RF power meter.
    c) absorption wavemeter.
    d) passive oscillator.

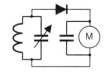

Fig.17

17. Referring to fig.17. What is this device suitable for?
    a) Accurate RF voltage measurement.
    b) Accurate RF power measurement.
    c) Coarse frequency checking and testing for harmonics.
    d) Generating calibration markers.

18. Referring to fig.17. What are the common uses of this device?
    a) Accurate power and frequency measurement.
    b) Checking for correct harmonic multiplication, spurious emissions and parasitic oscillation.
    c) VSWR and impedance measurement.
    d) Checking the accuracy of standard frequency transmissions.

19. The absorption wavemeter shown in fig.17 has an inductance of 20μH. When loosely coupled to an RF source, the peak occurs when the capacitor is adjusted to 140.7pF. What is the approximate frequency of the RF source?
    a) 1MHz
    b) 3MHz
    c) 5MHz
    d) 10MHz

20. Which instrument from the list below would you use to give an approximate indication of the resonant frequency of a non-energised tuned circuit?
    a) Grid dip oscillator (GDO) or a FET dip oscillator.
    b) Digital frequency meter.
    c) RF spectrum analyser.
    d) Peak reading power meter.

21. What is the name given to the type of instrument which beats the incoming signal with an accurate internal variable frequency oscillator (VFO) to produce an audible beat note?
a) Heterodyne wavemeter.
b) Carrier dip detector.
c) Audible crystal calibrator.
d) Digital crystal calibrator.

22. What is one of the disadvantages of the instrument referred to in Q 21?
a) It will only measure high power transmitters.
b) Licences are no longer issued for the use of this device.
c) It will only operate below 2MHz.
d) Harmonics and other spurious emissions might give misleading results.

23. A device used to generate accurate markers for calibration purposes, at known frequency spacing is a-
a) frequency standard transmission.
b) mark - space tester.
c) free-running oscillator.
d) crystal calibrator.

24. The digital frequency meter (DFM), or frequency counter, is-
a) one of the most complex of instruments to operate.
b) the least accurate of the frequency measuring instruments.
c) very accurate, easy to use; but unable to measure harmonics on a signal.
d) highly unreliable.

25. The accuracy of the digital frequency meter is dependent upon the-
a) precise frequency of the a.c. mains.
b) accuracy and long term stability of the internal clock oscillator.
c) impedance of the source being measured.
d) accuracy of the MSF signal to which it was initially calibrated.

26. The term 'resolution' applied to a digital frequency meter refers to the-
a) smallest division to which a reading can be taken.
b) time taken to reset the instrument.
c) upper frequency limit of the instrument.
d) amount of overload it can tolerate.

27. Fig.18 shows the schematic diagram of a basic cathode ray oscilloscope. The timebase provides-
a) voltage stabilisation for the cathode ray tube.
b) the calibrated horizontal 'X' deflection.
c) a calibration voltage for the signal amplifier.
d) the calibrated vertical 'Y' deflection.

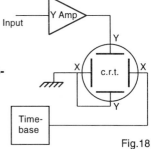

Fig.18

Measurement

28. What is the purpose of the 'Y' amplifier in the cathode ray oscilloscope?
a) It provides line flyback suppression.
b) It ensures that frequency calibration is maintained.
c) It produces the timebase deflection voltage.
d) It amplifies the input signal to give a suitable deflection on the screen.

29. A sinusoidal waveform is displayed on an oscilloscope; see fig.19. The timebase is adjusted to 2ms/division, and the Y amplifier to 2V/division. What is the approximate period, frequency, and peak-to-peak amplitude of the wave?
a) 200ms, 100Hz, 32Vp-p
b) 20ms, 50Hz, 16Vp-p
c) 10ms, 10Hz, 16Vp-p
d) 5ms, 5Hz, 8Vp-p

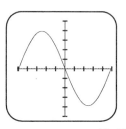
Fig.19

30. From the lissajous figure displayed in fig.20, the frequency of the unknown signal may be determined. In this case it is-
a) 50Hz
b) 100Hz
c) 200Hz
d) 400Hz

fx 100Hz
Reference oscillator

fy Unknown signal

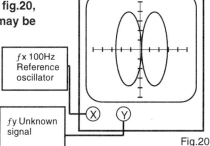
Fig.20

31. The lissajous figure shown in fig.21, indicates that the signals on the X and Y inputs are of equal frequency-
a) with no phase difference.
b) and vary in phase.
c) and have a phase difference of 90° or 270°.
d) and have a phase difference of 180°.

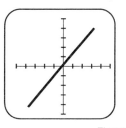
Fig.21

32. The lissajous figure shown in fig.22, indicates that the signals on the X and Y inputs are of equal frequency-
a) with no phase difference.
b) and vary in phase.
c) and have a phase difference of either 90° or 270°.
d) and have a phase difference of 180°.

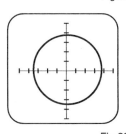
Fig.22

Measurement

33. Fig.23 shows an oscilloscope connected
to display a trapezoidal pattern from which
the modulation percentage 'M' can be
calculated by using the formula:-

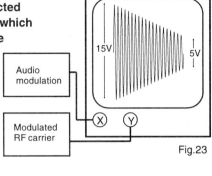

$$M = \frac{E_{Max} - E_{Min}}{E_{Max} + E_{Min}} \times 100\%$$

What is the modulation percentage
of the pattern shown?
a) 15%   b) 33%
c) 50%   d) 66%

Fig.23

34. Use the formula in the question above to
calculate the modulation percentage of
the AM wave shown in fig.24?
a) 40%   b) 50%
c) 60%   d) 70%

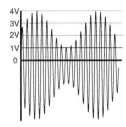

35. Which one of the instruments listed below
is suitable for measuring the carrier power
of an AM or FM transmitter?
a) Absorption wavemeter.
b) Directional RF wattmeter.
c) Heterodyne frequency meter.
d) Dip oscillator.

Fig.24

36. Fig.25 shows the circuit diagram of a simple-
a) noise bridge.   b) wheatstone bridge.
c) bolometer.   d) reflectometer.

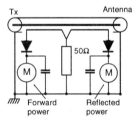

37. Referring to fig.25. Which statement is true when
the meter is used for RF power measurement?
a) The instrument is not accurate above 50 watts.
b) The calibration is independent of frequency.
c) The instrument is not suitable for use at VHF.
d) The calibration of the instrument varies with frequency.

Fig.25

38. The instrument shown in fig.25 is used for-
a) accurate frequency measurements.
b) measuring VSWR and checking for mismatch on feeder and antenna systems.
c) checking for second, and preferably the third harmonic of a transmission.
d) frequency calibration of synthesised receivers.

39. Refer to fig.26. What voltage standing wave ratio (VSWR) would you expect to be indicated on the VSWR meter?
a) 1 : 1
b) 2 : 1
c) 3 : 1
d) Infinity

Fig.26

40. Referring to fig.26. What VSWR will be indicated on the VSWR meter if the 50Ω load is disconnected?
a) 1 : 1   b) 2 : 1
c) 3 : 1   d) Infinity

41. A simple 50Ω 20W dummy load could be constructed from-
a) fifty 10W 20Ω carbon resistors in series.
b) twenty 1W 50Ω carbon resistors in parallel.
c) ten 2W 500Ω carbon resistors in parallel.
d) ten 2W 500Ω wirewound resistors in parallel.

42. What are desirable features in a dummy load?
a) Non-reactive. Purely resistive at all frequencies. Fully screened.
b) Reactive. Purely resistive. Non-screened. Variable impedance.
c) Inductive. Able to radiate. Constant impedance.
d) Inductive. Non-reactive. Able to radiate.

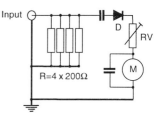

43. The instrument shown in fig.27 is a typical-
a) line terminating, or dummy load power meter.
b) resistance measuring meter.
c) absorption wavemeter.
d) d.c.power meter.

44. The 4 terminating resistors in fig.27 have the same value (200Ω). What is the input resistance of the meter, and what is special about the resistors?

Fig.27

a) 50Ω / non-inductive, i.e. carbon.   b) 50Ω / inductive, i.e. wire-wound.
c) 200Ω / capacitive.   d) 800Ω / non-inductive.

45. What is the purpose of the diode D and the preset resistor RV in fig.27?
a) To convert the frequency to wavelength and the adjust the input resistance.
b) To prevent the load overheating and regulate the diode current.
c) To convert the RF to direct current and calibrate the meter.
d) To save using a bridge rectifier and convert the the d.c. back to a.c.

Measurement

46. The meter in fig.27 is required to read 20 watts maximum power. What is a suitable power rating (watts) for each of the 4 resistors?
   a) 2W
   b) 4W
   c) 10W
   d) 50W

47. An RF voltage of 31.6V is developed across the 4 resistors in fig.27. What is the approximate power dissipated in the load?
   a) 0.63W
   b) 20W
   c) 40W
   d) 100W

48. The meter shown in fig.27 shows a power of 10 watts. What is the approximate total RF current in the 50Ω load?
   a) 0.45A
   b) 0.2A
   c) 5A
   d) 50A

49. The output power of an SSB transmitter is measured in-
   a) PEP (Peak envelope power).
   b) PWP (Peak wattage power).
   c) P-P (Peak-to-peak power).
   d) SSP (Single-sideband power).

50. The usual output test for an SSB transmitter is to use-
   a) a single RF tone applied to the audio modulator input.
   b) two non-harmonically related audio tones of equal amplitude applied to the audio input.
   c) one non-harmonically related audio tone of half amplitude applied to the audio input.
   d) a d.c. ammeter in the antenna feeder.

51. Fig.28 shows the output of an SSB transmitter under test conditions monitored on an oscilloscope. The waveform represents the-
   a) RF output with an audio two tone test signal applied.
   b) RF output with a single audio test tone applied.
   c) d.c. input to the PA stage.
   d) d.c output from the PA stage.

Fig.28

52. Fig.29 shows the output of an SSB transmitter under test conditions monitored on an oscilloscope. The waveform represents the-
   a) RF output with an audio two tone test signal applied.
   b) RF output with a single audio test tone applied.
   c) d.c. input to the PA stage.
   d) d.c output from the driver stage.

Fig.29

Measurement

53. A two-tone test oscillator for the alignment of a single sideband transmitter must be able to provide two-
   a) harmonically related audio frequency tones.
   b) non-harmonically related, equal amplitude, audio frequency tones.
   c) harmonically related radio frequency signals of equal amplitude.
   d) non-harmonically related radio frequency signals of half amplitude.

54. A single audio tone is applied to the input of an SSB transmitter, which is connected to a dummy load and monitored by an oscilloscope.
   The average output power is 100 watts. What is the average power dissipated in the dummy load when a second, and non-harmonically related tone, of equal amplitude to the first is applied to the transmitter input?
   a) Zero   b) 141.4 watts
   c) 200 watts   d) 400 watts

55. Fig.30 shows the output waveform of the transmitter in Q54 with the two tone test signal applied. With the two audio tones removed, a speech signal is applied, and its level adjusted so that the RF modulation peaks, observed on the CRO screen, are equal to the maximum deflection caused by the two tone test signal.
   What is the peak envelope power of the RF output signal?
   a) 14.4 watts   b) 141.4 watts
   c) 200 watts   d) 400 watts

Fig.30

56. The output of a transmitter with a 2 tone test signal applied, as in Q54, is shown in fig.30. This waveform is similar to-
   a) a 100% modulated AM transmitter.
   b) a 50% modulated AM transmitter.
   c) an unmodulated transmitter.
   d) an overmodulated AM transmitter.

57. Referring to fig.31. The transmitter output power is 100W, and the power dissipated in the load is 10W.
   What is the feeder loss in dB?
   a) 1dB   b) 10dB
   c) 100dB   d) 200dB

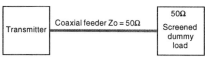

Fig.31

58. Where is the missing 90W between transmitter and load in Q57 above?
   a) Radiating in space.
   b) Radiating in the transmitter.
   c) Escaping from the dummy load.
   d) Being dissipated as heat in the feeder.

Measurement

59. A transmitter connected as shown in fig.31, has an output power of 10W.
Due to feeder loss the power measured at the load is only 2 watts.
What is the feeder loss measured in dB?
a) 3dB   b) 5dB
c) 7dB   d) 20dB

60. A transmitter connected as shown in fig.31, has an output power of 150W.
The feeder loss is 3dB. What power will be dissipated in the load?
a) 3W   b) 75W
c) 150W   d) 450W

61. Your power meter has a quoted accuracy of ±10%. Although the output
power of your transmitter is 100 watts, the power meter is likely to indicate
any power between-
a) 99 and 101 watts.   b) 10 and 110 watts.
c) 80 and 120 watts.   d) 90 and 110 watts.

62. All initial tests, measurements and adjustments to a transmitter, should
be made with the transmitter connected to-
a) a dummy load.   b) a 2m earth spike.
c) a 500mA meter.   d) an oscilloscope.

63. The voltmeter shown in fig.32 is switched to the
100V range and has a resistance of 1000Ω/V.
What voltage will it read?
a) 10V   b) 100V
c) 33.3V   d) 66.6V

64. The voltmeter used for the measurement in
Q63 and fig.32 is changed to a digital meter
having an input resistance of 10MΩ.
What reading will it display?
a) 49.75V   b) 50.25V
c) 50V   d) 100V

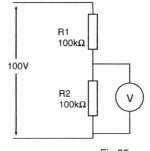

Fig.32

65. What is the d.c. input power to the
circuit shown in fig.33?
a) 50W   b) 138W
c) 150W   d) 207W

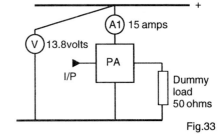

Fig.33

Measurement

66. The power level supplied to the antenna is quoted in dBW. What does dBW mean?
   a) That a reference power level of 1 watt equals zero dB is used, and that the actual power level is 'X'dB above or below the reference level.
   b) That all decibels are measured in watts.
   c) That logarithmic units will not be used in calculations.
   d) That only d.c. input power will be measured.

67. Convert a power level of 15dBW to watts. Use the following formula.

$$Power\ (watts)\ =\ Antilog\ \frac{dBW}{10}$$

   a) 1.5W   b) 10W
   c) 15W   d) 31.6W

68. Convert 26dBW to watts. Use the above formula.
   a) 2.6W   b) 0.42W
   c) 26W   d) 400W

69. A power of 100W is measured. What is this expressed as dBW? Use the following formula- $dBW = 10\ Log_{10}\ Power\ (watts)$
   a) 10dBW   b) 20dBW
   c) 26dBW   d) 200dBW

70. A power of 160W is measured. What is this expressed as dBW?
   a) 16dBW   b) 22dBW
   c) 26dBW   d) 160dBW

Answers - Measurement

1	a	16	c	31	a	46	c	61	d
2	b	17	c	32	c	47	b	62	a
3	c	18	b	33	c	48	a	63	c
4	d	19	b	34	c	49	a	64	a
5	b	20	a	35	b	50	b	65	d
6	a	21	a	36	d	51	b	66	a
7	b	22	d	37	d	52	a	67	d
8	d	23	d	38	b	53	b	68	d
9	a	24	c	39	a	54	c	69	b
10	b	25	b	40	d	55	d	70	b
11	b	26	a	41	c	56	a		
12	d	27	b	42	a	57	b		
13	d	28	d	43	a	58	d		
14	d	29	b	44	a	59	c		
15	a	30	c	45	c	60	b		

Answers - Measurement

1. The basic moving coil meter movement is only capable of responding to direct current. It will not measure alternating current.

2. To extend the voltage range of the basic movement a resistor called a multiplier is connected in series.

3. The meter coil needs a current of 1mA for full scale deflection, so a multiplier resistor R_M is added to limit the current to 1mA maximum when 10V is applied.-

    $$R_M = \frac{Range\,fsd}{fsd\,current} - Meter\,resistance = \frac{V}{I_m} - Rm = \frac{10}{1 \times 10^{-3}} - 100 = 9,900\Omega.$$

4. The sensitivity of a voltmeter is normally expressed in Ohms per Volt (Ω/V). The higher Ω/V the greater the sensitivity of the meter and the less loading effect it will have on the circuit under test. E.g. a meter with a quoted sensitivity of $2000\Omega/V$ will have a resistance of $20,000\Omega$ switched to its 10V range.

5. The current range of the basic meter movement can be extended by using a parallel connected resistor called a shunt. The shunt is a low resistance and bypasses the difference in current between meter movement fsd and required range fsd. Use the formula-

    $$R_S = \frac{V_m}{I_s} = \frac{I_m \times R_m}{I_T - I_m} = \frac{1 \times 10^{-3} \times 100}{100 \times 10^{-3} - 1 \times 10^{-3}} = \frac{0.1}{0.099} = 1.010\Omega.$$

6. $$R_S = \frac{V_m}{I_s} = \frac{I_m \times R_m}{I_T - I_m} = \frac{100 \times 10^{-6} \times 500}{1 \times 10^{-3} - 100 \times 10^{-6}} = \frac{0.05}{0.0009} = 55.55\Omega.$$

7. Fig.13 is the basic configuration of an ohmmeter. Initially the terminals are 'shorted' and VR adjusted for fsd, the unknown resistance is then substituted for the 'short'. The scale - calibrated to read resistance - may be read directly. Resistor R is to protect the meter if VR is set to too low a value.

8. The meter with a sensitivity of $1M\Omega/V$ will have the least loading effect on the circuit.

9. Fig.14 is an a.c. voltmeter. The bridge rectifier converts the a.c. to d.c. and the resistor is the range multiplying resistor.

10. A.c. instruments are normally calibrated in RMS values unless otherwise stated.

11. For the measurement of alternating current, a current transformer is used.

12. The thermocouple element. Current passing through the heater (H-H) raises the temperature at the junction of two dissimilar metals, causing an emf to be produced and a current to flow in the meter circuit.

13. Thermocouple instruments read RMS values independent of waveform, and by careful design can operate from d.c. to over 500MHz. The scale is non-linear.

Answers - Measurement

14. The hot wire ammeter, not encountered often these days, was used to measure RF antenna currents in LF and MF transmitters.

15. The moving iron ammeter, not encountered much these days. Often found on old battery chargers and car instrument panels.

16. The basic absorption wavemeter. The tuned circuit is tuned to resonate with the transmission being checked, the diode converts the RF to d.c. and the meter peaks at resonance. The variable capacitor has a pointer that indicates the resonant frequency on a calibrated scale.

17,18. The absorption wavemeter has no great accuracy, about 5 -10% is typical. It will indicate order of frequency and check for harmonics. It can be used as an RF monitor. Current amateur regulations require that the frequency coverage must extend up to the second, and preferably the third harmonic.

19. $f_r = \dfrac{1}{2\pi\sqrt{LC}} = \dfrac{1}{2\times\pi\times\sqrt{20\times10^{-6}\times140.7\times10^{-12}}}$

   $= \dfrac{1}{333.3\times10^{-9}} = 3\times10^{6}Hz\ (3MHz)\ Approx.$

20. The GDO. When the instrument's oscillator is tuned through the resonant frequency of a nearby tuned circuit, energy will be sucked out of the GDO's oscillatory circuit - by the circuit under test - causing a dip on the meter. The instrument is calibrated much the same as an absorption wavemeter. It can also double as an absorption wavemeter when its oscillator is switched off.

21,22. The heterodyne wavemeter beats the incoming signal with an accurate internal variable frequency oscillator (VFO). Zero beat indicating that the two frequencies are equal. Calibration tables may be included with the instrument. The internal VFO is checked against an internal crystal calibrator. Transmitter harmonics, spurious emissions, and strong local transmissions can give misleading beat notes. Not in general use today.

23. The crystal calibrator generates a harmonic-rich output signal from an accurate 100kHz or 1MHz crystal oscillator. Useful for calibrating non-synthesised receivers.

24. The digital frequency meter is very easy to use and very accurate if the clock oscillator is of high stability. It will not measure harmonic frequencies.

25,26. The accuracy of the digital frequency meter depends on the accuracy and stability of its internal clock oscillator. The resolution is determined by the smallest division to which a reading can be taken, e.g. if the incoming frequency is 145537500Hz, a device with a four digit display would not be much good however accurate the crystal clock oscillator.

27. The CRO timebase causes the horizontal 'X' deflection. The timebase is calibrated in Time per division, e.g. 10ms/cm.

28. The 'Y' amplifier amplifies the signal to a suitable voltage to give a satisfactory 'Y' deflection on the screen. It is calibrated by means of an input attenuator in Volts per Division or Volts/cm.

29. A complete cycle of waveform occurs in 10 horizontal 'X' divisions on the screen, since each division represents 2ms, the complete cycle takes 20ms; this is the period of the waveform. From the period we can find the frequency-

$$Frequency = \frac{1}{Period} = \frac{1}{20 \times 10^{-3}} = 50Hz.$$

The 'Y' amplifier is switched to 2V/division, the peak-to-peak amplitude of the wave is 8 divisions. The peak-to-peak voltage 16 volts.

30. Lissajous figures are used to compare frequencies. They are obtained by replacing the timebase with a variable frequency sinewave oscillator fx, and connecting the unknown frequency fy to the 'Y' plates. By counting the loops along the top, and the number down the side, a frequency ratio of $fy : fx = 2:1$ is determined. In this case the unknown signal frequency is twice the 100Hz reference frequency i.e. 200Hz.

31. The phase difference of signals of the same frequency may be determined. The straight inclined line of fig.21 indicates a phase difference of zero degrees.

32. The full circle of fig.22 indicates that the signals are equal in frequency and have a phase difference of either 90° or 270°.

33. $M = \dfrac{E_{MAX} - E_{MIN}}{E_{MAX} + E_{MIN}} \times 100 = \dfrac{15-5}{15+5} \times 100 = \dfrac{10}{20} \times 100 = 0.5 \times 100 = 50\%.$

34. $M = \dfrac{E_{MAX} - E_{MIN}}{E_{MAX} + E_{MIN}} \times 100 = \dfrac{4-1}{4+1} \times 100 = \dfrac{3}{5} \times 100 = 0.6 \times 100 = 60\%.$

35. A directional RF wattmeter may be used for measuring carrier power.

36. Fig.25 is the circuit of a basic reflectometer or through-line power meter.

37. When power measurements are made with this type of meter the manufacturers correction factor - if provided - should be used.

38. The reflectometer shown in fig.25 can be used for checking for mismatch and matching antenna/feeder systems. It can provide forward and reflected power measurements, which, with the aid of a graph or formula can be converted to VSWR.

39. Fig.26 shows a perfectly matched system - all impedances are 50Ω and match. In this case there is no reflected power and the VSWR is 1:1.

40. With an open ended, or short circuit feeder, all the forward power will be returned to the source. The VSWR meter will read infinity. (Assuming no feeder loss.)

41. The dummy load must be constructed from non-reactive components, in this case ten, 500Ω, 2W carbon resistors will be used. Total dissipation 20W. The resistance of similar value resistors in parallel is given by-

$$R_T = \frac{Resistance\ of\ one\ resistor}{Number\ of\ resistors} = \frac{500}{10} = 50\Omega.$$

42. The dummy load must be non-reactive, exhibit a constant and pure resistance (e.g. 50Ω or 75Ω) over the frequency bands on which it will be used. It should also be screened to prevent RF signals radiating from it.

43. This is a simple dummy load power meter.

44. The 4 x 200Ω resistors connected in parallel form the dummy load - 50Ω. The resistors should be non-inductive types, such as carbon.

45. Diode D converts the alternating current RF signal to d.c. The preset resistor RV is to calibrate the meter.

46. The 20 watts maximum power dissipation must be divided among the 4 resistors, therefore each resistor must dissipate a minimum of 5 watts. The best option from the choice given is the 10 watt resistors, this leaves a good margin of safety.

47. $P_{Watts} = \dfrac{V^2}{R} = \dfrac{31.6^2}{50} = 20W\ (Approx).$

48. $I = \sqrt{\dfrac{P}{R}} = \sqrt{\dfrac{10}{50}} = 0.45A\ (Approx).$

49. Because the output power of an SSB transmitter is varying at the syllabic rate of the speech waveform, the peak envelope power (PEP) is measured.

50. Output and linearity tests on SSB transmitters are carried out using an audio two tone test oscillator. The tones are normally equal in amplitude and non-harmonically related.

51. A single audio tone applied to the transmitter input will produce a single RF output signal displaced from the suppressed carrier, this is similar to the output of a CW transmitter, and is shown in fig.28.

52. When two audio tones of different frequency, and equal amplitude, are applied to the transmitter input, the resultant output will be two RF signals, displaced from the suppressed carrier, and spaced from one another by their frequency difference. The oscilloscope waveform shown in fig.29 results from the two RF signals beating together.

53. See answer 50.

54. The average output power will be 200W. (Twice that for a single tone.)

55. With the two-tone test signal adjusted to produce an average or mean power of 200W in the load, the envelope of the RF output will vary between a maximum and minimum value, this is observed on an oscilloscope as shown in fig.30. The peaks of the displayed waveform representing 400W PEP. The speech modulated RF output power will be 400W PEP when the modulation peaks cause the same maximum deflection as the two-tone test signal.

56. The transmitter output waveform with a two-tone test signal applied is similar to a 100% amplitude modulated wave.

57. Transmission loss in dB is given by- $Loss\,(dB) = 10\,Log_{10}\dfrac{Power\,sent}{Power\,received}$

$(Loss)\,dB = 10\,Log_{10}\dfrac{100}{10} = 10\,Log_{10}\,10 = 10 \times 1 = 10dB$

We say that "the feeder has a loss of 10dB".

58. Since the input power is 100W and the output power is only 10W, 90W is wasted in the feeder and dissipated as heat.

59. $Loss\,(dB) = 10\,Log_{10}\dfrac{10}{2} = 10\,Log_{10}\,5 = 10 \times 0.6989 = 7dB\,Approx$

The feeder loss in this case is approximately 7dB.

60. $Loss\,(dB) = 10\,Log_{10}\dfrac{P_{Sent}}{P_{Received}}$

$3 = 10\,Log_{10}\dfrac{150}{P_{Received}}$

$\therefore\; Antilog\dfrac{3}{10} = \dfrac{150}{P_{Received}}$

and $P_{Received} = \dfrac{150}{Antilog\,0.3} = \dfrac{150}{2} = 75W$

Note. The antilog on the calculator is usually the second function of the Log key, i.e. $\boxed{\text{SHIFT}}\,\boxed{10^{x}}$

61. An accuracy of ±10% indicates that readings can differ by up to 10 parts - in either direction - for every 100 parts measured. In this case the actual power is 100W, so the instrument could read anything from 90 up to 110W.

62. A transmitter should be connected to a dummy load - not the antenna - for all initial tuning and adjustments. This avoids interference and other tuning signals being radiated.

63. The resistance of the voltmeter, R_M, is $100 \times 1000\Omega = 100k\Omega$. This is in parallel with R2, also $100k\Omega$. The resultant resistance (R_R), of the voltmeter and R2 in parallel is therefore $50k\Omega$. This in series with R1, is across the 100V supply. Using the voltage division formula we can calculate the voltage V_M across the meter.

$$V_M = V \times \frac{R_R}{R1 + R_R} = 100 \times \frac{50,000}{100,000 + 50,000} = 100 \times 0.333 = 33.3V.$$

64. First - calculate the resistance of R2 and the voltmeter in parallel (R_R):-

$$R_R = \frac{100 \times 10^3 \times 10 \times 10^6}{100 \times 10^3 + 10 \times 10^6} = 99010\Omega \ (Approx)$$

Next - calculate the voltage across the meter, V_M :-

$$V_M = V \times \frac{R_R}{R1 + R_R} = 100 \times \frac{99010}{100,000 + 99010} = 100 \times 0.4975 = 49.75V.$$

Note. The shunting effect of the two voltmeters in Q63 and Q64 is different, hence the different readings. The higher the meter resistance, the less the shunting effect, and the less the error due to the presence of the meter.

65. To measure the d.c. input power to a stage, measure the supply voltage and supply current to that stage, and use the formula:-
Power (watts) $= V \times I = 13.8 \times 15 = 207W.$

66. E.g. 20dBW means that the power level is 20dB relative to 1W.

67. *Power (watts)* $= Antilog \frac{dBW}{10} = Antilog \frac{15}{10} = Antilog\ 1.5 = 31.6W.$

68. *Power (watts)* $= Antilog \frac{dBW}{10} = Antilog \frac{26}{10} = Antilog\ 2.6 = 400W\ (Approx).$

69. $dBW = 10\ Log_{10}\ Power (watts) = 10\ Log_{10}\ 100 = 10 \times 2 = 20dBW.$

70. $dBW = 10\ Log_{10}\ Power (watts) = 10\ Log_{10}\ 160 = 10 \times 2.2 = 22dBW.$

Above.   Absorption   Wavemeter.   Marconi   Instruments   TF643B,   circa
1942. Operating range 20MHz - 300MHz. Showing plug-in high Q coils
and calibration charts. A separate chart is drawn for each coil.
The wavemeter is tuned to resonate with the transmitter (indicated
by a peak on the meter), and the dial reading converted to frequency
MHz by reference to the calibration chart for the coil in use.
The circuit diagram of the meter is shown below.

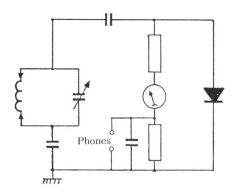

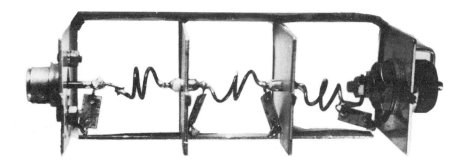

Above. Low pass filter for 50 watt VHF transmitter, showing inductors and capacitors. Each section is in a separate screened compartment. Shown with cover removed and 2/3 actual size.

Above. 10 watt, 50 ohm dummy load.

16. Transmitter Interference

This section will cover :-
1. frequency stability and out of band radiation.
2. spurious emissions, harmonics, causes and prevention.
3. overmodulation, overdeviation and parasitic oscillation, causes and prevention.
4. frequency checking.

Transmitter interference
An incorrectly adjusted, and poorly designed and constructed transmitter will not only be inefficient - in which case only the user will be affected - but; more importantly, it is likely to cause interference to many other services and people.

Interference precautions
Fig.1, related to the list that follows it, shows a transmitter and some of the basic precautions to be taken during construction and in the event of interference.

Each case of transmitter interference should be regarded as individual to that layout and installation, since generally speaking no two cases are the same, and not all of the items shown will be necessary.

In the modern transceiver of today most of the items on the diagram are likely to be taken care of at the design stage.

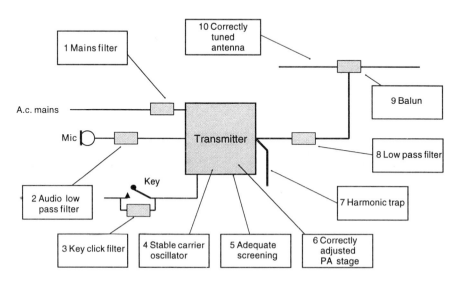

Fig.1 Showing some of the precautions necessary to ensure that a transmitting installation is environmentally friendly. See numbered list on next page ⇒

Transmitter Interference

Interference precautions (see fig.1)

1. **Mains filter.** Mains borne interfering RF signals and transients can travel both in, and out, of a piece of equipment by way of its mains power cable. A mains filter should be fitted as close to the equipment chassis/cabinet as possible.

2. **Audio low pass filter.** To prevent a wide modulation bandwidth the audio modulation is restricted to a maximum frequency of about 3000Hz (3kHz). This giving a 6kHz RF bandwidth on AM and a 3kHz RF bandwidth on SSB.

3. **Key click filter** slows the rise and decay of the keying current. This reduces 'splatter' and long distance interference on adjacent channels.

4. **Carrier oscillator.** If this is not stable the transmitter is likely to drift into other channels and services. Crystal and synthesised carrier oscillators will be more stable than free running L/C oscillators.

5. **Adequate screening** is necessary to ensure that RF energy does not leave any point other than the antenna socket. Screening may be applied to the microphone and keying leads, and also the various stages within the transmitter to prevent feedback between stages causing oscillation and spurious signals.

6. **Correct adjustment of the PA** drive levels and operating conditions is necessary to avoid sideband splatter and the generation of harmonics.

7. **The harmonic trap** may be a simple L/C resonant tuned circuit or a λ/4 coaxial stub, cut to resonate at the frequency of an unwanted emission or harmonic at the output of the transmitter.

8. **The low pass filter** (LPF) passes all frequencies below its design cut-off frequency and attenuates or blocks all frequencies above the cut-off frequency. VHF transmitters will normally use a bandpass filter (BPF).

9. **The balun** - *bal*ance to *un*balance transformer - is used to match a balanced antenna to an unbalanced coaxial feeder. It may, by its turns ratio, match the feeder impedance to the antenna impedance.

10. **A correctly tuned** and matched antenna will not reflect any of the incident power and standing waves will not be set up on the feeder. A tuned and resonant dipole can reduce the level of transmitted spurious and harmonic emissions.

Transmitter Interference

1. **You have set the carrier frequency of an AM telephony transmitter 1kHz inside its allocated band, it is then modulated with a speech signal which contains frequency components in the range 300-3000Hz. What is wrong?**
   a) Nothing.
   b) You should be using FM this close to the band edge.
   c) One of your modulation sidebands will extend 2kHz into the adjacent frequency band.
   d) Your complete signal has been inverted.

2. **You are operating an AM telephony transmitter 3kHz inside your permitted band edge, what might now cause you to infringe the regulations?**
   a) Nothing.
   b) The transmitter might drift outside its allocated band.
   c) The distant receiver might be switched to the CW mode.
   d) You might not be radiating enough harmonics.

3. **You are operating a frequency modulated transmitter near the centre of the 2 metre amateur band, but due to the deviation limiter being incorrectly adjusted, your deviation is wider than it should be. This is likely to result in-**
   a) harmonics of the carrier frequency causing TVI.
   b) detuning of the frequency multiplier stages.
   c) image channel interference at the receiver.
   d) interference to receivers on adjacent channels.

4. **Your transmitter has an unacceptable amount of frequency drift. What is the most likely cause?**
   a) The multiplier stages, if used, are drifting.
   b) The cut-off frequency of the low pass filter is drifting with temperature.
   c) The carrier frequency oscillator is drifting.
   d) The power supply is locking the oscillator.

5. **The most likely cure for the problem encountered in Q 4 above is-**
   a) better ventilation of the multiplier stages.
   b) increasing the pass band of the low pass filter.
   c) voltage and temperature stabilisation of the carrier frequency oscillator.
   d) improved power supply filtering.

6. **Excessive transmission bandwidth is undesirable because it-**
   a) always interferes with TV receivers.
   b) might damage receiver IF filters.
   c) reduces the effectiveness of the low pass filter.
   d) will cause adjacent channel interference and waste frequency spectrum.

7. What precautions should be taken in the transmitter modulator stage to ensure that the transmitted bandwidth is only that necessary for the transmission of intelligible speech?
   a) Include an audio low pass filter.
   b) Place a block of polystyrene over the audio transistors.
   c) Stabilise the modulator power supply.
   d) Include an audio high pass filter.

8. The typical upper cut-off frequency for the audio low pass filter in the modulation amplifier stage of an amateur transmitter is about-
   a) 450 - 500Hz   b) 455 - 470kHz
   c) 10 - 100Hz   d) 2500 - 3000Hz

9. The RF bandwidth of a typical double sideband (DSB) amateur transmission is of the order of-
   a) 3kHz   b) 6kHz
   c) 10kHz   d) 75kHz

10. The RF bandwidth of a typical single sideband (SSB) amateur transmission is of the order of-
    a) 3kHz   b) 6kHz
    c) 10kHz   d) 75kHz

11. The RF bandwidth of a typical on-off keyed CW transmission will be-
    a) 3kHz.
    b) equal to the oscillator drift.
    c) zero, no bandwidth is used in on-off keying.
    d) fairly narrow, but proportional to the keying speed and the characteristics of the 'key-click filter'.

12. It is bad practice to key the transmitter VFO because it might affect the oscillator stability and also cause a-
    a) chirp at the distant receiver.
    b) very large 3rd harmonic.
    c) very large 5th harmonic.
    d) heavy drain on the power supply.

13. A CW transmitter has a keying current waveform as shown in fig.1. What is the associated problem?

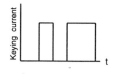

Fig.2

   a) There is no problem.
   b) There will be no harmonic content.
   c) The filters might suffer flashover effect.
   d) Excessive sidebands will be generated causing clicks in adjacent channels.

14. Which one of the keying current waveforms shown below will give the cleanest RF output spectrum from a CW transmitter?

a)   b)   c)   d)

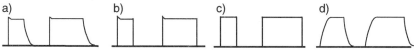

15. Which one of the circuits shown below is suitable for use as a 'key-click filter' in the key of a CW transmitter?

a)   b)   c)   d)

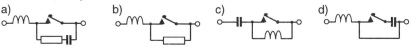

16. Sparking at the key and radiation from the keying lead is likely to cause-
   a) 'whistler waves' which radiate world-wide.
   b) local, short distance interference.
   c) overheating of the PA stage.
   d) flashover at the mains supply cable.

17. It might be possible to reduce or eliminate the problem referred to in Q16 by-
   a) fitting a band pass filter in the antenna.
   b) keying a very low current point in the transmitter, using screened leads from the key to the transmitter, and suppressing the key contact.
   c) the use of large heat sinks on the PA transistors.
   d) the use of silicon rubber insulated cable for the key.

18. What are spurious emissions?
   a) The modulated sidebands.
   b) Various temperature differentials emitted from the case of the transmitter.
   c) Any frequency at the output of a transmitter other than that intended.
   d) Any band of frequencies not present at the output of a transmitter.

19. From what point in a transmitter are spurious emissions likely to be radiated?
   a) The antenna only.
   b) Directly from the low pass filter.
   c) From any part of the transmitter, cabinet, wires, filters, and components etc.
   d) From the main radio station earth only.

20. What are harmonics?
   a) Musical notes emitted from the low pass filter during CW transmissions.
   b) Overtones of the crystal oscillator which appear at the distant receiver.
   c) Signals at multiples of the final output frequency, or multiples of frequencies used to generate the final frequency.
   d) Two co-channel signals causing additive mixing on an antenna.

21. The amplitude modulated wave shown
in fig.3 is said to be-
a) undermodulated.
b) overmodulated.
c) underpowered.
d) overpowered.

Fig.3

22. When the output signal of an AM transmitter is as shown in fig.3-
a) all is well.
b) it is switched to the CW mode.
c) the power supply has failed.
d) it is likely to be causing splatter in adjacent channels.

23. Listed below are four classes of emission, which one is the least likely to
cause interference to TV and radio reception?
a) A1A. CW on-off telegraphy.
b) A3E. Double sideband amplitude modulation.
c) J3E. Single sideband suppressed carrier.
d) F3E. Frequency modulation.

24. What are parasitic oscillations?
a) Unwanted oscillations that occur at any frequency, anywhere in a
transmitting or receiving system.
b) The wanted oscillations and harmonics from a crystal oscillator.
c) Wanted oscillations produced by a heterodyning process.
d) Oscillations that occur only in a resonant antenna due to a high standing
wave ratio at the antenna/feeder junction.

25. When the drive to a PA stage is removed, a transmitter produces some RF
output power on a frequency different to that to which it is tuned.
The most likely cause is-
a) parasitic oscillation.
b) inductive lag.
c) capacitive lag.
d) a faulty oscillator crystal.

26. Parasitic oscillations in any stage of a transmitter are likely to cause-
a) spurious emissions at the transmitter output.
b) key clicks on distant receivers.
c) severe overheating of the mains filter.
d) severe fading of the transmission in the ionosphere.

Transmitter Interference

27. Harmonics are present at the output of all transmitters, but those with the highest harmonic output levels usually employ-
   a) overdriven class C output stages.
   b) linear class A output stages.
   c) low pass filters with high attenuation in the pass band.
   d) low pass filters with high attenuation in the stop band.

28. How would you reduce the level of harmonics present in the output signal of an HF band transmitter before they are fed to the antenna?
   a) Fit a small neon lamp at the tip of the antenna.
   b) Leave the SWR meter in the antenna feeder at all times.
   c) Use a variable voltage power supply for the PA stages.
   d) Use a low pass filter in the transmitter RF output.

29. Fig.4 shows the block diagram of a basic VHF transmitter. The RF output is a carrier wave and some spurious signals which are related to the various multiplier stage harmonics.
   What could be done to reduce the level of the spurious signals?
   a) QSY to another frequency.
   b) Fit a VHF band pass filter in the transmitter output.
   c) Fit an audio band reject filter in the transmitter output.
   d) Fit an RF filter in the microphone lead.

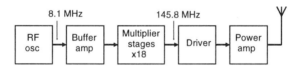

Fig.4

30. Using information from fig.4, calculate the frequency of the third harmonic of the output signal.
   a) 24.3MHz   b) 145.8MHz
   c) 437.4MHz   d) 729MHz

31. Refer to fig.4. What is the frequency of the fifth harmonic of the output signal, and where is it likely to fall?
   a) 291.6MHz / In the VHF TV band.
   b) 729MHz / In the UHF TV band.
   c) 89.1MHz / In band 2. VHF sound broadcasting.
   d) 10GHz / In the 10GHz police radar band.

Transmitter Interference

32. What could be used at the output of a transmitter to reduce the level of a second harmonic?
   a) A quarter-wave, short-circuit coaxial stub, or harmonic trap.
   b) An earthed isolating switch.
   c) A ground-plane radio active coaxial socket.
   d) A band stop filter tuned to the carrier frequency.

33. A harmonic trap in the form of a λ/4 short-circuit coaxial stub is to be fitted at the output of the transmitter in fig.4 to reduce a strong second harmonic. The stub is to be made from 50Ω coaxial cable having a VF of 0.65. The transmit frequency is 145.8MHz. What is the approximate stub length?
   a) 1.02m   b) 0.66m
   c) 0.26m   d) 0.33m

34. You are likely to encounter some, or all of the filters shown below. Select their correct order.

a) 1 HPF	b) 1 LPF	c) 1 BSF	d) 1 BSF
2 LPF	2 BPF	2 HPF	2 HPF
3 BSF	3 HPF	3 LPF	3 BPF
4 BPF	4 BSF	4 BPF	4 LPF

  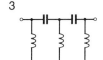 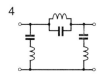

35. Below are the symbols associated with the filters above. Select their correct order.

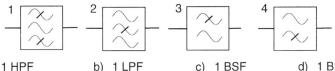

a) 1 HPF	b) 1 LPF	c) 1 BSF	d) 1 BPF
2 LPF	2 BPF	2 HPF	2 BSF
3 BSF	3 HPF	3 LPF	3 LPF
4 BPF	4 BSF	4 BPF	4 HPF

36. What type of filter has the response curve shown in fig.5?
   a) BPF   b) BSF
   c) LPF   d) HPF

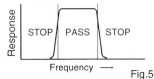

Fig.5

Transmitter Interference

37. What type of filter has the response curve shown in fig.6?
   a) BPF   b) BSF
   c) LPF   d) HPF

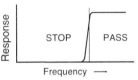

Fig.6

38. What type of filter has the response curve shown in fig.7?
   a) BPF   b) BSF
   c) LPF   d) HPF

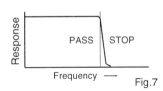

Fig.7

39. Fig.8 shows the spectrum of the fundamental frequency and harmonics at the output of a 28MHz transmitter. What type of filter would you select to reduce the level of the harmonics?
   a) LPF
   b) BPF
   c) HPF
   d) BSF

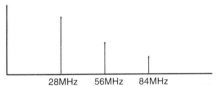

Fig.8

40. Fig.9 shows the spectrum of the signals present at the output of a 2 metre transmitter. The carrier frequency is at 145MHz. What type of filter would you select to reduce the level of the unwanted signals?
   a) LPF
   b) BPF
   c) HPF
   d) BSF

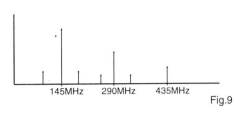

Fig.9

41. To obtain the maximum reduction of RF radiation from the case or cabinet of a radio transmitter-
   a) a dummy load must be used.
   b) a dummy load must not be used.
   c) all earthed wires must be screened.
   d) RF stages must be individually screened, decoupled and grounded.

42. Select the circuit shown below which you consider the most suitable for filtering the d.c. power supply lead to a screened oscillator or RF stage.

a)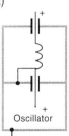

b)

c)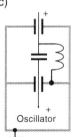

d)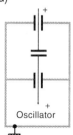

43. From the circuits shown below, which would be the most suitable for the reduction of mains-borne interference from a radio transmitter?

a)

b)

c)

d)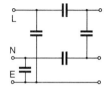

44. You wish to transmit on a frequency of 21.225MHz, but your measuring instrument only has an accuracy of ±1%.
Between which two limits might your transmission fall?
a) 21.012750 and 21.437250MHz
b) 21.203780 and 21.246230MHz
c) 21.000120 and 21.004370MHz
d) 21.000010 and 21.000430MHz

45. Your frequency meter has an accuracy of ±0.05%. Between which two limits might your transmission fall when you set up on a frequency of 21.020MHz?
a) 21.330330 and 21.660660MHz
b) 21.003000 and 21.006000MHz
c) 21.009490 and 21.030510MHz
d) 21.094900 and 21.305550MHz

Answers - Transmitter Interference

1	c	11	d	21	b	31	b	41	d
2	b	12	a	22	d	32	a	42	b
3	d	13	d	23	d	33	d	43	a
4	c	14	d	24	a	34	b	44	a
5	c	15	a	25	a	35	d	45	c
6	d	16	b	26	a	36	a		
7	a	17	b	27	a	37	d		
8	d	18	c	28	d	38	c		
9	b	19	c	29	b	39	a		
10	a	20	c	30	c	40	b		

1. An AM (A3E) transmission is a double-sideband transmission. Amplitude modulation produces two sidebands, one either side of the carrier, an upper and a lower. The highest frequency transmitted will be f_c + 3kHz and the lowest frequency will be f_c - 3kHz. When operating with the carrier frequency 1kHz inside the allocated band, either the upper sideband, or the lower sideband, will extend 2kHz into the adjacent band.

2. Having made allowances for the transmission bandwidth in A1 above, i.e. by setting the carrier 3kHz inside the band edge, a further allowance has to be made for the drift characteristic of the transmitter. This will vary between transmitters.

3. The deviation limiter controls the maximum deviation of the carrier wave. A carrier that is overdeviated will have a wider bandwidth than necessary and splatter into adjacent channels.

4. Carrier frequency drift is an oscillator problem. It may be due to poor temperature stability, poor mechanical and electrical construction, components ageing, or changes in power supply voltage.

5. Attention to all the points mentioned in A4 above should solve the problem.

6. Transmission bandwidth should not be wider than that necessary for intelligible communication, or be kept to the lowest value which technology and the nature of the service permits, thus ensuring the most efficient use of the frequency spectrum and minimising the possibility of adjacent channel interference.

7,8. For commercial quality speech, frequencies of up to 3kHz only, are required. (For high quality sound and music up to 15kHz.) An audio low pass filter may be included in the microphone or modulator stage, it should have a cut-off frequency of about 2.5 - 3kHz. FM transmitters will also require deviation limiting circuitry.

9. For a DSB transmission the RF bandwidth is twice the highest modulating frequency f_m. When f_m is 3kHz the RF bandwidth is $2f_m$ = 6kHz.

Answers - Transmitter Interference

10. An SSB transmission uses half the bandwidth of a DSB AM transmission. If the audio bandwidth is 3kHz the RF bandwidth is 3kHz.

11. The bandwidth of a CW transmission will be determined by the keying speed and the characteristics of the key click filter. The bandwidth will be narrow.

12. When an oscillator is keyed it may take a short time to settle, i.e. for its frequency to stabilise. This can cause a 'chirp' effect at the receiving end.

13. If the keying voltage or current, from key-up to key-down occurs too rapidly, a rectangular pulse is formed containing high frequency components which produce sidebands either side of the carrier, resulting in key clicks on the transmission. These sidebands are radiated with the signal and cause 'long distance' interference.

14. To reduce the sidebands that cause key-clicks, the rise and decay of the keying pulse of fig.2 must be slowed, the keying pulse will then resemble waveform d).

15. The required keying waveform may be achieved using the key-click filter circuit, diagram a). The inductor controls the rise time while the decay is controlled by the time constant of the resistor and capacitor. Typical rise and decay time is 5 - 10ms.

16. A spark at the key contacts may cause a broad band of RF energy to be radiated, causing local, or short distance RF interference to nearby receivers.

17. Keying high current parts of the circuit , such as the PA stage, should be avoided where possible. The key can be suppressed and the leads screened.

18. Spurious emissions are emissions other than those necessary for transmission. They include harmonics, parasitics, and intermodulation products.

19. Spurious emissions may be radiated from any part of a transmitter, such as the cabinet, wiring, mains leads, badly screened filters, and the feeder and antenna.

20. Any periodic waveform can be split into up into a number of sinusoidal waves of different frequencies, e.g. f, $2f$, $3f$, $4f$, and so on. Where f is the fundamental, $2f$ the second harmonic, $3f$ the third harmonic etc:. If the fundamental frequency is 1MHz any second harmonic present will be 2MHz. The shape of the periodic wave being determined by the number and amplitude of the harmonics. A square wave, for example, will consist of a fundamental and an infinite number of odd harmonics. A perfect sinewave will have no harmonics.

21. The amplitude modulated wave shown is overmodulated, it is over 100% modulated and broken up. Modulation depth should be kept below 100%.

22. An overmodulated transmission is likely to cause splatter in adjacent channels and possibly interference to local broadcast reception.

23. A frequency modulated transmission has no amplitude changes that can be detected and converted to audio by diode junctions in a receiver. FM is least likely to cause problems to local radio and TV installations.

24. Parasitic oscillations are unintended oscillations. They can occur in any piece of electronic or radio equipment (usually due to poor design). They do not always impair the operation of such equipment and often their presence is undetected. To avoid parasitics, attention must be given to internal and external screening, circuit layout and design, and component values and positioning.

25. If the RF drive to a PA stage is removed, and there is RF power at the output, then the PA stage is in oscillation.

26. Parasitic oscillations in a transmitter can appear at the output and be radiated. Not all parasitics will reach the output and may go undetected.

27. Overdriving an amplifier stage will cause distortion of the waveform, resulting in harmonics being produced, also, class C amplification is non-linear.

28. Harmonics can be reduced by careful adjustment of the transmitter. A low pass filter for HF transmitters and a band pass filter for VHF transmitters is normally fitted at the output circuit. Filters exhibit a small loss in their pass band but should not be omitted for this reason.

29. Spurious emissions can be produced by harmonics of the multiplier stages reaching the PA stage. They can occur both above and below the carrier frequency. A band pass filter, to pass the operating frequency band, or a notch filter or stub should be used to attenuate any particular spurious emission. If the spurious signal is close to the wanted signal it may not be possible to remove it by filtering at the output, and attention will have to be given to the stage where it is generated.

30. 3rd *Harmonic* $= 3 \times f_c = 3 \times 145.8 = 437.4MHz.$

31. 5th *Harmonic* $= 5 \times f_c = 5 \times 145.8 = 729MHz.$ In the UHF TV band.

32. A reduction in even harmonics may be achieved by using a quarter-wave, short-circuit, coaxial stub. It may be connected into the feeder with a coaxial 'T' connector. Caution! Stubs are tuned to one frequency, or a narrow band of frequencies, hence changing frequency is likely to cause a severe mismatch.

33. The stub is $\lambda/4$ at the transmission frequency, and short-circuit at the free end.

Wavelength of transmission $\lambda = \dfrac{300 \times 10^6}{145.8 \times 10^6} = 2.06 \ metres$

since $\lambda = 2.06 \ then \ \dfrac{\lambda}{4} = 0.51m$

Multiply $\lambda/4$ by the velocity factor (0.65) to get the approximate stub length.

$0.51 \times 0.65 = 0.33m \ or \ 33cm.$

34. From 1 to 4 the filters are Low pass, Band pass, High pass, and Band stop.

35. From 1 to 4 the symbols are Band pass, Band stop, Low pass, and High pass.

36. Fig.5 shows the response curve of a band pass filter.

37. Fig.6 shows the response curve of a high pass filter.

38. Fig.7 shows the response curve of a low pass filter.

39. A low pass filter with a cut-off frequency just above 30MHz will reduce the level of the second and third harmonics.

40. Use a band pass filter with a bandwidth of about 3MHz and centred on 145MHz.

41. In an ideal situation all RF stages within a transmitter will be individually screened. Attention may also be given to the screening properties of the cabinet to prevent further RF leakage. Efficient grounding is also advisable.

42. Circuit b) is the option that will work. The filter and oscillator are in separately screened compartments. Feedthrough capacitors effectively ground any RF present on the supply lead. The choke provides a high impedance path to the RF while allowing a low resistance path for direct current.

43. Filter circuit a) can be fitted into the mains supply lead of any electronic equipment to reduce the effects of mains-borne interference. The filter will normally be fitted close to the equipment, it may even be an integral part of the supply socket on the equipment. It will reduce both incoming and outgoing interference given suitable component values.

44. 1% of 21,225,000Hz $\quad 21,225,000 \times \dfrac{1}{100} = 212,250 Hz$

The frequency limits are $\quad 21,225,000 + 212,250 = 21,437,250 Hz$

$21,225,000 - 212,250 = 21,012,750 Hz$

45. 0.05% of 21,020,000Hz $\quad 21,020,000 \times \dfrac{0.05}{100} = 10,510 Hz$

The frequency limits are $\quad 21,020,000 + 10,510 = 21,030,510 Hz$

$21,020,000 - 10,510 = 21,009,490 Hz$

17. Electromagnetic Compatibility

This section will cover :-
1. the effects of an amateur station operating in close proximity to other electronic equipment and methods of improving the immunity of affected equipment.
2. sources of interference and paths by which interference can arrive at domestic TV and radio equipment, and improving station design to reduce EMC problems.
3. the steps to be taken when investigating EMC problems.

Electromagnetic compatibility

EMC defines the ability of a device or system to operate satisfactorily in its electromagnetic environment without introducing intolerable electromagnetic disturbances to any other equipment operating in that environment.

All electronic and radio equipment is capable of electromagnetic radiation, sometimes it is intentional, and sometimes unintentional. If the radiation level is small, and the device isolated by distance from other electronic equipment, It is not likely to impair the operation of that equipment. However; if the electromagnetic radiation is at a higher power level, it may radiate directly, or be conducted via the mains (mainsborne) and invade the environment of other equipment. Whether the operation of the other equipment will be impaired or not, will depend on its susceptibility and the strength of the invading signal.

All electronic equipment should be designed to operate satisfactorily in the electromagnetic fields to which it is likely to be subjected. Screening the complete device, and filtering and decoupling all supply and control leads may be essential.

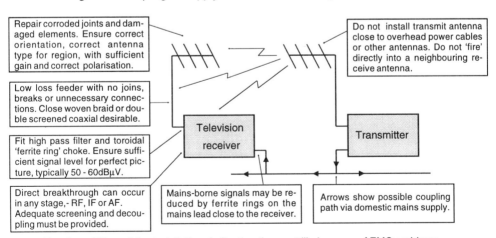

Fig.1 Showing a TV receiving installation. Indicating the most likely cause of EMC problems when close to a transmitter, and the possible cure. The transmitter radiates only from the antenna on its allocated frequency.

Electromagnetic Compatibility

Sources of interference and their effect on TV and radio

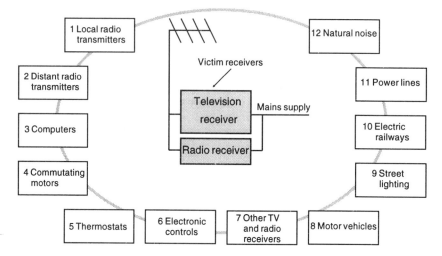

Fig.2 Showing a TV and radio receiver surrounded by some of the most likely sources of interference and pollution to the electromagnetic environment. All of the sources shown are capable of impairing reception. (See numbered list below.)

1. **Local radio transmitters.** An unwanted signal can enter the victim receiver via the antenna, antenna feeder screen, loudspeaker leads, or the mains supply (mains-borne interference). It can overload the receiver front-end, and also break through directly onto the receiver chassis (direct breakthrough). It may cause sound distortion, patterns on the screen or complete picture and/or sound wipe-out.

2. **Distant transmitters.** Not very likely to cause interference unless using the same channel (co-channel) as the victim receiver. Examples are TV patterning under abnormal atmospheric conditions, and night-time interference to MF broadcasting.

3. **Computer interference** is usually of a local nature, it can affect LF, HF, and VHF reception in the radio shack, and is both directly radiated and mains-borne. It is due to the harmonics generated by the sharp rise and fall of the digital pulses with which the machine operates. Screening the computer (not always possible), filtering its mains lead and repositioning it may solve the problem.

4. **Motor commutator** sparking causes a very wide spectrum of both mains-borne and directly radiated interference. Chokes and capacitors are used for suppression. TV and radio affected.

5. **Thermostats** are used to control central heating, refrigerators, electric cookers, and electric water heaters etc. Sparking at the contacts may be caused by worn contacts or the high back-emf of an inductive circuit. Spark-quench circuits are available for contact suppression. Interference is mains-borne and radiated .

6. **Electronic controls** employing digital circuitry will cause similar problems to the computer; mains-borne and directly radiated interference.

7. **Other TV and radio** receivers can cause interference by local oscillator radiation, although not very common. The line time-base and switched mode power supply of a TV receiver will cause mainly mains-borne interference. It will affect LF and MF broadcast bands and sensitive HF communications receivers.

8. **Motor vehicles** having faulty or unsuppressed ignition systems can cause Interference to both TV and radio.

9. **Street lighting.** Sodium and fluorescent lighting can cause mains-borne interference. It will affect LF and MF broadcast bands and sensitive HF communications receivers. The cure may be to change the lamp or fit mains filters close to the lamp. This type of interference can travel several hundred yards over the mains.

10. **Electric railways** can affect TV and radio due to sparking on the rails. Flutter on the TV picture may be observed when trains pass, this may be curable by improvements to the TV antenna system.

11. **Power lines.** High voltage overhead pylon routes can cause interference to sensitive HF and VHF communication receivers, and in some cases TV receivers. This is mainly due to corona discharge at the insulators. Ghosting on TV can occur due to signal reflection from the metal pylons.

12. **Natural noise.** This is made up of cosmic noise, lightning and electrostatic discharge etc. More noticeable when listening to weak signals in the HF band. It can be partly overcome by using high power levels to increase the signal-to-noise ratio.

Strong signal and overload effects

Intermodulation. When two or more frequencies are present at the input to a *linear* device or system, the output will contain only the original frequencies. However, when two signals, f_1 and f_2, are present at the input to a *non-linear* device or system, other frequencies will be generated and the output will contain f_1, f_2, and the second order intermodulation products ($f_1 \pm f_2$). There will also be some harmonics of f_1 and f_2, and higher order intermodulation products will be produced. For example third order intermodulation products ($2f_1 \pm f_2$), and ($2f_2 \pm f_1$), and so on.

E.g. Two frequencies in the amateur two metre band, $f_1 = 145\text{MHz}$, $f_2 = 145.1\text{MHz}$. If these two signals are of sufficient strength to develop a voltage across a non-linear device, third order intermodulation products falling in the two metre band will be generated as follows, and cause interference to adjacent channels.

$$2 f_1 - f_2 = (2 \times 145) - 145.1 = 144.9 MHz \quad \text{and:-}$$
$$2 f_2 - f_1 = (2 \times 145.1) - 145 = 145.2 MHz$$

In addition to the intermodulation products above, there will be others which fall in another part of the frequency spectrum.

Electromagnetic Compatibility

Transmitter Intermodulation can occur between closely coupled transmitters when some of the output power from one transmitter is fed - usually via the antenna - to the output stage of the other. Since the output stage is likely to be non-linear, intermodulation will occur, this is likely to be radiated from the antenna. If these intermodulation products fall in the passband of a nearby receiver, interference will result. Transmitter intermodulation cannot be cured at the receiver.

External intermodulation occurs when two or more strong signal voltages are present across any non-linear junction, including oxidised and corroded connections on antennas and lightning conductors, and rusty nuts and bolts on radio towers.

If the interference is somewhat weather dependent it will be due to external site problems rather than a receiver problem.

Receiver intermodulation can occur in a receiver due to two or more strong unwanted signals at the input of the receiver. Providing there is sufficient separation between the signals causing the intermodulation, and the wanted signal, then it can most likely be cured by a 'stop' filter on one of the unwanted signal frequencies.

Blocking or desensitisation is noticed as a change, usually a reduction in output power or signal-to-noise ratio when the receiver is tuned to the wanted signal. It is caused by a strong unwanted signal on another frequency reducing the gain of the stage concerned. When the offending transmission is removed, maybe by use of a filter, the gain will be restored.

Cross modulation is a similar mechanism to blocking, it occurs when the gain of the stage concerned is varied in sympathy with the modulation of the interfering signal.

Devices susceptible to strong electromagnetic fields

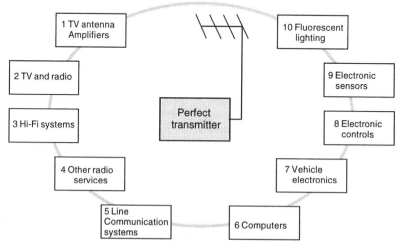

Fig.3 Showing typical devices and systems that can be affected by a perfect radio transmitter, i.e. one that has no harmonics or other spurious emissions in its output. (See numbered list.) ⇒

Electromagnetic Compatibility

1. **TV masthead amplifiers** are wideband amplifiers. They are likely to suffer from strong signals driving the amplifier into its non-linear region, causing blocking, cross-modulation and intermodulation.

2. **TV, radio and video recorders,** in addition to the points listed in 1 above, can be attacked by direct breakthrough and both mains-borne, and mains-radiated interference. (See fig.1.)

3. **Hi-Fi systems** can suffer from audio-breakthrough due to pick-up on any of the external connecting leads, including the loudspeaker leads. Any interfering signals entering the equipment can be rectified and 'detected' by any non-linear device, such as the base-emitter junctions of the semiconductors in the audio stages. Bypassing emitter-base junctions, decoupling speaker leads and input leads to RF may be necessary. Suitable RF chokes, capacitors and filters are available.

4. **Other radio services** e.g. Police, Fire, Ambulance etc, can suffer from strong signal overload. In general they are designed to a tighter specification than domestic equipment and are less likely to be affected by an amateur transmission.

5. **Line communication systems,** including telephones, telephone switchboards, data transmission systems, and cable TV etc. can suffer from breakthrough. With this form of interference, strong signals may cause errors in the data, and audio interference which may sound like a crossed line.

6. **Computer** operation can be impaired. Errors in data and VDU (on screen) disturbances are common. Separation of source and victim may be the easy solution to the problem.

7. **Vehicle electronics** can operate incorrectly as a result of strong RF fields. It may be advisable to check the functions of all vehicle systems when installing a transceiver in a vehicle. Consult the vehicle manufacturer if problems exist.

8. **Electronic controls.** RF energy may be picked up on any of the external control or sensor leads, amplified and/or rectified by the semiconductor junctions, and result in false operation, or non-operation of the system. Screening, RF decoupling, and moving the transmit antenna further away will cure the problem.

9. **Electronic sensors.** Typical devices that can be triggered by strong RF fields are intruder alarms and external security lighting employing passive infra-red (PIR) detectors. Possible solutions may be Screening, RF decoupling, moving the transmit antenna further away or reducing transmitter power. Also try changing the sensor or control unit to a type that has better immunity to RF fields.

10. **Fluorescent lighting** can flicker in sympathy with AM, SSB and CW modulation. FM will normally have little effect. May be cured be moving transmitter antenna and feeder away from house wiring. Avoid using a long-wire antenna.

Electromagnetic Compatibility

Propagation of Interference

Fig.4

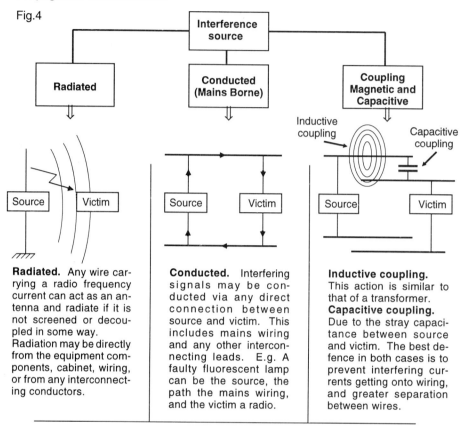

Radiated. Any wire carrying a radio frequency current can act as an antenna and radiate if it is not screened or decoupled in some way. Radiation may be directly from the equipment components, cabinet, wiring, or from any interconnecting conductors.

Conducted. Interfering signals may be conducted via any direct connection between source and victim. This includes mains wiring and any other interconnecting leads. E.g. A faulty fluorescent lamp can be the source, the path the mains wiring, and the victim a radio.

Inductive coupling. This action is similar to that of a transformer. **Capacitive coupling.** Due to the stray capacitance between source and victim. The best defence in both cases is to prevent interfering currents getting onto wiring, and greater separation between wires.

The Interference Spectrum

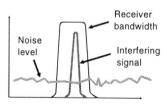

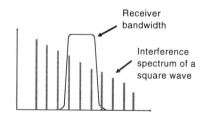

Fig.5. Comparing the receiver bandwidth to a narrow band interfering signal, such as produced by an unmodulated carrier wave, harmonic, or RF oscillator. The noise level is broadband, and consists of contributions from many sources, often unidentifiable. Its level will vary with time and location.

Fig.6. Showing the typical spectrum of interference caused by a circuit employing a square wave digital oscillator (clock), such as a computer. The square wave generates an infinite series of odd harmonics. Changing the frequency of the clock will change the frequency (and spacing) of the harmonics.

Electromagnetic Compatibility

1. **One of the aims of EMC is to-**
   a) prevent the RF spectrum becoming polluted with unwanted electromagnetic emissions from radio, electronic and other electrical equipment.
   b) ensure a narrower spectrum for radio users.
   c) create a hostile environment for interfering emissions.
   d) enable electromagnetic emissions to propagate unimpaired.

2. **Good EMC practice ensures that all radio and electronic equipment, whether using, or not using the RF spectrum, can be operated satisfactorily in the presence of-**
   a) strong electromagnetic fields.
   b) a.c. mains variations.
   c) d.c. power fluctuations.
   d) a heavily ionised ionosphere.

3. **All efforts to cure amateur EMC problems should-**
   a) be carried out under supervision of the DTI.
   b) be investigated by the local repeater group.
   c) begin by informing the DTI on form P18.
   d) begin in the amateur radio station.

4. **The production of spurious signals when two or more signals are combined or mixed in a nonlinear device, e.g. semiconductor junctions or diodes in receivers, rusty nuts and bolts on metal towers and masts, corroded copper water pipes in contact with others, and oxidised metal roofs and gutters etc. is known as-**
   a) interpolarisation.   b) intermodulation.
   c) crossmodulation.   d) mixer effect.

5. **Intermodulation in a receiver is caused by-**
   a) deficiencies in the loudspeaker coils.
   b) linear amplification of the wanted signal and its sidebands.
   c) the mixing of two or more frequencies in any non-linear stage or component of the receiver.
   d) lack of ozone in the depletion layers of the semiconductors.

6. **Corroded antenna elements and feeder connections, and badly fitting antenna plugs on a receiver are likely to cause-**
   a) intermodulation.
   b) Marconi effect.
   c) mains-borne interference.
   d) local oscillator drift in the receiver.

17-7

7. The transfer of intelligence from an unwanted signal to a weaker wanted signal is referred to as-
   a) crosspolarisation.
   b) crossfertilisation.
   c) crossmodulation.
   d) intermodulation.

8. Crossmodulation can occur when a receiver stage is overloaded by a strong modulated interfering signal which-
   a) varies the gain of that stage in sympathy with the modulation.
   b) reduces the supply rail voltage to 30% of its nominal value.
   c) splits into two equal parts, f_1 and f_2.
   d) frequency modulates the supply rail voltage to the audio stage.

9. The effect of crossmodulation is most noticeable when-
   a) the wanted signal is stronger than the interfering signal.
   b) both wanted signal and interfering signal are at the same level.
   c) both interfering signal and wanted signal are 120° out of phase.
   d) the interfering signal is much stronger than the wanted signal.

10. When crossmodulation has occurred in a receiver's RF or mixer stages it-
   a) can be cured by improving the IF selectivity.
   b) can be cured by improving the sensitivity of the audio amplifier.
   c) cannot be cured by modification to subsequent stages.
   d) can be tuned-out using the BFO.

11. Blocking is the-
   a) restriction on PSU current in the presence of strong signals.
   b) loss or reduction in level of the wanted signal when a strong unwanted signal is present.
   c) loss or reduction of the unwanted signal when a band stop filter is fitted.
   d) loss or reduction of the unwanted signal when a band pass filter is fitted.

12. Blocking can occur when a receiver is overloaded by a strong signal which-
   a) overcomes the supply rail voltage and causes current depression.
   b) reduces the gain of the stage concerned.
   c) increases the audio power to the 600 ohm output jack socket.
   d) detunes the first IF amplifier.

13. Intermodulation, crossmodulation, and blocking effects, occurring in a TV or broadcast receiver can often be minimised at the receiver by-
   a) reducing the gain of the audio stage.
   b) fitting braid breakers, suitable filters and better screening in the receiver.
   c) fitting RF filters in the microphone leads.
   d) fitting high Q tuned circuits in the power supply leads at the mains transformer.

Electromagnetic Compatibility

14. A UHF TV receiver is being blocked by a strong local amateur transmission on a frequency of 145MHz. A suitable cure at the TV might be to fit a-
a) high pass filter at the TV end of the antenna downlead.
b) low pass filter at the TV end of the antenna downlead.
c) 30dB attenuator in the TV antenna downlead.
d) wideband masthead TV signal preamplifier in the TV antenna.

15. If the blocking signal is a keyed CW transmission, the-
a) level of the wanted signal will follow the keying speed and sequence.
b) IF amplifier detuning effect will be most noticeable.
c) transit time of the emitter current in the IF stages will change.
d) interference will not be noticed.

16. Co-channel interference occurs when-
a) wideband IF filters are used.
b) narrow band audio frequency filters are incorrectly adjusted.
c) there is no rejector circuit in the antenna lead.
d) the wanted signal and the unwanted signal are the same frequency.

17. It might be possible to reduce co-channel interference by-
a) fitting a co-channel stop filter in the antenna feeder.
b) fitting a co-channel stop filter in first IF amplifier.
c) lowering the drive level of the receive local oscillator.
d) making use of directional properties of the receive antenna.

18. Adjacent channel interference may be due to-
a) poor selectivity in the IF amplifier and IF filters.
b) wide bandwidth of the RF amplifier.
c) insufficient bandwidth in the IF amplifier.
d) signals mixing in the IF stage and causing co-channel interference.

19. If adjacent channel interference is due to a receiver deficiency, what steps can be taken to improve its performance?
a) Increase the attenuation of the channel reject filter in the antenna.
b) Improve the selectivity of the IF stages.
c) Increase the bandwidth of the IF stages.
d) Increase the frequency response of the audio amplifier.

20. The non-linear properties of semiconductors and diodes-
a) help reduce frequency mixing.
b) reduce intermodulation effects.
c) reduce crossmodulation effects.
d) can cause unwanted signals to be produced.

Electromagnetic Compatibility

21. If an EMC cure seems a bit elusive, it may be worth while-
    a) checking the sunspot number.
    b) reducing transmitter power.
    c) increasing transmitter power.
    d) increasing the mains voltage.

22. The harmonics of a multiband HF transmitter, capable of operating in the amateur bands between 1.8 and 30MHz are causing interference to VHF radio and UHF TV services. A suitable choice of filter will be-
    a) high pass filter in the transmitter output with a cut off below 30MHz.
    b) high pass filter in the receiver with a cut off frequency at 600MHz.
    c) low pass filter in the transmitter with a cut off frequency at 30MHz.
    d) band pass filter in the receiver with a pass band of 1.8 to 30MHz.

23. A broadcast receiver is being affected by key clicks from a local CW transmitter. What might be the first course of action?
    a) Retune the receiver local oscillator so that it is below the signal frequency.
    b) Retune the wanted signal so that it is above the local oscillator frequency.
    c) Increase the keying speed of the transmission.
    d) Ensure that an effective key click filter is fitted to the transmitter.

24. Direct radiation from oscillators and RF amplifier stages can be reduced or prevented by-
    a) bypassing all semiconductors in the radiating stage with 1pF capacitors.
    b) enclosing the stage in a mu-plastic box with silver plated screws.
    c) lengthening all power feed wires with high resistivity conductors.
    d) ensuring that the stage is in a completely screened enclosure with adequate decoupling for the power supply rail.

25. An unwanted amateur transmission entering a nearby TV via the antenna can often be effectively reduced by-
    a) making a $\lambda/2$ air gap in the inner conductor of the TV feeder cable.
    b) using a wideband preamplifier on the TV antenna.
    c) using a tuned coaxial stub at the TV antenna input.
    d) using low loss feeder at the transmitter.

26. A strong local 145MHz transmission is entering a TV via the antenna and causing blocking. It is decided that a $\lambda/4$ open-circuit coaxial stub fitted across the TV antenna input might cure the problem. The velocity factor of the coaxial feeder used for the stub is 0.67. What is the approximate length of the stub?
    a) 0.347m   b) 1.67m
    c) 2.0m   d) 4.0m

27. Your neighbour's TV is being blocked by your 432MHz transmission, but due to the cost of the filter required to cure the receiver you go for the cheaper option, and make your neighbour a half-wave short-circuit stub from a length of scrap coaxial cable having a velocity factor of 0.67. To what approximate length should it be cut?
   a) 11.5cm   b) 23cm
   c) 35cm   d) 70cm.

28. The input impedance of a half-wave short-circuit stub at the resonant frequency is-
   a) very low   b) 300 ohms
   c) 600 ohms   d) 1200 ohms

29. Adjustment of an open-circuit stub can be made by cutting the stub longer than calculated, connecting it across the antenna feeder at the receiver, either soldered or with a coaxial T connector, - first ensuring that the installation is not live and that there is no risk of electrocution, and then-
   a) gradually slicing off the open end of the stub, watching for maximum reduction of interference.
   b) squeezing the stub with a pair of pliers until all the moisture comes out of it, using high grade cable will avoid this problem..
   c) pushing a pin through the stub every fraction of an inch and watching for a maximum reduction of interference as the pin shorts the stub, permanently short the stub end at this point.
   d) stroking it with a strong magnet until the interference is reduced.

30. One of the advantages of using a stub is that-
   a) it traps all unwanted signals on the antenna.
   b) it offers high impedance to the interfering signal.
   c) it is simple and cheap to construct and tune
   d) its cut off frequency is above that of LC filters.

31. Amateur transmissions are being heard on a TV receiver even when the audio volume control is fully off.
   To which stage of the receiver do you associate the problem?
   a) The second IF stage.
   b) The first IF stage.
   c) The mixer stage.
   d) The audio amplifier stage.

Electromagnetic Compatibility

32. A type of filter consisting of a number of turns of coaxial cable wound on one or two ferrite rings is shown in Fig.7. It is often fitted in the antenna feeder of a TV or VHF broadcast receiver to increase the impedance of the outer screen and reduce the flow of RF currents.
It is known as a-
   a) ferrite ring choke.
   b) grid stopper.
   c) harmonic reducer.
   d) signal reducer.

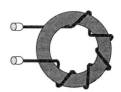

33. **In an effort to reduce mains-borne interference from** Fig.7
   an amateur transmitter, it would be advantageous to-
   a) reduce the length of the crystal socket pins.
   b) ensure that the mains fuses are of a BS1362 type.
   c) fit a low pass filter on the microphone lead.
   d) chose separate routes for the mains and antenna feeder cables.

34. **A portable broadcast receiver, operating on internal batteries is affected by mains-borne interference from an amateur telephony transmitter.**
   What course of action might solve the problem?
   a) Complain to the local club committee and insist they fit mains low pass filters.
   b) Fit a mains supply filter on the receiver conforming to BS800.
   c) Fit a mains supply filter at the transmitter and ensure that there is adequate separation between the transmitter antenna system and all mains wiring.
   d) Fit a transient suppressor on the receiver supply rail.

35. **Referring to Q34 above. You might also improve the situation by-**
   a) moving the victim receiver further from the house mains wiring.
   b) ensuring the transmitter PA stage is operating in class C.
   c) ensuring the transmitter PA stage is operating in class D.
   d) ensuring the key click filter is effective.

36. **Which of the circuit arrangements shown below will best reduce the level of an unwanted signal at the input to a receiver?**
   (All LC circuits shown are tuned to the interfering signal.)
   a)   b)   c)   d)

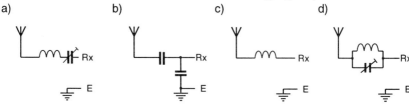

37. When a receiver is being affected at or near the intermediate frequency by interfering signals entering via the antenna, an effective cure might be to-
   a) fit ferrite beads over the transistor leads of the IF amplifier.
   b) fit RF chokes and decoupling capacitors in the audio stage.
   c) reduce the level of the local oscillator at the mixer stage.
   d) fit an IF rejector or trap in the antenna feed.

38. To reduce the level of an interfering signal, at or around the intermediate frequency, an IF rejector is fitted at the receiver antenna input socket. What is the most likely construction?
   a) A capacitor and resistor in series with the antenna lead.
   b) A low Q inductor and a high Q resistor connected across the antenna.
   c) Six turns of 8 s.w.g. silver plated copper wire on a 1/2" iron bar, connected in series with the antenna
   d) A parallel LC circuit, tuned to the IF, in series with the antenna input.

39. Where parallel or series tuned LC circuits are used to reduce or eliminate unwanted signals entering a receiver, they are respectively known as-
   a) signal enhancers and de-enhancers.
   b) interference couplers and decouplers (frequency traps).
   c) rejector and acceptor circuits (wave traps).
   d) circulators and isolators (signal traps).

40. IF breakthrough on a broadcast or TV receiver can usually be identified-
   a) since both intensity and frequency increase at noon.
   b) because it is usually present on all stations to which the receiver is tuned.
   c) since it only occurs in receivers tuned to 10.7MHz.
   d) as a '100Hz tone' when the receiver is tuned to the wanted station.

41. An amateur transmission is virtually free of all spurious emissions, but neighbouring TV and hi-fi installations are being affected. The most probable reason is-
   a) lack of immunity in the affected receivers.
   b) power supply faults in the affected receivers.
   c) severe ozone deficiency in the transmitter PA stage.
   d) faulty earth bonding at the local substation.

42. Digital equipment relies on, and produces square waves for, and during, its operation. The perfect square wave consists of a fundamental frequency and-
   a) several even harmonics.
   b) an infinite series of odd harmonics.
   c) an infinite series of even harmonics.
   d) a third harmonic only.

43. Digital circuitry should be-
a) adequately screened and have decoupled power supply leads.
b) operated at 3.5V and have decoupled power supply leads.
c) operated with maximum current from a logic power supply unit (PSU).
d) coupled only via the interstage power supply leads.

44. Fig.8 shows components C_d and L_d associated with the supply rail of an RF amplifier. What are they for?

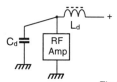

Fig.8

a) Voltage regulation.
b) Current regulation.
c) Decoupling the supply rail.
d) Reducing signal frequency gain.

45. When parasitic oscillation is detected in an RF stage it may be possible to cure it by-
a) screening the input and output circuit from each other.
b) increasing the coupling between the output and input.
c) increasing the coupling between the input and output.
d) soldering a 10µF capacitor between the output and ground.

46. Parasitic oscillations in RF amplifier stages can be caused by unwanted feedback within the amplifier, and also-
a) the self resonance of RF chokes.
b) linear metal oxide resistors.
c) exhausted 9V grid bias batteries fitted in some receivers.
d) reverse conduction within some of the linear resistors.

47. Overdeviation of a frequency modulated carrier wave -
a) is a normal situation for greater talk power.
b) is standard practice in telephony transmitters.
c) will generate excessive side frequencies and cause splatter and noise in adjacent channels.
d) is normally used to reduce 5th harmonic interference.

48. Long wire antennas brought directly into a house, and terminated directly onto a transmitter are-
a) most likely to cause interference problems to neighbouring receivers.
b) least likely to cause interference to neighbouring receivers.
c) the best for general propagation.
d) a sure cure for all EMC problems.

49. Wideband TV preamplifiers in common use are-
a) the best means possible of reducing TVI.
b) likely to be susceptible to overload from strong transmissions.
c) usually fitted as a precaution against lightning strikes.
d) recommended for reducing interference from nearby transmitters.

50. Which one of the devices listed is most likely to cause broadband LF, MF, and sometimes HF interference to domestic and amateur radio receivers?
a) A 2kW electric fire.
b) Incandescent lighting.
c) Fluorescent lighting.
d) A clock with a λ/4 pendulum.

51. A sensitive amateur receiver is suffering from some form of harsh continuous wideband noise interference, which sometimes disappears late in the evening and returns about 0900 hrs next morning. It might be-
a) a neon shop sign.
b) a Japanese hi-fi system using a faulty infrared controller.
c) sunspot activity.
d) An RF welding unit at a local factory.

52. When operating your mobile transceiver in the car, you notice that the instrument panel warning lights operate when you transmit. What should you do?
a) Stop transmitting and consult the manufacturers agent.
b) Fit RF rejector circuits in the plug leads.
c) Use an internal wideband antenna fitted near the rear window.
d) Change to a British manufactured sparking plug.

53. A hi-fi system picks up an amateur VHF transmission via its long loudspeaker leads. The most probable cure may be to-
a) fit audio bandstop filters at the the loudspeaker terminals of the amplifier.
b) insert 4.7pF ceramic capacitors in series with the loudspeaker leads.
c) use heavy duty, low inductance, speaker leads.
d) pass the speaker leads through ferrite beads at the amplifier end of the leads, or fit suitable RF chokes at the same point and use screened leads.

54. A stub or a filter, fitted in a TV antenna feeder, will not solve an EMC problem when-
a) the mains power is asymmetrically fed.
b) the TV antenna is the wrong type for the received transmission.
c) narrow band FM (NBFM) signals are the cause of the EMC problem.
d) the interference does not enter via the antenna.

Electromagnetic Compatibility

55. What is the best defence against the direct pick-up of interfering signals?
a) Use ear defenders, wireless operators for the use of, type 1B.
b) Complete RF screening of the affected equipment (not always practicable).
c) Band pass filters in the antenna downlead.
d) High pass filters in the antenna downlead.

56. Although functioning correctly from a practical point of view, which of the items below will be most capable of generating broad band interference?
a) A carrier oscillator.
b) The PA stage of a transmitter.
c) The computer, fluorescent lighting, the ignition circuit of a car, vacuum cleaner, and any electric motor with a sparking commutator.
d) The hi-fi amplifier, electric kettle, analogue voltmeter, battery clock, car radio, electric cooker element, 150W filament bulb, and a mains induction motor.

57. Calculate the field strength to which a neighbouring TV could be subjected when it is 10 metres from, and in the direction of maximum radiation of, your antenna. Your effective radiated power (erp) in this case is 100 watts.
{Note. Further questions on field strength appear in Chapter 13 Q111 on.}
a) 7.02V/m   b) 4.9V/m
c) 3.5V/m   d) 1.1V/m

58. To avoid interference to a neighbouring TV, you reduce your output power to 10W (ERP), and increase the spacing between the transmitting antenna and receiving antenna to 20m.
What is the approximate field strength in the vicinity of the TV antenna?
a) 7.02V/m   b) 4.9V/m
c) 3.5V/m   d) 1.1V/m

59. A station has an erp of 1000 watts (1kW). At what distance is the field strength approximately 1 V/m?
a) 2.22m   b) 22.2m
c) 222m   d) 1000m

60. EMC problems due to high field strengths can be reduced or cured by-
a) reducing the power of the source and increasing the separation between the source and the victim receiver.
b) decreasing the separation between the source and the victim receiver.
c) increasing the field strength of the interfering signal, and decreasing the separation between the source and victim to about one wavelength.
d) decreasing the attenuation path between the source and the victim, and coating any screens with highly conductive graphite oil.

61. A good EMC conscious amateur will always operate with-
a) full legal power.
b) a class C, 2kW linear amplifier.
c) only sufficient power to maintain reliable communication.
d) an extra 10dB of power to ensure S9+20dB signals at the far end.

62. The mains supply filter will help prevent mains-borne RF interference getting out of the radio station, it will also-
a) reduce mains-borne interfering signals entering the station.
b) match the mains impedance to the load and give a better power transfer.
c) enable you to take advantage of wattless power and save on electricity bills.
d) provide a better match for the antenna.

63. Where possible a long wire antenna should-
a) be made of resistance wire to give it a wider bandwidth.
b) be kept away from the house and fed by a single unscreened resistance wire.
c) be kept as far from houses and other buildings as possible.
d) have a balun fitted at the centre.

64. When a balanced antenna, e.g. a centre-fed dipole, is fed from an unbalanced coaxial feeder, it is necessary to-
a) load each end of the dipole with an 88mH coil.
b) short-circuit the centre of the dipole to prevent harmonic radiation and oscillation, and to reduce the VSWR.
c) check for parasitic oscillation in the feeder.
d) fit a balun transformer at the dipole centre

65. The best position for an antenna tuning unit; although not always practicable, is-
a) close to the transmitter.
b) in the centre portion of the feeder.
c) close to the tip of the dipole.
d) as close to the antenna as possible.

66. Coaxial feeders used at a radio station-
a) should have a high quality carbon dielectric and a closely woven braiding or a solid copper screen.
b) should be of a high quality low loss type, with closely woven braiding or a solid copper screen.
c) must have a conducting polythiene outer conductor, high resitivity centre conductor and be capable of screen radiation.
d) must have air gaps in the centre conductor to allow the VSWR to equalise.

67. Because it could, under certain circumstances be instrumental in generating harmonics the-
   a) low pass filter should have a notch at the carrier frequency.
   b) modulator should never be modulated.
   c) VSWR meter should be fitted before any output filters.
   d) PA stage must always be overdriven.

68. Fig.9 shows the diagram of a typical-
   a) antenna signal clarifier.
   b) blocking oscillator.
   c) blocking transformer.
   d) braid-breaking transformer.

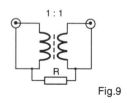

Fig.9

69. The braid-breaker is useful when-
   a) IF signals are present at the antenna.
   b) mains hum affects the audio stages.
   c) wideband FM signals need an improvement in fidelity.
   d) strong signals flowing on the outside of the screen of a coaxial feeder cable must be blocked.

70. Fig 10 shows a filter with its associated response curve. What type of filter is it?
   a) Low pass filter (LPF).
   b) High pass filter (HPF).
   c) Band pass filter (BPF).
   d) Band stop filter (BSF).

 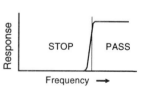

Fig.10

71. The filter shown in fig.10 is preferred when it is necessary to-
   a) attenuate the level of strong unwanted signals below the wanted signal.
   b) attenuate the level of strong wanted signals above the unwanted signal.
   c) pass all transmissions below cut-off and reject the rest.
   d) match a folded dipole to a 50 ohm feeder.

72. A good quality filter will have-
   a) very low attenuation in the passband.
   b) very high attenuation in the passband.
   c) 30dB attenuation in the passband.
   d) 60dB attenuation in the passband.

Electromagnetic Compatibility

73. Fig.11 shows a filter with its associated response curve.
    What type of filter is it?
    a) Low pass filter
    b) High pass filter.
    c) Band pass filter.
    d) Band stop filter.

 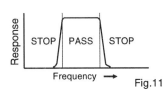

Fig.11

74. The impedance of any filters fitted in an antenna system should match the impedance of the antenna, the feeder, and the equipment.
    In the case of amateur radio transmitting equipment the antenna and feeder impedance is normally-
    a) 17.3 ohms   b) 25 ohms
    c) 43 ohms   d) 50 ohms

75. The impedance of any filters fitted in an antenna system should match the impedance of the antenna, the feeder, and the equipment.
    In the case of domestic TV, the antenna and feeder impedance is-
    a) 43 ohms   b) 50 ohms
    c) 75 ohms   d) 100 ohms

76. Your station is capable of operating in four modes of transmission, CW, AM, FM and SSB. Which mode is the least likely to cause audio break-through problems with neighbouring TV, radio and hi-fi equipment?
    a) CW   b) AM
    c) FM   d) SSB

77. Owners of affected receivers should take steps to ensure that-
    a) the manufacturer has fitted high pass filters where necessary.
    b) they are using a resonant length mains feeder.
    c) they are using adjustable set top indoor antennas.
    d) their apparatus has a reasonable standard of immunity.

78. In difficult EMC cases it may be necessary for the amateur to-
    a) have his neighbours viewing hours restricted by law.
    b) buy new receiving apparatus for neighbours within 1km of his boundary.
    c) apply to the CCIR for an Essential User Licence.
    d) modify his transmission practice.

1	a	16	d	31	d	46	a	61	c	76	c
2	a	17	d	32	a	47	c	62	a	77	d
3	d	18	a	33	d	48	a	63	c	78	d
4	b	19	b	34	c	49	b	64	d		
5	c	20	d	35	a	50	c	65	d		
6	a	21	b	36	d	51	a	66	b		
7	c	22	c	37	d	52	a	67	c		
8	a	23	d	38	d	53	d	68	d		
9	d	24	d	39	c	54	d	69	d		
10	c	25	c	40	b	55	b	70	b		
11	b	26	a	41	a	56	c	71	a		
12	b	27	b	42	b	57	a	72	a		
13	b	28	a	43	a	58	d	73	c		
14	a	29	a	44	c	59	c	74	d		
15	a	30	c	45	a	60	a	75	c		

1. Care must be taken at the design stage of any electrical, electronic and radio equipment to ensure that it complies with the relevant EMC standards laid down by the country in which it is to be used. The standards cover a whole range of equipment from radio transmitters to cordless telephones and vehicle ignition systems to thermostats.

2. Practically all electrical, electronic and radio equipment can be affected by strong electromagnetic fields. Manufacturers are aware of this problem and hopefully build immunity into their equipment to ensure satisfactory operation under adverse conditions.

3. Attention should be given to the set-up and layout of a radio station before complaints of interference are received. If complaints arise the equipment in the station should be checked before any other action is taken.

4,5. Sometimes two frequencies are deliberately mixed in a non-linear device to produce other frequencies, such as in the mixer stage of a superheterodyne receiver. However, unintentional mixing can occur by a similar mechanism, resulting in the production of unwanted intermodulation products which may fall in a wanted channel and cause interference.

6. Any corroded metallic joints or junctions are likely to create the ideal non-linear characteristic for intermodulation to occur. Once generated the intermods can radiate from any associated wiring that acts as an antenna.

7. Crossmodulation is the transfer of intelligence from one signal to another.

8. Crossmodulation occurs when a strong AM, SSB, or CW signal overloads a

stage in a receiver, varying its gain in sympathy with the modulation.

9. The effect is more noticeable when the unwanted signal is much stronger than the wanted signal.

10. Cross modulation cannot be cured after it has taken place. The unwanted signal should be attenuated to prevent it overloading the receiver.

11,12. A very strong signal can cause overloading of the RF or mixer stages. This will effectively reduce the gain of the overloaded stage, reducing or completely *blocking* the wanted signal. The unwanted signal will not be heard at the output.

13. When a receiver suffers from Intermodulation, crossmodulation and blocking, the cause is normally due to strong unwanted signals entering the receiver, usually via the antenna. Generally speaking, readily available high pass filters, and tuned coaxial stubs can be used in the TV feeder. Notch filters and suitable high pass or band pass filters may be used for VHF radio problems. The ferrite ring choke used as a braid breaker can be used when the unwanted signal is entering via the outside of the screen of the feeder cable.

14. Use a high pass filter close to the TV. The 145MHz signal will be attenuated.

15. Loss of sensitivity will only occur when the blocking signal is present. When a receiver is being blocked by an on-off keyed carrier wave, the wanted signal will appear between code characters. (Depends on receiver AGC characteristic.)

16. Co-channel interference occurs when the unwanted signal is the same frequency as the wanted signal.

17. Since a co-channel station is on the same frequency as a wanted station, attempts to filter it out will also result in attenuation of the wanted station. For VHF/UHF radio and TV it may be possible to use the directional characteristics of a high gain yagi antenna, provided that both stations are not in the same direction from the receiver.

18,19. Interference from adjacent channels may be due to a number of causes. The offending transmission itself may be overdeviated or overmodulated and cause splatter. Where the problem lies in the receiver it is likely to be due to a wide IF bandwidth. Improving the selectivity of the IF stages and selecting a suitable IF filter may solve the problem.

20. Two or more signal voltages developed across any non-linear device are likely to produce sum and difference frequencies.

21. Intermodulation, crossmodulation and blocking effects depend on the level of the signals involved. Even a small reduction in the power of one of the contributory transmitters may cure the problem.

Answers - Electromagnetic Compatibility

22. Use a low pass filter at the transmitter output. In this case all frequencies below 30MHz will be passed, and all frequencies above 30MHz will be attenuated.

23. Ensure that there is an effective key click filter and that the keying leads are suitably screened.

24. Direct radiation from oscillators and RF stages must be avoided because it may interfere with other parts of the circuit, and cause spurious responses and emissions. RF screening and power feed decoupling is necessary at each stage. A screened and decoupled stage will also prevent unwanted signals entering.

25. Where a single frequency, or a narrow band of frequencies has to be stopped from entering a receiver, it is possible to use a tuned length of coaxial cable, referred to as a 'stub', across the antenna input to the receiver.

26. One end of the λ/4 stub is connected across the antenna feeder near the TV, and the free, open-circuit end is left hanging. The condition at the end connected across the feeder will be a very low impedance, almost a short-circuit at the resonant frequency, in this case 145MHz.

$$Full\ wavelength\ \lambda\ at\ 145MHz = \frac{300 \times 10^6}{145 \times 10^6} = 2.069\ metres$$

$$Length\ of\ stub = \frac{\lambda}{4} \times VF = \frac{2.069}{4} \times 0.67 = 0.347m\ or\ 34.7cm\ (Approx)$$

27. One end of the λ/2 stub is connected across the antenna feeder near the TV, and the free, short-circuit end is left hanging. The condition at the end connected across the feeder will be a very low impedance, almost a short-circuit, at the resonant frequency, in this case 432MHz.

$$Full\ wavelength\ \lambda\ at\ 432MHz = \frac{300 \times 10^6}{432 \times 10^6} = 0.694\ metres$$

$$Length\ of\ stub = \frac{\lambda}{2} \times VF = \frac{0.694}{2} \times 0.67 = 0.23m\ or\ 23cm\ (Approx)$$

28. The input impedance of the short-circuit stub (at the end connected across the antenna) is very low, almost a short-circuit.

29. Various practical methods may be used to tune a stub. A simple method requiring no test equipment is to cut the stub slightly longer than calculated, install it in the antenna system and gradually slice off the end until the interference is minimum. However, you may pass through the minimum point and need to cut another stub based on the measurements of the first. It should be noted that stubs will resonate at certain multiples of the fundamental frequency, and cause attenuation resulting in possible loss of a wanted TV signal.

30. The stub is simple to construct and tune, it is also cheap and effective.

31. The audio amplifier stage and loudspeaker leads are the prime suspects.

32. Currents flowing on the outside of the feeder screen and onto the chassis of the receiver can be reduced by increasing the inductance, and hence the reactance, of the screen. This is achieved by winding several turns of the feeder on to one or more ferrite rings. Such an arrangement is referred to as a *ferrite ring choke, coaxial choke,* or *braid breaker,* since it effectively breaks the braid by choking-off the RF currents flowing on its surface. Ferrite rings can also be used in a similar manner for choking mains leads and loudspeaker leads. Small ferrite beads can be slipped over transistor leads as parasitic stoppers.

33. In order that RF coupling between the antenna and antenna feeder, and the domestic mains is kept small, antennas and antenna feeders should be installed as far away from the mains supply as practical circumstances allow.

34. First check the radio station, it may be that the action in Q33 above is required. It may also improve the situation by fitting a mains filter or ferrite ring choke in the transmitter mains supply lead close to the transmitter.

35. Moving the receiver away from - RF radiating - house wiring may solve the problem.

36. The parallel tuned - high impedance - rejector circuit, connected in series with the antenna, as shown in diagram d), will reduce the level of the unwanted signal entering the receiver. It should be tuned to the unwanted frequency.

37. The parallel tuned rejector circuit of the previous answer may be used, and should be tuned to the unwanted IF frequency.

38,39. Parallel tuned rejector circuits, and series tuned acceptor circuits may be used to reduce the level of unwanted signals reaching a receiver. Parallel circuits are connected in series with the antenna and series circuits across the antenna terminals.

40. Normally, the RF stages of a receiver offer sufficient protection to prevent break-through of signals at the intermediate frequency. The unwanted IF signal cannot be removed by tuning to a new station or channel.

41. A receiver lacks immunity when its operation is impaired by signals to which it is not tuned. Usually the unwanted signals are of a high level.

42. The perfect square wave consists of a fundamental frequency and an infinite series of odd harmonics.

43. Digital equipment should be adequately screened and decoupled, else it may cause local and mains-borne interference.

44. The power supply input to any stage should be decoupled to prevent RF currents entering that stage or being fed from that stage to other stages. The capacitor C_d bypasses the currents to ground, and L_d has a high impedance to RF, ensuring RF does not return to the power supply. L_d has a low resistance to DC.

45. Parasitic oscillation is an unwanted self-oscillation within an amplifier or device. Stray coupling between input and output may be the cause, therefore, Adequate screening between the input and output circuitry should be provided.

46. Parasitic oscillation can occur near the required frequency or many megahertz away. Parasitic oscillation is often unstable and its frequency and amplitude liable to change due to 'hand' capacitance. RF chokes possess self capacitance, making them resonant at some frequency. In addition stray circuit capacitances can cause a choke or inductor to resonate at unpredicted frequencies.

47. An over deviated carrier will cause splatter into adjacent channels. Transmitter deviation must be adjusted to suit the system in which it is operating.

48. A long wire, or end fed antenna, brought straight into the radio station will be radiating along its whole length, including any associated earth return system. Since this type of antenna is likely to be close to mains wiring and neighbouring TV receivers, breakthrough may result.

49. Masthead amplifiers must have a bandwidth wide enough to accommodate all of the TV channels for that region. They can suffer crossmodulation, intermodulation and blocking from strong unwanted signals.

50. Fluorescent lighting can cause mains-borne interference, particularly in the lower frequency bands, and when the lighting is concentrated, i.e. such as in a shopping centre or industrial complex. It can be due to one particular tube, or the addition of the electrical noise of many tubes. Tube replacement and/or suppression at the source should be considered.

51. Typical of neon shop sign. Detective work may tie the time down to business hours. Often due to faulty high voltage connections on the tubes and transformers.

52. Any electronic system can malfunction in a strong RF field. Since failure in this case can be dangerous, consult the manufacturers. They may have the answer.

53. The RF must be prevented from entering the amplifier. Winding several turns of the loudspeaker lead on ferrite rings, in addition, and with the manufacturers approval, 100pF or 470pF capacitors, fitted from each speaker terminal to ground, and keeping all leads as short as possible may solve the problem.

54. When interference is caused by direct breakthrough onto the chassis, or mains-borne, filters and stubs fitted on the antenna will not cure the problem.

55. Complete RF screening is the best solution to counter direct breakthrough. This is not always very practicable, and in the case of a TV receiver problems are best referred back to the manufacturer.

56. Any of the items listed in c) are likely to cause wideband interference, both directly radiated and, in most cases, mains-borne.

57. $e = \dfrac{7.02\sqrt{ERP}}{d} = \dfrac{7.02\sqrt{100}}{10} = \dfrac{70.2}{10} = 7.02\,V/m$

58. $e = \dfrac{7.02\sqrt{ERP}}{d} = \dfrac{7.02\sqrt{10}}{20} = \dfrac{7.02\times3.16}{20} = \dfrac{22.2}{20} = 1.1\,V/m$

59. $d = \dfrac{7.02\sqrt{ERP}}{e} = \dfrac{7.02\sqrt{1000}}{1} = \dfrac{7.02\times31.6}{1} = 222\,m$

60. EMC problems can often be completely eliminated by reducing transmitter power and increasing the distance between the source and the victim.

61. With EMC and spectrum re-use in mind, only the transmitter power necessary for reliable communication should be used.

62. Mains power feed filters can prevent mains-borne interference leaving the radio station as well as preventing it entering.

63. The Long wire antenna radiates along its whole length, it is therefore likely to cause EMC problems when close to local mains supplies, houses, and Television.

64. Centre-fed antennas are balanced devices, and equal capacitance to ground should exist on both elements. Connecting an unbalanced coaxial feeder will upset the balance condition on the antenna and may cause currents to flow back along the outside of the screen or braid of the feeder and radiate. To overcome the problem of connecting a balanced antenna to an unbalanced feeder, a balance to unbalance transformer *(balun)* is used.

65. The antenna tuning unit (ATU) will ideally be fitted at the antenna/feeder junction. This is not usually practical, so it is fitted at the transmitter end between the filter and the antenna. Its purpose is to match the transmitter to the antenna.

66. Coaxial feeders. At VHF/UHF feeder loss will be noticeable when long runs are necessary, therefore, use a low loss feeder. A good quality coaxial cable will have a tightly woven or double braid screen. The best coaxial cables have a semi-flexible solid copper screen.

67. The VSWR meter. Because there may be some possibility of low level harmonics being generated due to the diodes in it, the VSWR meter, when fitted, should be connected between the transmitter and any external filters.

68,69. The braid breaker blocks the flow of RF currents picked up on the outside of the screen of the coaxial cable. The ferrite ring choke, or coaxial choke has previously been shown. Fig.9 shows a small 1:1 RF transformer which will pass only the wanted antiphase signal currents on the inner. The resistor is for static discharge.

70. A high pass filter. The higher frequencies are passed by the low Z capacitors. The lower frequencies are blocked by the capacitors and pass to ground via the inductors.

71. A high pass filter designed for use on UHF TV frequencies will block or attenuate signals below about 470MHz and pass all signals above this frequency.

72. All filters possess some attenuation in their passband, usually this is small, about 1 to 2dB.

73. The filter shown is a bandpass filter. The top arms are acceptor circuits tuned to pass the required frequency band and offer high Z to frequencies outside the band. The parallel circuit has a high Z at the resonant frequency and shunts frequencies outside resonance.

74. The impedance of equipment, feeders, antennas and filters must match in order to obtain maximum power transfer. Although other impedances are used, 50Ω is typical for most amateur radio transmission systems.

75. The impedance of equipment, feeders, antennas and filters must match in order to obtain maximum power transfer. 75Ω is used for domestic TV.

76. The FM carrier has constant amplitude and is unlikely to cause breakthrough type interference. CW, AM, and SSB transmissions incur rapid changes in RF level, these changes, and subsequent rectification in the victim receiver, are usually the cause of breakthrough.

77. Owners of receivers should take steps to ensure that their equipment has a reasonable standard of immunity and is installed and tuned correctly.

78. In difficult cases of EMC, it may be necessary for the amateur to modify his operating practice. This may mean using lower power, not beaming the antenna into the affected receive antenna, avoiding the use of a particular frequency, or in some cases, restricting operating times until the problem can be solved. There is no set answer to EMC cures, each case must be treated on its merits.

    Neighbours must be handled with care. The amateur should be aware that to carry out modifications on neighbours equipment might result in a claim for damages at a later date.

    If it is demonstrated that a filter will cure a neighbours reception problems it may be in the amateurs interests to pay for the filter.

    When there is no amicable or practical solution to TVI and EMC problems, advice may be sought from the Radio Agency or the RSGB EMC committee.

18. Operating Practices and Procedures

This Section will deal with aspects of :-
1. the calling procedures used for telegraphy and telephony.
2. the use of Q codes, phonetic alphabet and signal reports.
3. maintaining a station Log, amateur repeaters, and safety precautions.

Good operating practices and procedures are essential to the efficient use of the allocated frequency bands, and will result in minimum interference to other services. Using well established, and internationally accepted practices and procedures, operators of different countries are able to communicate with a minimum of misunderstanding.

The Q code is an internationally agreed series of questions and answers. Q code abbreviations sent as a question are followed by question mark.

Although primarily intended for morse telegraphy, where its use cuts across the language barrier and speeds operation, it is common practice to use it in a more informal form in telephony.

A list of the more common Q codes and their abbreviated/informal meaning

QRA	Address.	QRT	Closing down.
QRK	Readability/Signal strength.	QRZ	Who is calling me.
QRM	Interference from other stations.	QRX	Wait/Stand by.
QRN	Interference due to static.	QSB	Signals fading.
QRO	High power/Increase power.	QSL	Confirmation of contact.
QRP	Low power/Reduce power.	QSO	Radio contact.
QRQ	Send faster.	QSY	Change frequency.
QRS	Send more slowly.	QTH	Location.

The Recommended Phonetic Alphabet

A	Alpha	H	Hotel	O	Oscar	V	Victor
B	Bravo	I	India	P	Papa	W	Whiskey
C	Charlie	J	Juliet	Q	Quebec	X	Xray
D	Delta	K	Kilo	R	Romeo	Y	Yankee
E	Echo	L	Lima	S	Sierra	Z	Zulu
F	Foxtrot	M	Mike	T	Tango		
G	Golf	N	November	U	Uniform		

Signal Reports. The RST Code
Signal reports are based on the RST code (Readability - Signal Strength - Tone).
Tone T is applicable to telegraphy reports and not telephony.
Readability is on a scale of R1 to R5. 1 being unreadable and 5 being perfect.
Signal Strength is on a scale S1 to S9. 1 being just perceptible and 9 being very strong.
Tone is on a scale T1 to T9. 1 being extremely bad and distorted, 9 being a pure tone.

Operating Practices and Procedures

The CQ Call (CW and Telephony)
The CQ call is a general call inviting any station to reply. Before making any CQ call the operator should listen on the frequency to ensure that there is no operation (QSO) in progress, if there is, either change frequency (QSY) or wait until the frequency is clear. It is bad practice to call over the top of an established QSO.

Establishing a CW (morse telegraphy) A1A Contact
The following example is of a station, callsign G0OAT, making a general CQ call and inviting any station to reply -

CQ CQ CQ de G0OAT G0OAT G0OAT K.

Replies from any station are invited by including the final K. The CQ call should be sent at a speed no greater than the operator is prepared to receive. "de" means "from." A call may be directed to a specific country. The following is an example of a CQ call inviting only New Zealand stations to reply -

CQ ZL CQ ZL CQ ZL de G0OAT G0OAT G0OAT K.

The CQ call below is directed to a specific station only (no others to reply) by sending $\overline{KN}$ at the end. (The bar or line over $\overline{KN}$ indicates the characters are sent as one.)

G6SXV G6SXV G6SXV de G0OAT G0OAT G0OAT $\overline{KN}$.

Operating under poor signal conditions difficulty may be experienced in identifying the station answering a call, in this case send QRZ? (Who is calling me?) -

QRZ? QRZ? de G0OAT G0OAT G0OAT $\overline{KN}$.

Establishing a Telephony (voice) A3E, J3E or F3E Contact
As previously described, listen for a clear frequency, or if using a band with a dedicated calling frequency use that. Always use a clear voice, and when conditions are poor make use of the phonetic alphabet if necessary. Q codes are often used in speech, and have the same meanings as when used in telegraphy. Q codes are particularly useful when there are language problems.
The following examples are typical voice telephony general calls -

"CQ CQ CQ this is G0OAT calling and standing by."

Alternatively, and using the phonetic alphabet - "CQ CQ CQ this is Golf Zero Oscar Alpha Tango, Golf Zero Oscar Alpha Tango calling CQ and standing by."

If there is no reply, the call can be repeated at short intervals, avoid repeating the CQ call too many times in a short period. Directed calls can also be made using telephony.

The Station Log
The Station Log contains a permanent record of all transmission from the Main Station Address and all Temporary Locations. No Log need be kept in respect of Mobile or Maritime Mobile operations. The Log must be retained for inspection for a period of

at least six months from the date of the last entry. This also applies to a Log maintained on magnetic tape, disc or other electronic storage medium. When the Log is maintained in a book, it must not be loose leaf and there must be no gaps left between entries.

DATE	TIME UTC Start | End	FREQ MHz	MODE	POWER (Watts)	STATION Worked/Called	REPORT Sent | Rcvd	QSL Sent | Rcvd	COMMENTS
←		THIS DATA MUST BE RECORDED	→		←	RECORDING THIS DATA IS OPTIONAL →		

Fig.1 A typical station log.

Repeaters

Amateur repeaters are located on sites advantageous to good radio coverage. They enable the radio range of mobile and portable equipment in poor coverage areas to be extended. Repeaters are normally accessed by a 0.5s (500ms) burst of 1750Hz audio tone. Repeaters operate on two frequencies - the input frequency - and the output frequency. The input and output frequency separation for 2 metre repeaters is 600kHz and the separation for 70 cm repeaters is 1.6MHz.

Satellites

Whereas repeaters retransmit their input signal on another frequency in the same band, satellites typically retransmit a received band of frequencies into another band, they are transponders. E.g. 144 to 432MHz, 432 to 144MHz and 144 to 28MHz. Directional antennas capable of movement in both azimuth and elevation are desirable. Satellites do not require an access tone and can normally only be worked when above the horizon.

Safety Precautions

Safety precautions are often mistakenly regarded as common sense, some are, but some basic education is necessary regarding the nature of high voltages and currents, and also RF voltages, currents and radiation levels. Consideration must be given to correct earthing and the consequences of incorrect earthing. *If the reader is uncertain of any aspect of safety, advice should be sought from a competent person.* Some recommended precautions are: Never work on live equipment. Have all equipment controlled by one master switch in the radio station, which is clearly identifiable and known to others. Regard all voltages as potentially hazardous. Ensure that bleeder resistors are fitted across PSU capacitors where necessary. Use fuses of the correct rating.

Do not disregard non-electrical safety aspects, such as sharp metal corners on home constructed equipment. Safe erection of antennas. Tie ladders top and bottom before working from them. When driving do not use a hand microphone, and have the equipment and antenna correctly installed. Do not operate at filling stations or when refuelling. Do not operate near quarries where electrically detonated charges are in use.

Operating Practices and Procedures

1. **Before calling CQ on any frequency it is advisable to-**
   a) tune the transmitter to the antenna without the use of a dummy load.
   b) key-up the carrier for three minutes to the clear the channel.
   c) ensure that all other signals on that frequency are below S9.
   d) listen on the proposed operating frequency first.

2. **A station - G8CCJ - when making a general call (CQ) using CW telegraphy, and inviting any station to reply, should first listen the frequency, and then-**
   a) hold the key down for a period of three minutes to clear the frequency.
   b) set up an automatic call sender and leave it sending CQ for at least five minutes before announcing the call-sign.
   c) send CQ CQ CQ K K K G8CCJ CQ K CQ K.
   d) send CQ CQ CQ DE G8CCJ G8CCJ G8CCJ K.

3. **A station making a general call sends -**
   CQ CQ CQ DE G8CCJ G8CCJ G8CCJ K. Why is the 'K' sent?
   a) It invites Kentish stations only to reply.
   b) It invites any station to reply.
   c) It informs receiving stations that the message has been sent correctly.
   d) It announces that there is another CQ to follow.

4. **When sending messages by Morse telegraphy, the procedure signal for wait is A̅S̅. What does the line above the A and the S mean?**
   a) That you have just sent AS correctly.
   b) That the message is for American Stations only.
   c) That the message is for Amateur Stations only.
   d) That the individual letters are sent as one, with no space between them.

5. **When sending messages by Morse telegraphy it is inadvisable to-**
   a) talk when you are keying.
   b) send perfect Morse, this will tend to confuse Morse reading software.
   c) use a suppressed Morse key.
   d) send at a speed greater than you are able to receive.

6. **When attempting to establish a long distance (Dx) telephony contact on the HF bands it would be considered good procedure to-**
   a) repeat CQ Dx for five minutes followed by your call-sign.
   b) give your call-sign first then call CQ Dx for five minutes.
   c) call 'CQ Dog Xray' for 10 seconds, and repeat until somebody replies.
   d) call CQ Dx three or four times followed by your call-sign and listen for a reply; repeat if necessary.

7. **What is the Q code?**
   a) A series of internationally agreed abbreviations that speed telegraphy operation.
   b) A series of mandatory (RSGB agreed) operational status reports.
   c) An easy to remember series of UK/European operational status codes.
   d) An internationally agreed code which ensures great secrecy and speed of use.

8. **The international Q code for static interference and interference caused by electrical machines is-**
   a) QRM   b) QRN   c) QSO   d) QSL

9. **The international Q code for the interference caused by an adjacent radio transmission is-**
   a) QRM   b) QRN   c) QSO   d) QRT

10. **You have just received a report of severe QSB from a station you are in contact with; what does it mean?**
    a) That the distant station is receiving static interference.
    b) That the distant station is reducing his power.
    c) That your signals are suffering severe fading.
    d) That the neighbours have just requested the distant station to close down due to severe television interference.

11. **The international Q code for reducing power is-**
    a) QRN   b) QRT   c) QRP   d) QSY

12. **If you requested a distant station operator to QRO, he would-**
    a) change frequency.
    b) reply with the time.
    c) close down.
    d) increase power.

13. **The Q code QTH refers to-**
    a) sending tone.
    b) sending speed.
    c) location.
    d) height of antenna.

14. **On receipt of Q code QSA you-**
    a) report on the weather.
    b) report received signal strength.
    c) change to an alternate frequency.
    d) check your antenna.

15. A station sends QRT, his intentions are to-
   a) check the time.
   b) seek a temperature report.
   c) close down.
   d) change transmitting frequency.

16. A station sending QRP? is asking if he can-
   a) decrease power.   b) increase power.
   c) stop sending.   d) send faster.

17. The Q code for a radio contact is-
   a) QSO   b) QSC
   c) QRC   d) QRK

18. If you are in contact with a station that is sending morse code faster than you are able to read it, you should-
   a) send the code QSLOW QSLOW QSLOW
   b) reduce your BFO frequency to slow down the received transmission rate.
   c) plug in the microphone and tell him to slow down.
   d) send the Q code QRS.

19. An RST report gives the receiving station's assessment on-
   a) Readability, Strength and Carrier wave frequency.
   b) Reception, Standing Waves and Time.
   c) Readability, Signal strength and Time.
   d) Readability, Signal strength and Tone.

20. You receive a report that your telephony transmission is 5 and 9. What does that imply to you?
   a) That your signal is strength 5, and your readability is graded 9.
   b) That your readability is graded 5 on a quality scale 1 - 5, and your signal strength is graded 9 on a signal strength scale 1 - 9.
   c) That your signals are very low and unreadable.
   d) That the QSB is strength 5, and the QRM is strength 9.

21. When using telephony on any frequency band, and conditions are poor, it may be necessary to-
   a) reduce transmitter power.
   b) insert an attenuator in the receiver antenna to reduce the noise levels.
   c) spell words using the phonetic alphabet.
   d) check that the 'low pass filter' is fitted.

22. The recommended 'phonetic' spelling for the word 'STAR' is-
a) Sierra Tango Alpha Roger
b) Sierra Texas Alpha Romeo.
c) Sugar Tango Alpha Romeo.
d) Sierra Tango Alpha Romeo.

23. In order that a reasonable degree of harmony is experienced by all amateurs operating on the amateur bands, it is advisable to-
a) stick rigidly to one's rights.
b) observe the recommended band plan for the band on which you intend to operate.
c) demand that any high power stations operating in your neighbourhood close down while you are receiving weak signals.
d) ensure, if possible, that all your A.M. transmissions are overmodulated, and that all of your F.M. transmissions are overdeviated.

24. To use an amateur repeater, one first has to-
a) access it by the prescribed method for that particular repeater, normally a 1750Hz tone burst, or a carrier wave.
b) be a member of the RSGB.
c) obtain an additional licence from the regulatory authority.
d) access it by sending GA in Morse code using a 2.8MHz tone.

25. The advantage of using a repeater is that-
a) secrecy is maintained between the participants of the QSO.
b) general broadcasts to all amateurs, from any amateur and from any other source may be made.
c) once accessed, the superior coverage of the repeater is extended to the accessing station.
d) it may be used for passing business messages over wide areas.

26. The input and output frequencies of a 2 metre repeater are spaced by-
a) 17.50Hz.
b) 600kHz.
c) 1.6MHz.
d) 21MHz.

27. The input and output frequencies of a 70 cm. repeater are spaced by-
a) 17.50Hz.
b) 1750Hz.
c) 1.6MHz.
d) 2.8MHz.

28. Safety at the amateur station is the responsibility of the-
a) Amateur himself.
b) R.S.G.B.
c) Radio Regulatory Authority.
d) Local Electricity Authority.

29. Safety inspections of amateur radio stations-
a) are the responsibility of the amateur.
b) are carried out at regular intervals by the Radio Regulatory Authority.
c) take the form of a six-monthly questionnaire which has to be returned to the R.S.G.B. on completion.
d) are carried out by the local electricity authority at regular twelve monthly intervals from the date of issue of the licence.

30. In locations to which people have access, the power flux density on transmit must not exceed the currently recommended limit of-
a) $1000mW/cm^2$ b) $100mW/cm^3$
c) $10mW/cm^2$ d) $1mW/cm^2$

31. It is advisable that the mains power entering the amateur radio station is controlled by-
a) one two pole switch for each item of equipment.
b) one 30 Amp fuse that can be easily blown by throwing a shorting switch.
c) a separate toggle switch on each piece of equipment.
d) one master switch, clearly marked to be easily identified, which can isolate the power to the radio station.

32. If you walk into a radio station and find a person unconscious on the floor, and apparently in contact with live mains equipment, you should-
a) grab hold of him and lay him on a rubber mat so that he is insulated from the ground.
b) stand yourself on a rubber mat to insulate yourself, and gently pull him away from the live equipment before you begin resuscitation.
c) check his pulse, then switch off the mains power at the master switch.
d) first turn off the mains at the master switch, and then apply the appropriate first-aid action that you have been trained for.

33. All radio station wiring should be-
a) cotton insulated with a current carrying capacity of at least 1 amp.
b) enclosed in an RF screen.
c) adequately insulated and have sufficient current carrying capacity.
d) of the coaxial type.

34. It is recommended that all radio and test equipment is correctly-
a) fireproofed.   b) waterproofed.
c) pressurised.   d) earthed.

35. Before repairing any item of mains powered equipment-
a) it should first be stood on a rubber mat.
b) you should first stand on a rubber mat.
c) it should first be disconnected from the mains supply.
d) set the lowest voltage possible on the mains input adjustment panel.

36. When working on, or handling radio equipment that has been switched off or disconnected, it is possible to receive a severe electric shock from the-
a) valve heaters.
b) charged field around the P.A. coil.
c) charged field around the transistors.
d) charged capacitors, particularly those in the PSU.

37. What is often done to ensure that PSU capacitors discharge when the equipment is switched off?
a) They are short-circuited with a large toggle switch.
b) A lower value capacitor is switched in series with them.
c) A 'bleed resistor' is fitted in parallel with them.
d) A 'bleed resistor' is fitted in series with them.

38. When low-leakage capacitors are stored, you should-
a) pack them in a dry cardboard box.
b) wrap their terminals with insulating tape.
c) store them in a damp atmosphere.
d) short circuit their terminals.

39. In order to indicate that your equipment is live, you should-
a) fit a power output meter.
b) make sure that it has suitable indicator lamps fitted.
c) mount a thermometer on the transformer.
d) fit a transformer with noisy laminations.

40. If your transmitter fuse keeps blowing, and it is of the recommended value, you should-
a) disconnect the transmitter from the mains and check for a fault.
b) increase the rating of the fuse until you find one that does not blow.
c) replace the fuse with a nail, and allow the fault to burn itself out.
d) reduce the rating of the fuse, it may be rated too high for the application.

41. Before you change the fuse on a piece of equipment, you should-
- a) first tune to the lowest possible frequency.
- b) switch off and disconnect the equipment from the mains.
- c) disconnect the antenna.
- d) short circuit the mains supply.

42. When constructing equipment which uses high voltages, it is good practice to-
- a) use low voltage fuses.
- b) use thermal delay fuses.
- c) fit micro switches, so that when any cover exposing a high voltage is removed, the power supply is disconnected.
- d) design a built-in SWR meter.

43. The recommended mains switches for amateur equipment are-
- a) double pole types.
- b) single pole types.
- c) insulated gate types.
- d) screened dipole types.

44. Antennas should not be-
- a) higher than 50 feet above sea level.
- b) lower than 20 feet below sea level.
- c) fed with more than 100 Watts (20dBW) of RF power.
- d) allowed to come into contact with mains or d.c. voltages.

45. When transmitter h.t. voltages are decoupled from the feeder and antenna by the use of capacitors-
- a) a fuse must be fitted in the feeder.
- b) a neon light must be fitted at the tip of the antenna.
- c) a d.c. path to earth must be provided on the antenna side of the capacitor, usually by means of an RF choke.
- d) the tip of the antenna should be grounded to RF currents by using diodes.

46. Fuses should be fitted in the 12V supply from a car battery as close to the battery as possible, because a fault developing on the supply lead might-
- a) electrocute all the occupants in one go.
- b) jam aircraft beacons if you drive within half a mile of an airport.
- c) set the car on fire. (Always have a fire extinguisher on board).
- d) cause premature electrolytic corrosion, especially on imported models.

47. You must not transmit near quarries where-
- a) heavy lorries are crossing.
- b) the earth moving vehicles are radio controlled.
- c) quartz is being quarried.
- d) electrically detonated charges are being used.

48. When making adjustments on live equipment you should never-
- a) wear headphones or use both hands on the equipment.
- b) wear rubber boots and nylon socks because of the static.
- c) drink high conductivity liquids, such as lager.
- d) leave it connected to a radio frequency power meter.

49. For the measurement of high voltage circuits, you are warned not to use-
- a) electronic voltmeters.
- b) spark-gap voltmeters.
- c) meters with metal zero adjusting screws.
- d) voltmeters with a high Ω/V rating.

50. Equipment installed in a car should be in such a position that in the event of an accident it-
- a) does not injure the occupants of the car.
- b) can be removed easily to prevent further damage.
- c) can still be operated to call an ambulance.
- d) blows all its fuses.

51. When the operator is driving, he should not use a-
- a) loudspeaker other than the one in the transceiver.
- b) screened microphone cable.
- c) hand microphone.
- d) cassette player at the same time as the transceiver.

52. You should not operate your mobile radio transmitting equipment when-
- a) refuelling at a petrol station or near fuel tanks.
- b) on mountain roads in case your vehicle overturns and the radio causes a fire.
- c) you spot a radar speed trap, it might prevent you from being booked.
- d) you are close to a fire station.

53. A piece of radio equipment is rated 250 watts at 250 volts. Which fuse from the list below will you use?
- a) 500mA
- b) 750mA
- c) 2A
- d) 13A

54. One often overlooked cause of danger is-
a) worn rubber feet on old equipment.
b) grey paint used on ex-services equipment.
c) control knobs with metal retaining screws on live metal spindles.
d) the light emission from LED displays.

55. Metal cases of morse keys and microphones etc: should be-
a) grounded via low inductance RF chokes.
b) properly connected to the chassis or case of the equipment with which they are associated.
c) insulated with a plastic coating.
d) left unearthed.

56. You are about to fit a new antenna to the side of your house and you will be working from a ladder; your first duty will be to-
a) assemble the antenna on the ground.
b) ensure that the cable fixings will not cut the coax.
c) tie the ladder at the top and bottom before working from it.
d) check the insulation resistance of the ladder and the VSWR of the antenna.

57. Because of its high thermal conductivity, high resistivity and low dielectric loss, Beryllium oxide is sometimes used in the construction of power transistors, heat sinks and dummy loads. These devices should not be-
a) used in a low temperature environment.
b) used at frequencies above 200MHz.
c) broken, filed or ground to produce dust.
d) purchased without a special licence.

58. Damaged or broken devices which are known to contain Beryllia should be-
a) sealed in polythene bags and disposed of in accordance with the equipment or device manufacturers instructions.
b) saved until you have a reasonable quantity, and sent, by recorded delivery, to the local Environmental Health Officer of your district.
c) neutralised in hot salt water and buried locally.
d) neutralised in a strong RF field and sealed in plastic bags before disposal.

Answers-Operating Practices and Procedures

1	d	11	c	21	c	31	d	41	b	51	c
2	d	12	d	22	d	32	d	42	c	52	a
3	b	13	c	23	b	33	c	43	a	53	c
4	d	14	b	24	a	34	d	44	d	54	c
5	d	15	c	25	c	35	c	45	c	55	b
6	d	16	a	26	b	36	d	46	c	56	c
7	a	17	a	27	c	37	c	47	d	57	c
8	b	18	d	28	a	38	d	48	a	58	a
9	a	19	d	29	a	39	b	49	c		
10	c	20	b	30	c	40	a	50	a		

1. Listening on the frequency before you use it will determine if that frequency is in use and enable you to avoid causing interference to other stations. In the case of the HF bands it will determine if the bands are open.

2. A typical CW general call - CQ CQ CQ DE G8CCJ G8CCJ G8CCJ K

3. The K invites any station to reply. If $\overline{KN}$ is sent, only specific stations should reply.

4. The line, or bar above the letters means that they are to be sent as one. The letters AS sent separately, with a space between letters is ● —   ● ● ●, and sent as one, $\overline{AS}$ becomes ● — ● ● ● .

5. Do not send at a speed greater than you are able to receive, because the distant station is likely to reply at your sending speed.

6. Call - CQ DX CQ DX CQ DX this is G0OAT G0OAT calling and standing by. If no reply repeat the call a few times. The call can be directed to a particular country, Australia for instance, by calling - CQ VK CQ VK CQ VK from G0OAT Golf Zero Oscar Alpha Tango calling and standing by. The callsign can be repeated in phonetics for clarification.

7. A series of internationally agreed abbreviations to speed telegraphy operation.

8. QRN. Interference caused by static, atmospherics, and local electrical apparatus.

9. QRM. Refers to interference caused by other radio transmissions.

10. QSB. Are my signals fading? Your signals are fading.

11. QRP. Shall I decrease transmitter power? Decrease transmitter power.

12. QRO. Shall I increase transmitter power? Increase transmitter power.

13. QTH. What is your location? My location is . . . . .

14. QSA. What is the strength of my signals? The strength of your signals is . . . . .

15. QRT. Shall I stop sending? Stop sending .

16. QRP? Shall I decrease power?

17. QSO. Refers to a radio contact.

18. QRS. Shall I send more slowly? Send more slowly . . . (words per minute).

19. RST. Readability, Signal strength and Tone.

20. Only Readability and Signal strength is included in a telephony report. A report of R5 indicates that the readability is perfect - on a scale of 1 to 5, and the S9 signal is extremely strong, on a scale of 1 to 9.

21. When transmission conditions are poor, use should be made of the phonetic alphabet, this will reduce misunderstanding and improve clarity.

22. Sierra Tango Alpha Romeo.

23. Observing the appropriate band plan for the band in use will ensure that operation can take place with a minimum of annoyance to other users.

24. A repeater must first be accessed before a QSO can take place. Normally access is by transmitting a 1750Hz tone for a period of about 500ms.

25. The topographical coverage area of a repeater is very large due its location. When accessed by a mobile; for instance; the mobile's coverage, - via the repeater - will be the same as the repeater.

26. Input and output frequencies are spaced by 600kHz for a 2 metre repeater.

27. Input and output frequencies are spaced by 1.6MHz for a 70 cm. repeater.

28. Safety at the amateur radio station is the responsibility of the amateur himself.

29. Safety inspections at the amateur radio station are the responsibility of the amateur himself.

30. At the time of writing, an exposure limit of $10mW/cm^2$ should not be exceeded.

31. For safety purposes it is recommended that the power (a.c. mains) entering the radio shack should be controlled by one readily identifiable master switch. The position and purpose of the switch should be known to others using the house or club.

32. First turn-off the power, or you may become a victim yourself.

33. All wiring must have sufficient current-carrying capacity or it may overheat, burn-out, or worse, cause a fire. Always have a suitable fire extinguisher available.

34. All radio equipment should be correctly earthed. If in doubt about the method that should be used seek competent advice.

35. Switch-off all electrical equipment before working on it. If this is not possible, once again seek professional advice or refer to the manufacturers handbook.

36. Capacitors are able to retain a charge for several minutes, hours, days, or maybe weeks after the power has been removed from them.

37. Power supply capacitors should have bleed resistors fitted in parallel with them. This ensures that they are rapidly discharged after the supply has been removed.

38. Shorting the terminals of low-leakage capacitors, particularly paper and oil-filled types, will prevent them acquiring a static charge when stored.

39. Suitable indicator lamps will indicate the presence of mains supply voltage and also low voltage supply to equipment.

40. First disconnected the equipment from the mains, and/or other power supply, and investigate the cause of the fault.

41. Switch off and disconnect equipment from the mains before changing a fuse, as it is sometimes possible, usually with old style fuse holders, for the operator to come into contact with the supply if the fuse has not failed.

42. When the removal of equipment covers is likely to expose high voltage circuitry, micro switches should be fitted to break the power supply when the covers are removed for servicing.

43. In most cases it is desirable to fit double-pole mains switches to equipment so that both live and neutral are switched.

44. Antennas should be erected clear of power supply cables and other voltage sources.

45. A breakdown in the insulation/dielectric of the decoupling capacitor may, depending on the circuit, place a high d.c. potential at the antenna terminal. Fitting a radio frequency choke across the antenna side of the capacitor will ground this voltage and most likely blow the HT fuse.

46. In the event of a short-circuit or grounding along their length, the leads from a battery can become so hot that they melt and cause nearby materials to catch fire. Wiring should be safely routed, correctly fused, and have adequate current-carrying capacity for the equipment that it is required to supply. Always carry a suitable fire extinguisher in the car.

47. Operation should not take place near quarries where electrical detonation of explosives is employed.

48. When it is necessary to work on live equipment, i.e. for final tuning purposes etc. only the safe procedure and adjustments recommended by the manufacturer in that equipment's service manual should be carried out. Only the recommended insulated tools should be used, and hands and other parts of the body should be kept clear of all metalwork. Earphones should not be worn.

49. Some, particularly the older analogue instruments (including moving coil meters) may have a metal zero adjusting screw. In operation it is likely that this screw is at the same potential as the circuit being measured.

50. Equipment installed in a car should be firmly secured, so that in the event of an accident it does not fly around the car injuring the occupants. Leads should not be left trailing, these may cause passengers to trip when alighting.

51. A person driving a vehicle should not use a hand microphone, various hands-free units are available.

52. Due to the high concentration of petrol vapour, and the risk of sparking, particularly from poorly connected antennas and power feeds, you should switch off all transmitting equipment when refuelling.

53. $I = \dfrac{W}{V} = \dfrac{250}{250} = 1A$. A fuse rated at 1 amp continuous would be o.k. but on the limit. From those listed, the 2 amp fuse should be used.

54. It is advisable to check that metal control spindles, and control knobs with metal retaining screws are not 'live'. This is likely to be a particular problem associated with older, or home constructed equipment.

55. It is recommended that the metal cases, when fitted, of morse keys and microphones etc. should be connected to an appropriate earth/chassis point of the equipment to which they are associated. However, since safety is involved, always consult the manufacturer or dealer if in any way unsure. Danger! Some equipment, particularly domestic radio and TV equipment may have a live chassis. Do not attempt to connect to this.

56. Ladders should be tied top and bottom before working from them. Do not lean out to reach the work, reposition the ladder if necessary. Use a safety helmet and eyeshields when carrying out antenna work.

57. Beryllium oxide combines high thermal conductivity with high electrical resistivity. Because of these properties it is used in ceramic form in some special valves, power transistors and heat sinks. Do not attempt to dismantle, file or grind devices containing beryllium oxide. The devices are normally (but not always) marked with a warning. Refer to device manufacturer for advice.

58. All potentially hazardous materials should be handled and disposed of in accordance with the manufacturers instructions.

19. Licensing Conditions

It is essential that every student preparing for the Radio Amateurs' Examination obtains and studies, in conjunction with this section a current copy of 'How to Become a Radio Amateur' and 'Amateur Radio Licence (A) or (B) Terms, Provisions and Limitations Booklet BR68.' (Obtainable free of charge from the Radio Amateur Licensing Unit.)

However; the student should be aware that licensing conditions are liable to change from time to time. It is not therefore possible to ensure (neither should the student assume) that all the questions and answers given in this section will be correct or valid at the time they are read. Every effort will be made to ensure that future editions are updated as necessary.

When working through this section in conjunction with 'How to become a Radio Amateur' and 'BR68' the student will spot for himself any changes that have occurred and be able to make the necessary corrections as required. Course instructors will be covering licensing conditions and advise accordingly.

This section is aimed at making the student thoroughly read and search through the above mentioned booklets to find the answers.

Please note. There are no written answers to this chapter.

1. **Who runs the Radio Amateurs Examination?**
   a) The City and Guilds of London Institute on behalf of the UK licensing administration.
   b) The Radio Society of Great Britain (RSGB).
   c) The City and Guilds of London Institute on behalf of the RSGB.
   d) The Radio Investigation Service of the DTI.

2. **All U.K. amateur radio licences require a pass in-**
   a) the City and Guilds Radio Amateurs Examination.
   b) the morse test.
   c) GCSE Maths and English as a pre-course requirement.
   d) the novice 'A' licence.

3. **Amateur Radio Licence 'A' requires a pass in-**
   a) the C & G RAE only.
   b) the morse test only.
   c) both the RAE and the morse test.
   d) GCSE Maths and English, the C & G RAE and the morse test.

4. **The holder of an Amateur licence 'B' must have passed-**
   a) the C & G RAE.
   b) the morse test.
   c) both the RAE and the morse test.
   d) the DTI novice 'B' examination.

5. You have not previously passed the Novice RAE. Therefore, to apply for a full radio amateur licence you must have reached the age of-
   a) 10   b) 12   c) 14   d) 16

6. Who sets the amateur morse test?
   a) The RSGB.   b) The DTI.
   c) The Post Office Radio Division.   d) British Telecom.

7. A pass in the amateur morse test is valid for-
   a) 2 years.   b) 3 years.   c) 12 months.   d) life.

8. If situated within 1km of the boundary of an aerodrome, what is the maximum permitted height for an antenna or any mast or structure supporting it?
   a) 5m   b) 15m   c) 25m   d) 50m

9. You live within 1km of the boundary of an aerodrome and intend to use a vertical antenna which has a height when assembled of 3m. What is the maximum height of the supporting structure on which it may be erected?
   a) 18m   b) 15m   c) 12m   d) 9m

10. You receive a demand by a person authorised by the Secretary of State to close down or restrict operation of your radio station, you must comply-
    a) Immediately.   b) Within 24 hours.
    c) Within 7 days.   d) Within 28 days.

11. When a station is closed down on the demand of an authorised officer, it will be confirmed in writing-
    a) as soon as practicable   b) within 7 days.
    c) within 14 days.   d) within 28 days.

12. Upon revocation of the amateur licence-
    a) it must be destroyed immediately.
    b) it must be retained in a safe place.
    c) the validation document must be surrendered to the Secretary of State.
    d) it must be deposited at the nearest public library.

13. When must the licence renewal fee be paid?
    a) Within 14 days of receiving the renewal notice.
    b) Within 28 days of receiving the renewal notice.
    c) Within 30 days of receiving the renewal notice.
    d) Before the anniversary date of the Date of Issue in each year.

14. For a full licence, the morse test is conducted at a speed of-
    a) 8 wpm   b) 10 wpm   c) 12 wpm   d) 20 wpm

Licensing Conditions

15. On renewal of the licence, the licensee will be issued a-
a) certificate of competence.
b) complementary certificate signed by the Secretary of State.
c) copy of the International Radio Regulations.
d) document, referred to as the 'Validation Document'.

16. The Amateur Radio Licence A or B may be revoked or have its terms, provisions or limitations varied by publication of a general notice in-
a) the London, Edinburgh and Belfast Gazettes.
b) every town hall window.
c) the Radio Times.
d) the Sun newspaper on page 3.

17. Apart from notices published in the various Gazettes, how else might information regarding changes to the licence be brought to notice?
a) By the Independent Radio Authority.
b) By amateur repeater broadcasts at 10am on Sunday mornings.
c) Broadcast nationally by the BBC.
d) By a conference call from British Telecom.

18. The abbreviation 'CEPT' means-
a) Central England Portable Telecommunicators Conference.
b) Central European Parliamentary Telecommunications Conference.
c) European Conference of Postal and Telecommunications Administrations.
d) Conference of English Private Telecommunicators.

19. Which one of the following statements is incorrect?
a) The licence is not transferable.
b) The initial licence fee covers 3 years operation.
c) No log is required for /M or /MM operation.
d) Coordinated Universal Time may be regarded as GMT.

20. An amateur licence does not absolve the licensee from obtaining any necessary permission before entering on, or operating from private or public property; including-
a) a public transport vehicle.
b) the motorways on the U.K. mainland.
c) A class roads in the U.K. and the Channel Isles
d) private motor vehicles owned by the licensee himself.

21. Using the recommended phonetic alphabet spell the word RADIO.
a) Roger Alpha Delta India Ontario
b) Radio Able Dog Item Oscar
c) Rome Alpha Delta India Ontario
d) Romeo Alpha Delta India Oscar

Licensing Conditions

22. The holder of an Amateur Radio Licence B may only operate on frequency bands above -
    a) 21MHz   b) 30MHz   c) 144MHz   d) 432MHz

23. Which one of the first symbols/letters used to designate classes of emission indicates that the main carrier is frequency modulated?
    a) A   b) B   c) F   d) G

24. Which one of the first symbols/letters used to designate classes of emission indicates that the main carrier is amplitude-modulated double sideband?
    a) A   b) B   c) F   d) C

25. The second symbol of an emission code describes the nature of the signal(s) modulating the main carrier. Which symbol indicates that the modulating signal consists a single channel containing analogue information?
    a) A   b) 1   c) 2   d) 3

26. The third symbol of an emission code describes the type of information to be transmitted. Which letter describes a telephony transmission?
    a) A   b) E   c) 1   d) 7

27. What is the emission class code for hand sent, on/off keying of the carrier, i.e. morse telegraphy?
    a) A3E   b) J3E   c) F2A   d) A1A

28. What is the emission class code for amplitude modulated telephony?
    a) A3E   b) J3E   c) F3E   d) A1A

29. What is the emission class code for frequency modulated telephony?
    a) A3E   b) J3E   c) F3E   d) F2A

30. When operating a single sideband suppressed carrier telephony transmitter on 145MHz, what class of emission do you enter in your station log?
    a) A3E   b) J3E   c) S3E   d) A1A

31. The licensee of an amateur station shall use the station for the purpose of-
    a) self-training in communication by wireless telegraphy.
    b) re-transmitting general emergency and distress messages.
    c) participating in the National Radio Relay Service.
    d) monitoring codes and cyphers, and reporting on soviet spy activity.

32. The licensee may use or permit the use of the station during any operation conducted by a-
    a) User Service.   b) political broadcasting service.
    c) religious organisation.   d) commercial advertising agency.

33. **The Licensee may record and retransmit messages addressed to the Licensee from-**
    a) commercial television stations.
    b) commercial radio stations.
    c) unknown sources.
    d) other licensed amateurs with whom the licensee is in direct communication; or which are intended for retransmission to a specified licensed amateur.

34. **When retransmitting recorded messages from your main station address, whose call sign must you use?**
    a) Yours.
    b) That of the original sender.
    c) Both.
    d) None required, only a postcode is necessary for location identification.

35. **When operating your equipment from a temporary location, what suffix must you use with your call sign?**
    a) /A   b) /P   c) /M   d) /T

36. **When mobile, what suffix should be used?**
    a) /A   b) /P   c) /M   d) /V

37. **When operating from the main station address what suffix should be used?**
    a) /MA   b) /M   c) /QTH   d) None

38. **What suffix should accompany the call sign when operating from a vessel on tidal waters?**
    a) /T   b) /MM   c) /M   d) None

39. **What suffix should be added to the callsign when operating from a vessel on any inland waterway?**
    a) /M   b) /MM   c) /A   d) None

40. **When operating as a pedestrian the licensee shall use the suffix -**
    a) /A   b) /T   c) /M   d) /P

41. **What suffix should be used when travelling as a passenger in an aircraft?**
    a) /M   b) /A
    c) /P   d) None, operation is forbidden.

42. **On a vessel, the licensee shall install, use or make changes to the station-**
    a) only with written permission from the vessels master.
    b) with prior permission of the vessels master.
    c) after agreement with the harbour authorities.
    d) only with written permission from the admiralty.

43. A class B licensee may receive messages from other amateurs on all-
   a) amateur bands.
   b) bands above 30MHz.
   c) bands above 50MHz.
   d) bands above and including 144.0MHz.

44. Where a log is maintained in a book, the book shall -
   a) be kept in duplicate, so that one copy may be sent to the Radio Agency.
   b) be approved by the DTI.
   c) be supplied by the RSGB.
   d) not be loose-leaf.

45. Where a log is maintained in a book -
   a) annual inspection is required by the DTI.
   b) it must be sent to the DTI annually for verification.
   c) no gaps shall be left between entries.
   d) the reverse side of the pages must be left blank.

46. Where a log is maintained on a magnetic disk or tape, the tape or disk shall be used -
   a) only to keep the log.
   b) to maintain full personal details of the person with whom the QSO is held.
   c) to maintain all station operating programs in BASIC.
   d) only to keep the log and store specifications of the stations equipment.

47. The station log should record details of-
   a) all tests for spurious emissions, harmonics and interference.
   b) the names of persons contacted.
   c) the addresses of all stations contacted.
   d) the weather conditions at the far end.

48. When a call is logged, the time should be entered in-
   a) BST   b) DST   c) GMT+1 hour   d) UTC

49. For the purposes of the licence, UTC may be regarded as equivalent to-
   a) BST   b) DST   c) GMT   d) GMT + 1 hour

50. What is the abbreviation UTC?
   a) Coordinated Universal Time.   b) Corrected Universal Time.
   c) Uncorrected Clock Time.   d) Uncoordinated Clock Time.

51. Entries in the station log need not include-
   a) class of emission.   b) power.
   c) initial calls (CQ calls).   d) propagation path.

Licensing Conditions

52. Which entry need not be included in a station log?
a) The received signal strength.
b) The time in UTC.
c) The date.
d) The class of emission.

53. When CQ calls are made, they should-
a) not be entered in the log.
b) be repeated four times every two minutes.
c) be entered in the log.
d) be made within 1kHz of the appropriate band edge.

54. For a period specified by a person authorised by the Secretary of State the licensee may be required to -
a) log other matters.
b) stop keeping a log.
c) maintain specific gaps between entries.
d) record the licensees out-of-band operation.

55. Which item below is not required to be entered in the station log?
a) Dates of transmission.
b) Times of first and last transmission.
c) Content of messages transmitted and received.
d) Power.

56. For how long must the station log be retained following the last entry? At least-
a) 6 months
b) 12 months
c) 2 years
d) 6 years

57. Is it necessary to maintain a log for mobile and maritime mobile operation?
a) No, a log is not needed.
b) Yes, at all times.
c) No, the log is only required for maritime operation.
d) No, the log is only required for mobile operation.

58. Your licence has expired and you have no intention of renewing it. Do you need to retain your station log?
a) No.
b) Yes; for 4 weeks after the last entry.
c) Yes; for at least 3 months after the last entry.
d) Yes; for at least 6 months after the last entry.

59. The licensee shall address messages only to other licensed amateurs or-
a) the stations of licensed amateurs.
b) the stations of licensed amateurs or licensed CB users.
c) stations of the user services.
d) pirate radio stations to advise them of their illegality.

60. The licensee shall send only -
a) standard preprinted script as laid down by the CCIR.
b) generally broadcast signals (100% encyphered, or coded) which form part of, or relate to, the relaying of messages.
c) to any other user, on any band, remarks regarding regulations.
d) messages relating to technical investigations or remarks of a personal character.

61. The licensee shall transmit his callsign-
a) every 5 minutes.
b) every hour, on the hour.
c) at the beginning and end of each period of communication with a licensed amateur, and at the end of each 15 minute interval when the period of communication is longer than 15 minutes.
d) when the station is opened and at 20 minute intervals thereafter until the station closes, whether or not the station is in contact with other stations.

62. Messages and signals include communication by telephony, morse telegraphy, SSTV, FSTV, facsimile and -
a) high speed data and infrared beam modulation.
b) digital communications which include data, RTTY and AMTOR.
c) wideband F3E transmissions below 146MHz.
d) wideband C3F TV transmissions below 144MHz.

63. What messages or signals can an amateur send for general reception by other licensed amateurs?
a) Taped music identified by recording number.
b) Audio test tones.
c) Initial calls (CQ).
d) Recorded QSO's, identified by original callsign and date.

64. The licensee of an amateur station may send messages to groups of licensed amateurs as long as communication is-
a) restricted to 10 minutes in every hour.
b) first established separately with each amateur in the group.
c) first established separately with at least one licensed amateur in any such group.
d) maintained on an established channel, known as the 'net' channel.

65. Do the terms of the amateur licence in any way authorise you to transmit public or political broadcasts?
a) Yes.
b) No.
c) Yes - when authorised by the head of the local political party.
d) Yes - with the approval of the County Emergency Planning Officer.

66. On receiving the callsign GD8CCJ, the station operator could with some reasonable justification, point his antenna towards-
   a) Germany.   b) Wales.
   c) The Isle of Man.   d) Northern Ireland.

67. Which of the following callsign prefixes apply to the U.K. mainland?
   a) GW GM GI   b) GW GM G
   c) GI   GJ GU   d) GD   GU G

68. Which of the following are part of a class 'A' callsign?
   a) G2 G3 G4 G0   b) G1 G2 G3 G6
   c) G1 G3 G7 G8   d) G2 G4 G6 G8

69. Which of the following are part of a class 'B' callsign?
   a) G2 G3 G4 G0   b) G1 G2 G3 G6
   c) G1 G3 G7 G8   d) G1 G6 G7 G8

70. A licensee lives in Scotland, the first two letters of his callsign are-
   a) GH   b) GJ   c) GW   d) GM

71. A visitor to England from Guernsey has a home callsign GU1---.
   What will his callsign be when mobile in the county of Kent?
   a) GU1---/M   b) GE1---/P   c) G1---/M   d) GUE---/P

72. A station from the South of England, G8CCJ, when operating mobile in Scotland will use the callsign-
   a) GM8CCJ/M   b) G8MCCJ/M   c) GS8CCJ/M   d) GD8CCJ/M

73. The holder of an Amateur Licence B is in a small boat which springs a leak in the middle of Loch Ericht. Is he permitted to transmit his status to a mobile station near the bank?
   a) No.
   b) Yes, providing that he uses a /M (Loch Ericht is non-tidal) on his callsign and is operating in a band for which he is licensed.
   c) Yes, after prior written notice to the Inland Water Authority Inverness.
   d) Yes, providing that the /M station does not radiate in excess of 10W.

74. The holder of an Amateur Licence A is climbing a mountain somewhere in Wales. Which one of the following callsigns would be valid?
   a) GW3---/P   b) GW8---/M   c) GW3---/M   d) GW6---/M

75. On receiving a weak station with a GI3??? callsign. Your first reaction might be to turn your antenna in the direction of--
   a) Jersey.   b) Northern Ireland.
   c) Scotland.   d) Isle of Man.

76. Are you allowed to 'loan' your licence to the holder of a pass in the RAE?
    a) No.
    b) Yes, if the pass holder is over the age of 14.
    c) Yes, if the pass holder wishes to set-up and maintain an exhibition station.
    d) Yes, if the pass holder restricts operation to a vessel at sea.

77. Which of the following frequencies should not be used to meet the needs of international disaster communications?
    a) 3.5 - 3.8MHz, 7.00 - 7.10MHz and 10.10 - 10.15MHz
    b) 14.00 - 14.35MHz, 18.068 - 18.168MHz and 21.00 - 21.45MHz
    c) 24.89 - 24.99MHz, and 144.00 - 146.00MHz
    d) 28.00 - 29.70MHz, 1.810 - 2.000MHz and 430 - 440MHz

78. The Secretary of State shall be notified of any change of Main Station Address. Which one of the following apply?
    a) 7 days prior written notice.
    b) 14 days prior written notice.
    c) 28 days prior written notice.
    d) Prior written notice shall be given.

79. When necessary, to whom should prior written notice of a temporary location be given?
    a) The head postmaster of the nearest Post Office.
    b) The Secretary of State for Wireless Telegraphy.
    c) The Manager of the Radio Investigation Service office in whose district the operation is to take place.
    d) The Emergency Planning Officer of the local district council.

80. At a temporary location using your callsign with a suffix /P, how might you identify the location of your station? By-
    a) transmitting the full postcode or six figure National Grid Reference.
    b) transmitting the latitude and longitude in degrees and minutes.
    c) transmitting the address or other geographical description correct to 1km.
    d) using any of the above methods.

81. Who is responsible for conducting tests at the Amateur Station?
    a) The Amateur. (From time to time.)
    b) The Licensing Authority. (On a regular basis.)
    c) The RSGB. (When TVI complaints are received.)
    d) The CCITT. (At any time.)

82. When operating on frequencies above 1000MHz, you should ensure that (in locations to which people have access) the power flux density of your transmission does not exceed the currently recommended limit of-
    a) $0.1mW/cm$ b) $1mW/cm^3$ c) $10mW/cm^2$ d) $100mW/cm^2$

83. The licensee shall conduct tests-
a) before each period of operation.
b) after each period of operation.
c) on the anniversary of the licence, i.e. annually.
d) from time to time.

84. If any undue or harmful interference to wireless telegraphy is caused by the radiation of unwanted emissions or field strengths, they must be suppressed by the licensee-
a) to the degree satisfactory to the Secretary of State.
b) to produce less than 10mW/cm at a distance of 3m.
c) within 24 hours of receiving notice on form P18.
d) within 48 hours of receiving notice on form A252.

85. All apparatus comprised in the station shall-
a) conform to specification CB 27/81.
b) conform to FCC regulations and BS 800.
c) be capable of receiving transmissions in the standard frequency service.
d) be designed, constructed, maintained and used so as to cause no undue or harmful interference to any wireless telegraphy.

86. As far as current technical development of transmitting equipment allows, the amateur should ensure that the emitted frequency of the apparatus-
a) does not drift more than 25% of the band in use.
b) is as stable and free from unwanted emissions as possible.
c) does not drift more than 1Hz per 100MHz.
d) contains no harmonics greater than 60dB below the carrier power.

87. The station receiver must be capable of receiving all-
a) standard frequency service transmissions.
b) frequency bands covered by the licence.
c) harmonics of the highest frequency of transmission.
d) classes of emission and frequencies in use at the station for sending messages.

88. The bandwidths of emissions should be such as to ensure-
a) that all information is restricted to the HF bands.
b) that all information is contained within 25kHz of spectrum.
c) the greatest possible power saving at the transmitter.
d) the most efficient utilisation of the spectrum.

89. What is the lowest frequency band available to a class B licensee?
a) 28 - 29.7MHz   b) 50 - 52MHz   c) 70 - 70.5MHz   d) 144 - 146MHz

90. The lowest frequency band available to class A licence holders is-
a) 300 - 500kHz   b) 1.4 - 1.6MHz   c) 1.810 - 2.0MHz   d) 3.5 - 3.8MHz

91. Standard frequency transmissions are-
a) available to all licensees.
b) available to class A licensees only.
c) illegal for amateur use.
d) only to be used by holders of the Experimental C Licence.

92. Facsimile is the transmission of-
a) fixed or graphic images.
b) high speed data.
c) fast scan television signals.
d) machine-sent morse telegraphy.

93. In the schedule referring to frequency bands and powers etc; Maximum Power Level refers to the-
a) maximum d.c. input power to the PA device of the transmitter.
b) maximum r.f. input power to the PA device of the transmitter.
c) maximum r.f. power supplied to the antenna. Specified by 'Peak Envelope Power' (PEP).
d) peak d.c. input power supplied to the antenna. (Specified by PDC.)

Starting with the May 1996 examination candidates will be provided with a copy of the Schedule to the licence. This lists frequency bands in MHz, the status of allocations in the UK to the amateur service and to the satellite service, the maximum power level and permitted types of transmission. Questions on the Schedule will clearly state 'USE THE ATTACHED SCHEDULE TO FIND THE ANSWER'. (Check current syllabus for changes.) Use the schedule in your Amateur Licence (A) or (B) BR68 to answer the following.

94. You set up a station within 100km radius of Charing Cross, London. Which frequency band should you not use?
a) 144 - 146MHz   b) 51 - 52MHz
c) 432 - 440MHz   d) 431 - 432MHz

95. What is the maximum PEP permitted on the 144-146MHz band?
a) 10dBW   b) 16dBW
c) 26dBW   d) 144dBW

96. On which band is the maximum power level 16dBW erp?
a) 430 - 432MHz   b) 70 - 70.5MHz
c) 432 - 440MHz   d) 1240 - 1260MHz

97. Operation on the 70 - 70.5MHz band requires that the user does not exceed-
a) 15dBW PEP   b) 16dBW PEP
c) 20dBW PEP   d) 22dBW PEP

98. The maximum power level for a transmission on the 432 to 440MHz band is-
a) 10dBW   b) 16dBW
c) 20dBW   d) 26dBW

99. What is the maximum power level in the frequency band 51 - 52MHz?
a) 15dBW   b) 16dBW
c) 20dBW   d) 432dBW

100. In the 3.5, 7, 10, 14, 18, 21, 24 and 28MHz HF bands, the maximum power level in dBW (PEP) should not exceed-
a) 10dBW   b) 16dBW
c) 20dBW   d) 26dBW

101. You are transmitting FSTV (fast scan television) in the 7.00 - 7.1MHz band. What are you doing wrong?
a) Nothing.
b) You may not be in possession of a /TV extension to your licence.
c) You are not using morse telegraphy (A1A) in this band.
d) You are using FSTV below 430MHz.

Answers - Licensing Conditions

1	a	21	d	41	d	61	c	81	a
2	a	22	b	42	a	62	b	82	c
3	c	23	c	43	a	63	c	83	d
4	a	24	a	44	d	64	c	84	a
5	c	25	d	45	c	65	b	85	d
6	a	26	b	46	a	66	c	86	b
7	d	27	d	47	a	67	b	87	d
8	b	28	a	48	d	68	a	88	d
9	c	29	c	49	c	69	d	89	b
10	a	30	b	50	a	70	d	90	c
11	a	31	a	51	d	71	c	91	a
12	c	32	a	52	a	72	a	92	a
13	d	33	d	53	c	73	b	93	c
14	c	34	a	54	a	74	c	94	d
15	d	35	b	55	c	75	b	95	c
16	a	36	c	56	a	76	a	96	a
17	c	37	d	57	a	77	d	97	d
18	c	38	b	58	d	78	d	98	d
19	b	39	a	59	a	79	c	99	c
20	a	40	c	60	d	80	d	100	d
								101	d

Please note. There are no written answers to this chapter.

Notes

20. Circuit Recognition

It is important that every student of radio and electronics is able to recognise the various stages and components of a complete circuit diagram. At the end of a typical course the student will have been introduced to all, or most of the following circuits. This section has been included for self testing, group testing and group discussion on the circuits shown.

The circuit diagrams in this section are chosen to be representative of their type. In practice many other circuit configurations and diagram arrangements are possible for each of the stages shown. The actual, or practical circuit design and choice of components will depend on such factors as frequency of operation, signal amplitudes (levels) and operating voltages etc: and to some extent on the designer's own experience. Component labelling has only been included where it might assist recognition of the circuit. It must be noted that these diagrams are only typical examples and are not intended to be used for constructional projects.

Please note. The key is at the end of this chapter as in previous chapters. However; there are no written answers to this chapter.

To illustrate just how a circuit diagram can be rearranged, I have shown below, two possible circuit diagrams for a common base amplifier, all the components are in the same theoretical position and have the same value, only the drawing is different.

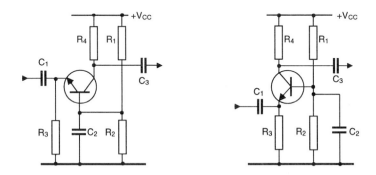

Two possible circuit arrangements for a common base amplifier.

Circuit Recognition

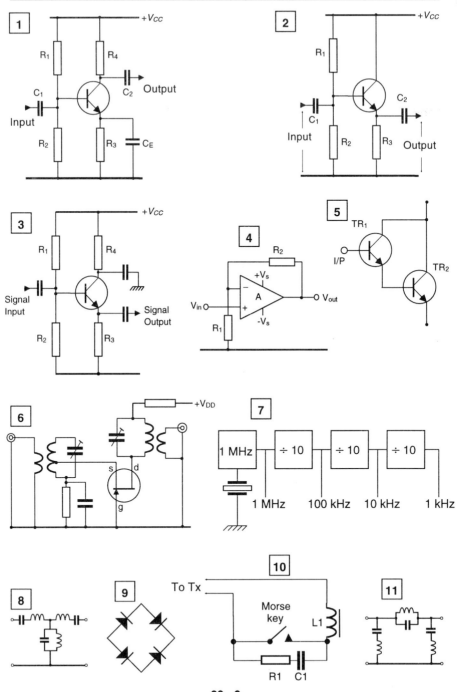

Circuit Recognition

12

+V

C₂ L₂
R1
TR1
L₁
C₁
R2 R3 C3

13

+V
Cd FB
R₁
Crystal
C₂
C₃
C₁
R₂ R₃

14

Tx   Antenna
R
50Ω
M   M

15

M

16

C L
$3f_c$
TR1
f_c

17

BFO
AF
C2
R1 C1
IFT

18

+V_DD
R_L
Signal
Input   d   Signal
g   C_C   Output
C_C   s
R_G   R_S   C_S

19

L
N
E

20

M
1V 10V 100V
+   −

20 - 3

Circuit Recognition

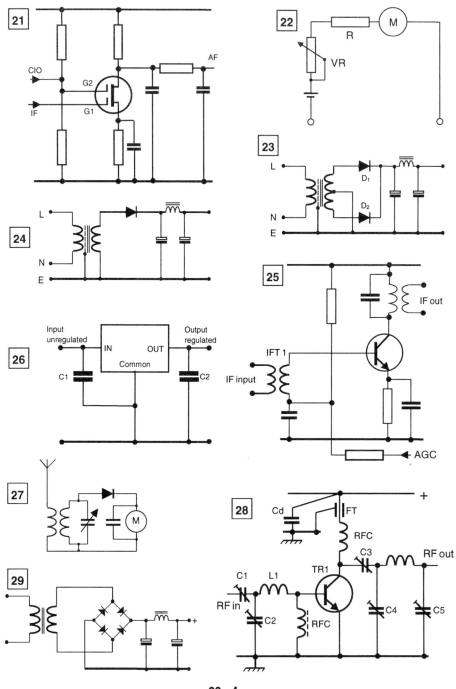

20 - 4

Circuit Recognition

30

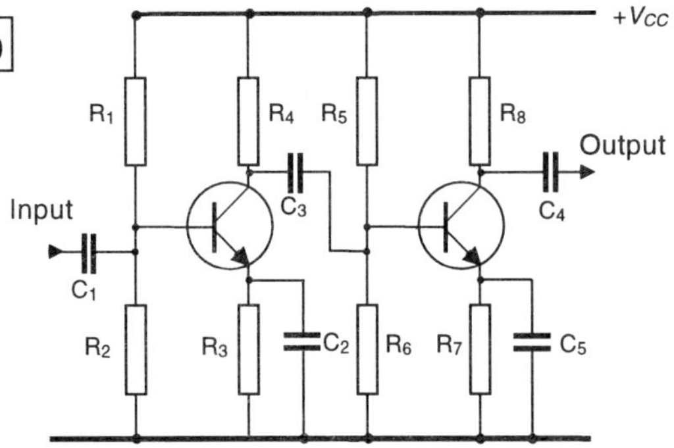

R₁ R₄ R₅ R₈

+V_{CC}

Output

Input

C₁ C₃ C₄

R₂ R₃ C₂ R₆ R₇ C₅

31

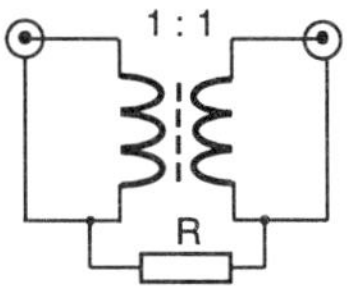

1 : 1

R

32

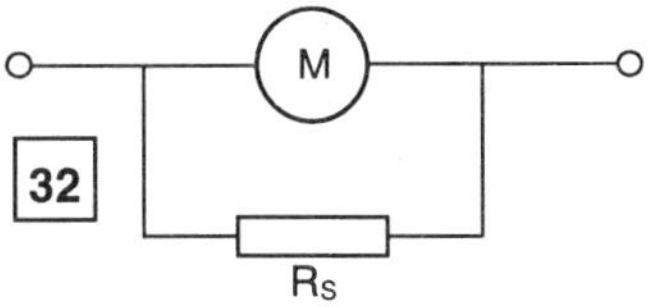

M

R_S

33

+V

C1

Last IF

AF Out

34

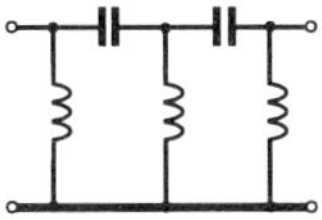

35

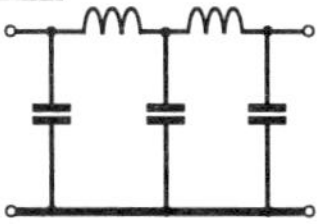

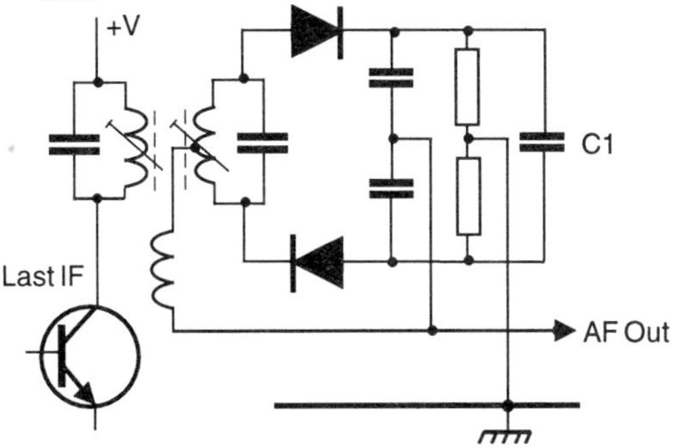

36

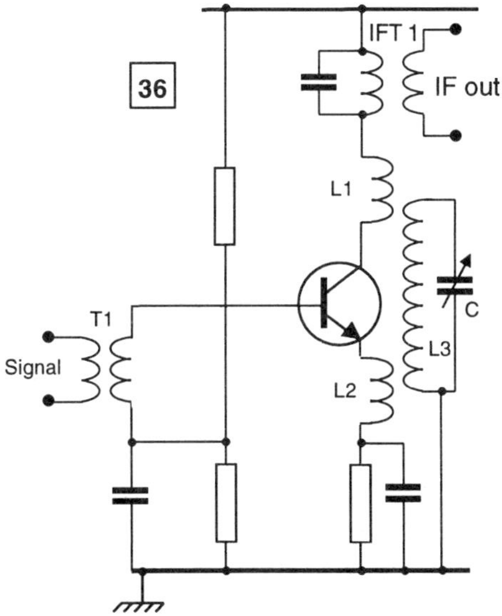

IFT 1

IF out

L1

C

L3

T1

Signal

L2

37

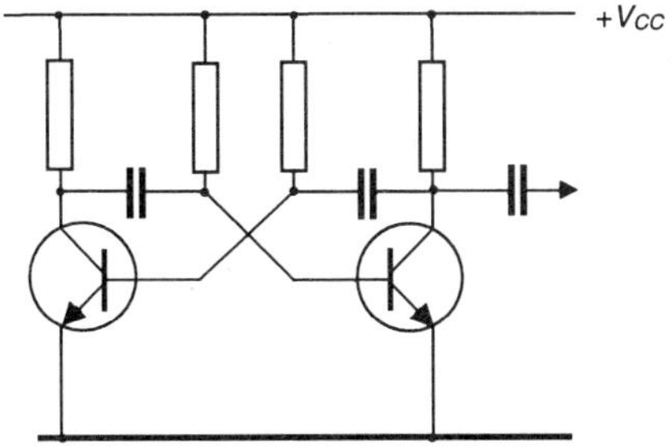

+V_{CC}

38

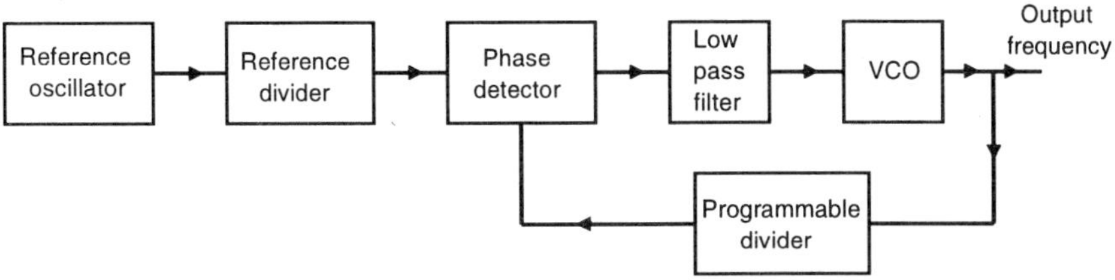

| Reference oscillator | → | Reference divider | → | Phase detector | → | Low pass filter | → | VCO | → | Output frequency |

Programmable divider

20 - 5

Answers - Circuit Recognition

1   Common emitter amplifier (general purpose).
2   Common collector amplifier (emitter follower).
3   Alternative configuration for the Common collector amplifier (emitter follower).
4   Basic integrated circuit operational amplifier.
5   Darlington pair configuration.
6   Grounded gate RF amplifier.
7   Crystal calibrator using digital integrated circuit dividers.
8   Band pass filter (Basic configuration).
9   Bridge rectifier unit.
10   Key click filter applied to a morse key.
11   Band stop filter (Basic configuration).
12   Common emitter RF amplifier (Transformer coupled).
13   Crystal oscillator.
14   VSWR meter or reflectometer.
15   Basic absorption wavemeter.
16   Frequency multiplier (X3)
17   AM detector with BFO injection.
18   Common source amplifier employing a junction FET.
19   Mains supply line filter.
20   Moving coil meter movement with multiplier resistors to extend voltage range.
21   SSB product detector.
22   Moving coil meter used as an ohmmeter.
23   Full-wave bi-phase rectified power supply.
24   Power supply unit (half-wave circuit).
25   Intermediate frequency amplifier stage with AGC applied.
26   Integrated circuit fixed voltage regulator.
27   An alternative configuration for the absorption wavemeter.
28   Radio frequency power amplifier.
29   Power supply unit (PSU) employing a bridge rectifier (Full-wave rectification).
30   2 stage RC coupled amplifier using NPN transistors.
31   Braid breaker for TV antenna feeder.
32   Moving coil meter with shunt resistor to increase current range.
33   A typical ratio detector for frequency modulation receivers.
34   High pass filter.
35   Low pass filter.
36   Self-oscillating mixer stage.
37   Multivibrator.
38   A basic frequency synthesiser circuit. Can be used in place of a VFO.

21. Using The Scientific Calculator

This chapter has been included to familiarise the student with the keying-in sequences necessary when using a hand-held scientific calculator to solve basic electrical theory problems. This chapter is not intended as a 'teach yourself maths' course.

The following examples are taken from this book and worked on a **Casio Fx 82s**, set to operate in **Normal mode 2**. Owners of other calculators may find the keying sequence different when using certain function keys. Consider using **Scientific mode** or **Fix mode** when you gain confidence. Always study the manufacturers handbook.

It should be noted that for keys with more than one function, the second function can normally only be executed by pressing the [SHIFT] key first. In the keying sequences given, shift key operation is not shown, however, the [SHIFT] key should be used when the desired function is a second function of a key.

Mathematical note. a times b may be written as $a \times b$ or simply ab. Similarly CR means $C \times R$ or C times R.

Also:- $\dfrac{a}{b}$ *means* $a \div b$ *or simply* a/b The latter to suit the text flow on the page.

When entering a number with an exponent, e.g. 8×10^{-12} the 10 does not appear on the display of some calculators, it is implied when the [EXP] key is pressed. E.g. the key sequence for entering 8×10^{-12} is 8 [EXP] 12 [+/-]. The [+/-] changes the sign of the exponent.

VALUE	SYMBOL & NAME	TYPICAL USAGE	EXPONENT ENTRY			
0.000000000001	10^{-12} p (Pico)	$4pW = 4 \times 10^{-12}W$	4	[EXP]	12	[+/-]
0.000000001	10^{-9} n (Nano)	$6nF = 6 \times 10^{-9}F$	6	[EXP]	9	[+/-]
0.000001	10^{-6} μ (Micro)	$4\mu H = 4 \times 10^{-6}H$	4	[EXP]	6	[+/-]
0.001	10^{-3} m (Milli)	$25mV = 25 \times 10^{-3}V$	25	[EXP]	3	[+/-]
1.0	10^{0}	Basic units. Volts, Amps, Hertz, Seconds, Metres, etc:				
1000	10^{3} k (Kilo)	$8kV = 8 \times 10^{3}V$	8	[EXP]	3	
1000000	10^{6} M (Mega)	$2MV = 2 \times 10^{6}V$	2	[EXP]	6	
1000000000	10^{9} G (Giga)	$4GHz = 4 \times 10^{9}Hz$	4	[EXP]	9	

Table showing units, unit value, and keying-in sequence for the exponents.

Using The Scientific Calculator

Example 1.
Chapter 1. Q14.
What is the effective resistance of the circuit shown?

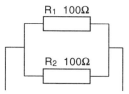

The two 100Ω resistors are connected in parallel.
There are two possible formulae to suit this case;-

Method 1. Using the general formula for any number of resistors in parallel

$$\frac{1}{R_T} = \frac{1}{R_1} + \frac{1}{R_2} = \frac{1}{100} + \frac{1}{100} = \frac{1}{0.02} = 50 \; ohms.$$

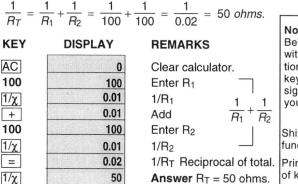

KEY	DISPLAY	REMARKS
AC	0	Clear calculator.
100	100	Enter R_1
1/χ	0.01	1/R_1
+	0.01	Add $\frac{1}{R_1} + \frac{1}{R_2}$
100	100	Enter R_2
1/χ	0.01	1/R_2
=	0.02	1/R_T Reciprocal of total.
1/χ	50	**Answer** R_T = 50 ohms.

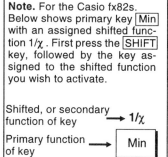

Note. For the Casio fx82s. Below shows primary key Min with an assigned shifted function 1/χ . First press the SHIFT key, followed by the key assigned to the shifted function you wish to activate.

Shifted, or secondary function of key ⟶ 1/χ

Primary function ⟶ Min of key

Example 2.
Chapter 1. Q14. Method 2. Using the formula for *two resistors only* in parallel.

When using the calculator bracket (parenthesise) the bottom line in this example.

$$R_T = \frac{R_1 \times R_2}{(R_1 + R_2)} = \frac{100 \times 100}{(100 + 100)} = \frac{10,000}{200} = 50\Omega .$$

KEY	DISPLAY	REMARKS
AC	0	Clear calculator.
100	100	Enter R_1
×	100	$R_1 \times R_2$
100	100	Enter R_2
=	10000	
÷	10000	Divide top by bottom.
(	0	Open brackets.
100	100	Enter R_1
+	100	$R_1 + R_2$
100	100	Enter R_2
)	200	Close brackets
=	50	**Answer** R_T = 50 ohms.

Using The Scientific Calculator

Example 3.
Chapter 1. Q15. In the previous example you calculated the total, or effective resistance of the two resistors connected in parallel. You now have to calculate the total supply current flowing when the combination is connected across a 10V supply.
From the previous example the total or effective resistance $R_T = 50\Omega$.

Using the formula- $I = \dfrac{V}{R} = \dfrac{10}{50} = 0.2A$ *or* $200mA$.

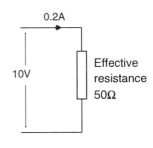

KEY	DISPLAY	REMARKS
AC	0	Clear calculator.
10	10	Enter V, 10 volts.
÷	10	Divide
50	50	Enter R, 50 ohms.
=	0.2	**Answer** 0.2 amps.
×	0.2	To convert to milliamps
1000	1000	we multiply by 1000.
=	200	**Answer** = 200mA.

Example 4.
Chapter 1. Q24. Calculate the power dissipated in the 12 ohm resistor when it is connected across a 12 volt supply.

Use the power formula- $W = \dfrac{V^2}{R} = \dfrac{12^2}{12} = \dfrac{144}{12} = 12\,watts.$

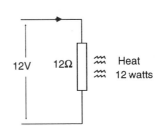

KEY	DISPLAY	REMARKS
AC	0	Clear calculator.
12	12	Enter V, 12 volts.
χ^2	144	Square voltage, V^2.
÷	144	Divide.
12	12	Enter R, 12 ohms.
=	12	**Answer** = 12 watts.

Using The Scientific Calculator

Example 5.
Chapter 1. Q56, 57. Two resistors of 10,000 and
20,000 ohms respectively are connected in series.
Calculate their effective resistance and the p.d.
developed across R_2.

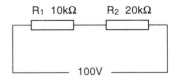

Total resistance of the series circuit:-
$R_T = R_1 + R_2 = 10,000 + 20,000 = 30,000$ *ohms* $(30k\Omega)$

KEY	DISPLAY	REMARKS
AC	0	Clear calculator.
10000	10000	Enter R_1, 10kΩ.
+	10000	Add. $R_1 + R_2$
20000	20000	Enter R_2, 20kΩ.
=	30000	**Answer** 30kΩ. Total resistance of the series circuit.

To calculate the p.d. across R_2, 20,000 ohms, first calculate the total current I_T.

$$I_T = \frac{V}{R_T} = \frac{100}{30,000} = 0.00333A \quad (3.33mA).$$

> If display reads 3.333333333^{-03} it is correct, but you are in Normal mode 1. If you wish to change it select Normal mode 2.

KEY	DISPLAY	REMARKS
AC	0	Clear calculator.
100	100	Enter V, 100 volts.
÷	100	Divide.
30000	30000	Enter R_T, 30,000 ohms.
=	0.003333333	**Answer** = 0.00333A. I've knocked off a few of the
×	0.003333333	recurring 3s. In **normal mode** the display is likely to fill
1000	1000	with unnecessary decimal figures. Multiply by 1000 to
=	3.333333333	convert to milliamps. **Answer** = 3.333mA. (Rounded)

This is the total current I_T and also the current in R_2.

Now that I_{R2} is known, the p.d. developed across R_2, V_{R2} can be calculated.
$V_{R2} = I_{R2} \times R_2 = 0.00333 \times 20000 = 66.6$ *volts*.

KEY	DISPLAY	REMARKS
AC	0	Clear calculator.
.00333	0.00333	Enter I_{R2}, 0.00333A. Notice that I didn't enter the zero
×	0.00333	before the decimal point.
20000	20000	Enter R_2.
=	66.6	**Answer** V_{R2} = 66.6 volts.

Using The Scientific Calculator

Example 6.
Chapter 2. Q 41. A radio station is listed as broadcasting on a wavelength of 208m.
To what frequency should your receiver be tuned?

$$f = \frac{300 \times 10^6}{\lambda} = \frac{300 \times 10^6}{208} = 1.4423 \times 10^6 Hz \ \ or \ \ 1442.3 kHz.$$

KEY	DISPLAY	REMARKS
AC	0	Clear calculator.
300	300	Enter top line of equation first.
EXP	300^{00}	Enter the Exponent. The 10 is implied.
6	300^{06}	The EXPonent has now been entered.
÷	300000000	Divide.
208	208	Enter wavelength in metres.
=	1442307.692	Frequency in hertz (Hz).
÷	1442307.692	Divide by 1000 to get answer in kHz.
1000	1000	
=	1442.307692	**Answer** = 1442.3kHz. (Rounded)

Example 7.
Chapter 3. Q 23. Calculate the total or effective capacitance of the series circuit
shown. I will use the general formula for any number of capacitors in series.

$$\frac{1}{C_T} = \frac{1}{C_1} + \frac{1}{C_2} = \frac{1}{20} + \frac{1}{10} = \frac{3}{20} \ \ Therefore \ \ C_T = \frac{20}{3} = 6.66pF.$$

When using this formula remember that all the units must be of the same type, i.e.
all pFs, nFs, μFs or farads. Do not use a mixture of units without first converting
them to a common unit.

C_1 20pF C_2 10pF

KEY	DISPLAY	REMARKS
AC	0	Clear calculator.
20	20	Enter C_1
1/χ	0.05	1/C_1 Reciprocal of C_1
+	0.05	Add
10	10	Enter C_2
1/χ	0.1	1/R_2 Reciprocal of C_2
=	0.15	1/C_T Reciprocal of total.
1/χ	6.666666667	**Answer** C_T = 6.66pF (Rounded)

Using The Scientific Calculator

Example 8.
Chapter 5. Q 16. What is the reactance of a 1000µF capacitor at a frequency of 50Hz? (Where C is entered in farads and frequency in hertz.)

$$X_C = \frac{1}{\omega C} = \frac{1}{2\pi f C} = \frac{1}{2 \times \pi \times 50 \times 1000 \times 10^{-6}} = \frac{10^6}{100,000 \times \pi} = 3.18\Omega .$$

Using the calculator it is often easier to solve the bottom line of the equation first.

KEY	DISPLAY	REMARKS
AC	0	Clear calculator.
2	2	
×	2	
π	3.141592654	Enter π (pi)
×	6.283185307	2 × π has now been entered.
50	50	Enter frequency 50Hz.
×	314.1592654	
1000	1000	Enter C in farads $1000\mu F = (1000 \times 10^{-6} F)$
EXP	1000^{00}	Enter EXPonent
6	1000^{06}	EXPonent entered.
+/-	1000^{-06}	Change sign of exponent.
=	0.314159265	Bottom line has been calculated.
1/χ	3.183098862	**Answer** = 3.18 ohms. (Rounded)

Example 9.
Chapter 6. Q 16. What is the reactance of a 5mH inductor at a frequency of 5MHz?

$$X_L = \omega L = 2\pi f L = 2 \times \pi \times 5 \times 10^6 \times 5 \times 10^{-3} = 50 \times \pi \times 10^3 = 157k\Omega.$$

KEY	DISPLAY	REMARKS
AC	0	Clear calculator.
2	2	
×	2	
π	3.141592654	Enter π (pi)
×	6.283185307	2 × π has now been entered.
5	5	Enter frequency $5MHz = (5 \times 10^6 Hz)$.
EXP	5^{00}	Enter EXPonent
6	5^{06}	EXPonent entered.
×	31415926.54	
5	5	Enter L in henrys. Continued at top of next page.

21 - 6

Using The Scientific Calculator

KEY		REMARKS
EXP	5^{00}	$5mH = (5 \times 10^{-3}H)$
3	5^{03}	Enter EXPonent, 3.
+/-	5^{-03}	Change sign of exponent.
=	157079.6327	**Answer** = 157079Ω (157kΩ Rounded)

Example 10.
Chapter 7. Q 11. What is the impedance of the circuit shown?
Where R = 30Ω and X_L = 40Ω.

$$Z = \sqrt{R^2 + X_L{}^2} = \sqrt{30^2 + 40^2} = \sqrt{900 + 1600} = \sqrt{2500} = 50\Omega.$$

Keying sequence for fx-115s (VPAM).

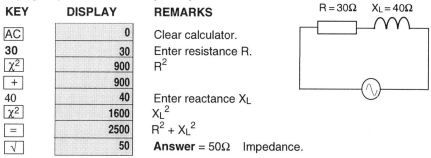

R = 30Ω X_L = 40Ω

KEY	DISPLAY	REMARKS
AC	0	Clear calculator.
30	30	Enter resistance R.
χ^2	900	R^2
+	900	
40	40	Enter reactance X_L
χ^2	1600	$X_L{}^2$
=	2500	$R^2 + X_L{}^2$
$\sqrt{}$	50	**Answer** = 50Ω Impedance.

Note. Some calculators, such as the Casio fx-115s, using the Casio VPAM operating system, have a different keying sequence. Some function keys (in this case the square root key) are pressed before the value is entered. Use the keying sequence below.

KEY	DISPLAY	REMARKS
AC	0	Clear calculator.
$\sqrt{}$	0	
(	0	
30	30	Enter resistance R.
χ^2	900	R^2
+	900	
40	40	Enter reactance X_L.
χ^2	1600	$X_L{}^2$
)	2500	$R^2 + X_L{}^2$ The square root is still pending.
=	50	**Answer** = 50Ω Impedance.

Using The Scientific Calculator

Example 11.
Chapter 8. Q 9. What is the resonant frequency of the circuit shown?

Where R = 5Ω   L = 10mH and C = 1μF.

Resistance R has no effect on the resonant frequency of the series circuit.

$$f_r = \frac{1}{2\,\pi\,\sqrt{L\,C}} = \frac{1}{2\times\pi\times\sqrt{10\times10^{-3}\times1\times10^{-6}}} = \frac{10^4}{2\times\pi} = 1592Hz.$$

There are several methods by which this problem can be solved with the calculator. For this example I will calculate the bottom line first, enclosing the values under the root sign in brackets, and finally using the reciprocal key for the answer.

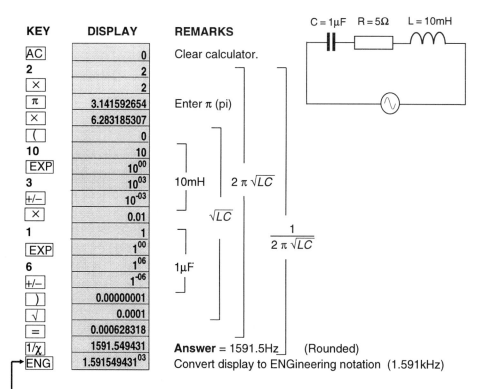

KEY	DISPLAY	REMARKS
AC	0	Clear calculator.
2	2	
×	2	
π	3.141592654	Enter π (pi)
×	6.283185307	
(	0	
10	10	
EXP	10^{00}	
3	10^{03}	10mH 2 π √LC
+/−	10^{-03}	
×	0.01	√LC
1	1	
EXP	1^{00}	
6	1^{06}	1μF
+/−	1^{-06}	
)	0.00000001	
√	0.0001	
=	0.000628318	
1/χ	1591.549431	**Answer** = 1591.5Hz (Rounded)
ENG	1.591549431^{03}	Convert display to ENGineering notation (1.591kHz)

Since the scientific calculator is able to display in 'Engineering Notation,' pressing the **ENG** key at this point will display the result as **1.591549431^{03}**
The exponent ^{03}, meaning 10 to the power of 3, or kilo (thousand).
Answer = 1.5915 x 10^{3}Hz = 1.5915kHz (Rounded).

Using The Scientific Calculator

Example 12.
Chapter 13. Q 112. A transmitter has an ERP of 400W.
What is the field strength at a distance of 30 metres?

$$e = \frac{7.02\sqrt{ERP}}{d} = \frac{7.02\sqrt{400}}{30} = \frac{7.02 \times 20}{30} = \frac{140.4}{30} = 4.68\,V/m.$$

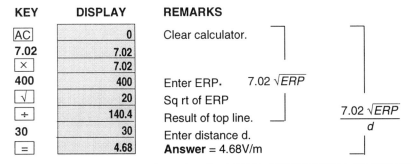

KEY	DISPLAY	REMARKS
AC	0	Clear calculator.
7.02	7.02	
×	7.02	
400	400	Enter ERP. $7.02\sqrt{ERP}$
√	20	Sq rt of ERP
÷	140.4	Result of top line.
30	30	Enter distance d.
=	4.68	**Answer** = 4.68V/m

$\dfrac{7.02\sqrt{ERP}}{d}$

> **Note.** The keying sequences used in this question are not correct for VPAM Casio scientifics, e.g. fx-115s.

Example 13.
Chapter 13. Q 115. Calculate the Effective Radiated Power (ERP) required to give a field strength of 2V/m at a distance of 15 metres.

$$ERP = \left(\frac{ed}{7.02}\right)^2 = \left(\frac{2 \times 15}{7.02}\right)^2 = \left(\frac{30}{7.02}\right)^2 = 4.27^2 = 18.26W\ (ERP)$$

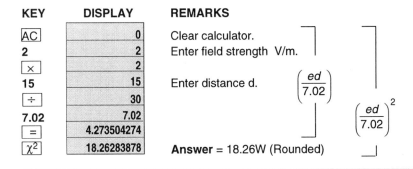

KEY	DISPLAY	REMARKS
AC	0	Clear calculator.
2	2	Enter field strength V/m.
×	2	
15	15	Enter distance d. $\left(\dfrac{ed}{7.02}\right)$
÷	30	
7.02	7.02	
=	4.273504274	
x^2	18.26283878	**Answer** = 18.26W (Rounded)

$\left(\dfrac{ed}{7.02}\right)^2$

Using The Scientific Calculator

Example 14.

Chapter 15. Q 67. Convert a power level of 15dBW to watts.

$$Power \,(watts) = Antilog \, \frac{dBW}{10} = Antilog \, \frac{15}{10} = Antilog \, 1.5 = 31.6W.$$

KEY	DISPLAY	REMARKS
AC	0	Clear calculator.
15	15	
÷	15	**Note.** 10^X is the Antilog key. It may be marked ANTILOG on some calculators. It is normally the second function of the LOG key. Press SHIFT to activate it.
10	10	
=	1.5	
10^X	31.6227766	**Answer** = 31.6W (Rounded)

Note. Keying sequences on this page are not suitable for VPAM type Casio calculators.

Example 15.

Chapter 15. Q 69. A power of 100W is measured. What is this expressed in dBW?

$$dBW = 10 \, Log_{10} \, Power \,(watts) = 10 \, Log_{10} \, 100 = 10 \times 2 = 20dBW.$$

KEY	DISPLAY	REMARKS	
AC	0	Clear calculator.	Do not do anything with this small 10. It implies that the logs are to the base of 10. **Note.** Logarithms are not normally encountered to-day because the scientific calculator has made them redundant as a calculating tool. However, they are still used in some formula.
10	10		
×	10		
100	100	Enter power in watts.	
LOG	2	Log of 100	
=	20	**Answer** = 20dBW.	

Example 16.

Chapter 15. Q 70. Express a power of 160W in dBW.

$$dBW = 10 \, Log_{10} \, Power \,(watts) = 10 \, Log_{10} \, 160 = 10 \times 2.2 = 22dBW.$$

KEY	DISPLAY	REMARKS
AC	0	Clear calculator.
10	10	
×	10	
160	160	Enter power in watts.
LOG	2.204119983	Log of 160
=	22.04119983	**Answer** = 22dBW (Rounded)

Appendix A1 - Frequency / Wavelength

Freq MHz	W/L Metres	Freq MHz	W/L Metres	Freq MHz	W/L Metres	Freq MHz	W/L Metres
0.1	3000.0	26	11.54	60	5.00	360	0.83
0.2	1500.0	27	11.11	65	4.62	380	0.79
0.3	1000.0	28	10.71	70	4.29	400	0.75
0.4	750.0	29	10.34	75	4.00	420	0.71
0.5	600.0	30	10.00	80	3.75	440	0.68
0.6	500.0	31	9.68	85	3.53	460	0.65
0.7	428.6	32	9.38	90	3.33	480	0.63
0.8	375.0	33	9.09	95	3.16	500	0.60
0.9	333.3	34	8.82	100	3.00	520	0.58
1	300.0	35	8.57	110	2.73	540	0.56
2	150.0	36	8.33	120	2.50	560	0.54
3	100.0	37	8.11	130	2.31	580	0.52
4	75.0	38	7.89	140	2.14	600	0.50
5	60.0	39	7.69	150	2.00	620	0.48
6	50.0	40	7.50	160	1.88	640	0.47
7	42.9	41	7.32	170	1.76	660	0.45
8	37.5	42	7.14	180	1.67	680	0.44
9	33.3	43	6.98	190	1.58	700	0.43
10	30.0	44	6.82	200	1.50	720	0.42
11	27.3	45	6.67	210	1.43	740	0.41
12	25.0	46	6.52	220	1.36	760	0.39
13	23.1	47	6.38	230	1.30	780	0.38
14	21.4	48	6.25	240	1.25	800	0.38
15	20.0	49	6.12	250	1.20	820	0.37
16	18.8	50	6.00	260	1.15	840	0.36
17	17.6	51	5.88	270	1.11	860	0.35
18	16.7	52	5.77	280	1.07	880	0.34
19	15.8	53	5.66	290	1.03	900	0.33
20	15.0	54	5.56	300	1.00	920	0.33
21	14.3	55	5.45	310	0.97	940	0.32
22	13.6	56	5.36	320	0.94	960	0.31
23	13.0	57	5.26	330	0.91	980	0.31
24	12.5	58	5.17	340	0.88	1000	0.30
25	12.0	59	5.08	350	0.86		

For Frequency to Wavelength conversion use the formula given.

$$f = \frac{3 \times 10^8}{\lambda} \qquad \lambda = \frac{3 \times 10^8}{f}$$

Appendix A2 - Power (watts) / dBW

Power Watts	Power dBW	Power Watts	Power dBW	Power Watts	Power dBW	Power Watts	Power dBW
1	0.0	50	17.0	175	22.4	300	24.8
2	3.0	55	17.4	180	22.6	310	24.9
4	6.0	60	17.8	185	22.7	320	25.1
6	7.8	65	18.1	190	22.8	330	25.2
8	9.0	70	18.5	195	22.9	340	25.3
10	10.0	75	18.8	200	23.0	350	25.4
12	10.8	80	19.0	205	23.1	360	25.6
14	11.5	85	19.3	210	23.2	370	25.7
16	12.0	90	19.5	215	23.3	380	25.8
18	12.6	95	19.8	220	23.4	390	25.9
20	13.0	100	20.0	225	23.5	400	26.0
22	13.4	105	20.2	230	23.6	410	26.1
24	13.8	110	20.4	235	23.7	420	26.2
26	14.1	115	20.6	240	23.8	430	26.3
28	14.5	120	20.8	245	23.9	440	26.4
30	14.8	125	21.0	250	24.0	450	26.5
32	15.1	130	21.1	255	24.1	460	26.6
34	15.3	135	21.3	260	24.1	470	26.7
36	15.6	140	21.5	265	24.2	480	26.8
38	15.8	145	21.6	270	24.3	490	26.9
40	16.0	150	21.8	275	24.4	500	27.0
42	16.2	155	21.9	280	24.5	510	27.1
44	16.4	160	22.0	285	24.5	520	27.2
46	16.6	165	22.2	290	24.6	530	27.2
48	16.8	170	22.3	295	24.7	540	27.3
50	17.0	175	22.4	300	24.8	550	27.4

$Power(dBW) = 10 \times Log_{10}(Actual\ Power\ in\ watts)$

$Power(watts) = Antilog \dfrac{dBW}{10}$

Tx power	Feeder loss (dB)			
(watts)	0dB	3dB	6dB	10dB
1	1	0.5	0.25	0.1
2	2	1	0.5	0.2
3	3	1.5	0.75	0.3
6	6	3	1.5	0.6
10	10	5	2.5	1
20	20	10	5	2
40	40	20	10	4
80	80	40	20	8
100	100	50	25	10
200	200	100	50	20
	Power in load (watts)			

Assumes that feeder and load are matched.

Example

Output power = 20W

Power in load = 10W

Feeder loss = 3dB

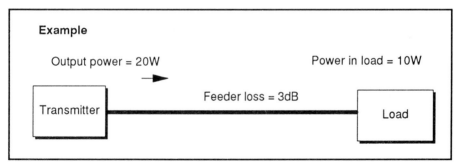

Transmitter

Load

Example

Output power = 80W

Power in load = 20W

Feeder loss = 6dB

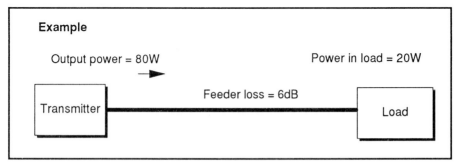

Transmitter

Load

Antenna gain dB	Power multiplying factor	Power at input to antenna		
		1 watt	10 watts	100 watts
0	x1	1	10	100
3	x2	2	20	200
6	x4	4	40	400
10	x10	10	100	1000
13	x20	20	200	2000
16	x40	40	400	4000
20	x100	100	1000	10000
		Effective Radiated Power (watts)		

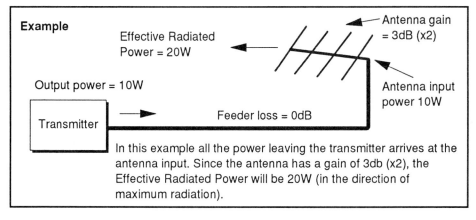

Example

Effective Radiated Power = 20W

Antenna gain = 3dB (x2)

Antenna input power 10W

Output power = 10W

Transmitter

Feeder loss = 0dB

In this example all the power leaving the transmitter arrives at the antenna input. Since the antenna has a gain of 3db (x2), the Effective Radiated Power will be 20W (in the direction of maximum radiation).

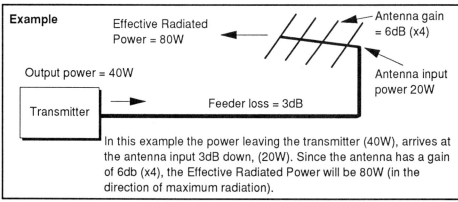

Example

Effective Radiated Power = 80W

Antenna gain = 6dB (x4)

Antenna input power 20W

Output power = 40W

Transmitter

Feeder loss = 3dB

In this example the power leaving the transmitter (40W), arrives at the antenna input 3dB down, (20W). Since the antenna has a gain of 6db (x4), the Effective Radiated Power will be 80W (in the direction of maximum radiation).

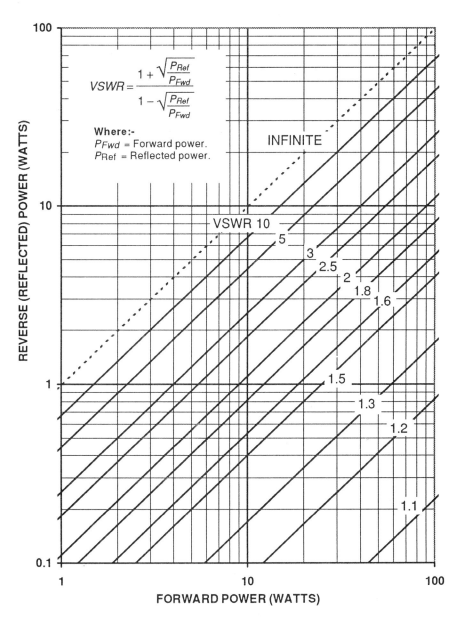

Nomograph for use with a through-line power meter. The VSWR on a transmission line or feeder may be ascertained when forward and reverse power are known.

Appendix A6 - Decibel Table

Power ratio	Voltage ratio	dB	Voltage ratio	Power ratio
Gain			Loss	
1.000	1.000	0.0	1.000	1.000
1.023	1.012	0.1	0.989	0.977
1.047	1.023	0.2	0.977	0.955
1.072	1.035	0.3	0.966	0.933
1.096	1.047	0.4	0.955	0.912
1.122	1.059	0.5	0.944	0.891
1.148	1.072	0.6	0.933	0.871
1.175	1.084	0.7	0.923	0.851
1.202	1.096	0.8	0.912	0.832
1.230	1.109	0.9	0.902	0.813
1.259	1.122	1.0	0.891	0.794
1.585	1.259	2.0	0.794	0.631
1.995	1.413	3.0	0.708	0.501
2.512	1.585	4.0	0.631	0.398
3.162	1.778	5.0	0.562	0.316
3.981	1.995	6.0	0.501	0.251
5.012	2.239	7.0	0.447	0.200
6.310	2.512	8.0	0.398	0.158
7.943	2.818	9.0	0.355	0.126
10.000	3.162	10	0.316	0.100
12.589	3.548	11	0.282	0.079
15.849	3.981	12	0.251	0.063
19.953	4.467	13	0.224	0.050
25.119	5.012	14	0.200	0.040
31.623	5.623	15	0.178	0.032
39.811	6.310	16	0.158	0.025
50.119	7.079	17	0.141	0.020
63.096	7.943	18	0.126	0.016
79.433	8.913	19	0.112	0.013
100.000	10.000	20	0.100	0.010
1.00E+3	31.623	30	0.032	1.00E-3
1.00E+4	1.00E+2	40	0.010	1.00E-4
1.00E+5	3.16E+2	50	3.16E-3	1.00E-5
1.00E+6	1.00E+3	60	1.00E-3	1.00E-6
1.00E+7	3.16E+3	70	3.16E-4	1.00E-7
1.00E+8	1.00E+4	80	1.00E-4	1.00E-8
1.00E+9	3.16E+4	90	3.16E-5	1.00E-9
1.00E+10	1.00E+5	100	1.00E-5	1.00E-10

The gain or loss of a system in decibels is given by:-

$$N_{dB} = 10 \times Log_{10} \frac{P_{out}}{P_{in}}$$

A system *gain* will result in a positive dB value. A system *loss* will result in a negative dB value.

Provided that the resistances through which the input and output current flow (or across which the input and output voltages are measured) are equal, the following formulae may be applied:-

$$N_{dB} = 20 \times Log_{10} \frac{V_{out}}{V_{in}}$$

$$N_{dB} = 20 \times Log_{10} \frac{I_{out}}{I_{in}}$$

Where:-
N_{dB} = Number of decibels. P_{out}, P_{in}, V_{out}, V_{in}, I_{out} and I_{in} are the output and input power, voltage and current levels.

Note 1. Adding decibels is the same as multiplying the ratios of voltage or power.

E.g. 6dB + 3dB = 9dB.

This is the same as multiplying the equivalent voltage ratios:-

1.995 x 1.413 = 2.818 = 9dB

Note 2. In the table, very small and very large numbers are shown in scientific notation.

E.g:-

$1.00E+3 = 1 \times 10^3 = 10^3 = 1000$

$1.00E-3 = 1 \times 10^{-3} = 10^{-3} = 0.001$

$3.16E+4 = 3.16 \times 10^4 = 31,600$

The examination syllabus and assessment pattern as published in Appendix B are valid for the December 1997 exam only. All later examinations will be to a revised syllabus and assessment pattern. A full copy of the Examination regulations and syllabus should be obtained from City & Guilds, there will be small charge. Course instructors will be aware and advise accordingly. The revised examination pattern and syllabus for examinations in May 1998 and onwards are as follows-

Examination Format and Assessment Pattern

The Radio Amateur Examination consists of one paper, 7650, containing 80 multiple choice questions. Questions are allocated to the syllabus sections as indicated below. Candidates must pass Part A to pass the examination as a whole.

The 7650 Radio Amateur Examination ($2^{1}/_{4}$ hours)

	Syllabus	Questions
Part A		
1	Licensing conditions	18
2	Operating procedures and practices	7
Part B		
3	Electronic principles and practice	6
4	Receivers, transmitters and transceivers	8
5	Transmitter interference	14
6	Electromagnetic compatibility	14
7	Propagation and antennas	7
8	Measurements	6
	Total -	80

Syllabus

Licensing conditions

1.1 Types of licence available and the qualifications necessary.

1.2 Terms provisions and limitations for Amateur Radio Licenses A & B, including a knowledge of booklet BR68, including the notes.

1.3 Schedule of frequency bands, power and types of transmission available to the Amateur Service and Amateur Satellite service.

Operating Procedures and Practices.

2.1 Operating procedures in telegraphy, telephony and digital communications: general calls to all stations and calls to specific stations.

2.2 Log keeping: Licensing requirements.

2.3 Use of satellites and repeaters: accessing a repeater.

2.4 Reasons for and use of Q codes and other abbreviations.

2.5 Band planning, purposes and advantages.

2.6 The phonetic alphabet, reasons for its use.

2.7 Safety in the amateur station. Precautions recommended by the RSGB. Reasons why equipment to be repaired should be disconnected from the mains supply and capacitors discharged.

Electronic principles and practice

3.1 The meaning of basic electrical terms; voltage, current, resistance, conductor, and insulator. - the relationship between voltage, current, resistance and power in a d.c. circuit.

3.2 The sine wave. definition of amplitude, frequency and period; peak, peak-to-peak, instantaneous, average and r.m.s. values. Simple explanation of the terms: phase angle, phase difference, phase lag and lead. - Inductance and capacitance; units, inductive and capacitive reactance. Reactance, impedance and power in an a.c. circuit.

3.3 Series and parallel tuned circuits, resonance, impedance, dynamic resistance, calculation of resonant frequency; amplification of current or voltage at resonance; Q (magnification) factor.

3.4 Function and uses of the transformer.

3.5 Simple explanation of how the decibel notation is used to express ratios of power and voltage and how it may also be used to define power levels.

3.6 Characteristics of junction diodes, npn, pnp and field effect transistors.

3.7 The common transistor circuit configurations, emphasising the biasing arrangements and conditions, and input and output impedances.

3.8 Use of solid state devices as - audio and radio frequency amplifiers - oscillators - mixers - demodulators - switches.

3.9 Rectification, smoothing and voltage stabilisation arrangements in low voltage power supplies.

Receivers, transmitters and transceivers

4.1 The superheterodyne principle of reception. Principles of reception of Morse and telephony (s.s.b. and f.m.) in terms of radio frequency amplification; frequency changing; demodulation or detection; audio amplification. - Advantages and disadvantages of high and low intermediate frequencies; adjacent channel and image frequency (second channel) interference and their avoidance. Typical receivers; use of beat frequency oscillator. Characteristics of a single sideband signal and the purpose of a carrier insertion oscillator. Characteristics of an f.m. signal and the purpose of a ratio detector. Reasons for automatic gain control; explanation of simple r.f. derived system.

4.2 Oscillators; stability of variable frequency and crystal controlled oscillators; factors affecting stability. Synthesisers, advantages and disadvantages: purpose of each stage with block diagram. - Transmitter stages; function of mixers, high and low power amplifiers (including linear types). Automatic level control (a.l.c.). - Methods of modulation and types of emission (s.s.b. and f.m.). Adjustment of modulation level. Relative advantages of Morse and telephony (s.s.b. and f.m.). - Valves and their application as r.f. power amplifiers; advantages and disadvantages.

4.3 Transceivers, block diagram; tuning and adjustment of controls. Use of dummy load.

5   Transmitter interference
5.1 Frequency stability; consequences of poor stability; risks of interference, out of band radiation.
5.2 Spurious emissions, causes and methods of prevention: harmonics of the radiated frequency, direct radiation fro the frequency determining stages (including synthesisers) and mixer stages of a transmitter, parasitic oscillations excessive sidebands due to overmodulation. Excessive deviation of f.m. transmitters (voice and data communications. Frequency synthesisers; problems of interference if out of lock.
5.3 Frequency checking.

6   Electromagnetic compatibility (E.M.C.)
6.1 E.M.C. the ability of a device, equipment or system to function satisfactorily in its electromagnetic environment without introducing intolerable electromagnetic disturbances to anything in that environment. E.M.C. problems that are likely to occur when an amateur station operates in close proximity to other electronic equipment.
6.2 Equipment used in an amateur station that is capable of generating broad band and narrow band interference.
6.3 Interfering signal paths: r.f., i.f., audio and mains borne.
6.4 Methods of improving the immunity of affected equipment; - use of toroidal chokes and filters (mains, high pass, low pass bandpass, notch or bandstop) - characteristics of filters, bandwidth, insertion loss and impedance - screening, lead lengths, and fitting ferrite rings and beads and bypass capacitors.
6.5 Improving station design - r.f. grounding - station mains filtering - screening - monitoring output power and calculations of field strengths - use of minimum transmitted power - monitoring output transmission for spuriou and harmonic levels, including key clicks - location of antennas and masts - type and size of antennas - use screened feeder cables, balanced lines and baluns.
6.6 Method of approach and basic checks required when investigating e.m.c. problems.
6.7 E.M.C. considerations for mobile installations - location of transceiver and connection to 12V supply - routing of d.c. power and antenna cables - location and grounding of antenna - possible effects of r.f. on vehicle electronic sys

7   Propagation and antennas
7.1 Explanation of basic terms: ionosphere, troposphere, atmosphere, field strength, polarisation, maximum usable frequency, critical frequency, skip distance, sunspot cycle.
7.2 Generation of electromagnetic waves; relationship between electric and magnetic components.
7.3 Structure of the ionosphere. Refracting and reflecting properties of the ionosphere and troposphere. Effect of sunspot cycle, winter and summer seasons, and day and night on the ionisation of the upper atmosphere; effect variations of ionisation on the propagation of electromagnetic waves.
7.4 Ground wave, ionospheric and tropospheric propagation.
7.5 Fade out and types of fading, including selective fading. Polarisation, absorption and skip.
7.6 Velocity of radio waves in free space; relationship between velocity of propagation, frequency and wavelength; calculation of frequency and wavelength.
7.7 Receiving and transmitting antennas. Operation and construction of typical antennas, including multiband and directional types: end fed, dipole, ground plane, yagi and quad. Their directional properties; polar diagrams. Coupling and matching.
7.8 Transmission lines: balanced and unbalanced feeders; elementary principles of propagation of radio waves alor transmission lines; velocity factor, standing waves.

8.   Measurements
8.1 Types of instrument used for the measurement of a.c., d.c. and r.f. voltages and currents; errors in measuremer analogue and digital meters, multimeters, oscilloscopes.
8.2 Measurement of - d.c. power input to power amplifiers - r.f. power output of power amplifiers - efficiency and dissipation.
8.3 Purposes, operation and use of absorption wavemeters, crystal calibrators and digital frequency meters; relative accuracies.
8.4 Dummy loads, their construction and use in adjusting transmitters.
8.5 Circuit and use of standing wave ratio meters.
8.6 Setting up and use of an oscilloscope to examine and measure waveforms.

Appendix B - Syllabus

Assessment pattern.

The Radio Amateurs' Examination consists of two separate papers, 7650-001 Licensing conditions, transmitter interference and electromagnetic compatibility and 7650-002 Operating procedures, practices and theory. 7650-001 contains 45 multiple- choice questions and 7650-002 contains 55 multiple-choice questions. Questions are allocated to the syllabus sections as indicated below.

7650-001 Licensing conditions, transmitter interference and electromagnetic compatibility. ($1^1/4$ hours).

	Syllabus	Questions
1	Licensing conditions	15
2	Transmitter interference	15
3	Electromagnetic compatibility	<u>15</u>
		<u>45</u>

There is a 15 minute break between the two papers.

7650-002 Operating procedures, practices and theory ($1^1/2$ hours).

	Syllabus	Questions
1	Operating procedures	9
2	Electrical theory	6
3	Solid state devices	7
4	Receivers	7
5	Transmitters	8
6	Propagation and antennas	9
7	Measurements	<u>9</u>
		<u>55</u>

The syllabus 7650-001 Licensing conditions, transmitter interference and E.M.C.

1   Licensing conditions
1.1   Types of licence available and the qualifications necessary.
1.2   Conditions (terms and limitations) laid down in the Amateur radio Licences (A) and (B), including a knowledge of the notes appended and an understanding of the schedule of frequency bands, power and types of transmission.

2   Transmitter interference
2.1   Frequency stability, consequences of poor stability; risks of interference, out-of-band radiation.
2.2   Spurious emissions, causes and methods of prevention: harmonics of the radiated frequency, direct radiation from frequency determining stages (including synthesisers) and frequency changing stages of of a transmitter, parasitic oscillations, excessive sidebands due to overmodulation. Excessive deviation of FM transmitters. key clicks; methods of suppression.
2.3   Frequency checking.

3   Electromagnetic compatibility
3.1   E.m.c.: the ability of a device, equipment or system to function satisfactorily in its electromagnetic environment without introducing intolerable electromagnetic disturbances to anything in that environment.
E.m.c. problems that are likely to occur when an amateur station operates in close proximity to other electronic equipment.

Appendix B - Syllabus

3.2 Equipment used in an amateur station that is capable of generating broad band and narrow band interference.
3.3 Interfering signal paths: r.f., i.f., audio and mains borne.
3.4 Methods of improving the immunity of affected equipment.
  1 use of toroidal chokes and filters (mains, high pass, low pass, bandpass, notch of bandstop)
  2 characteristics of filters, bandwidth, insertion loss and impedance
  3 screening, lead lengths, and fitting ferrite rings, beads and bypass capacitors.
3.5 improving station design
  1 r.f. grounding
  2 station mains filtering
  3 screening
  4 monitoring output power and calculations of field strengths
  5 use of minimum transmitter power
  6 monitoring output transmission for spurious and harmonic levels, including key clicks
  7 location of antennas and masts
  8 type and size of antennas
  9 use of screened feeder cables, balanced lines and baluns.
3.6 Methods of approach and basic checks required when investigating e.m.c. problems with a neighbours equipment.

The syllabus 7650-002 Operating procedures, practices and theory.

1 Operating procedures
1.1 Calling procedures in telephony and telegraphy: general calls to all stations and calls to specific stations.
1.2 Log-keeping: licence requirements.
1.3 Use of satellites and repeaters: accessing a repeater.
1.4 Reasons for and use of Q codes and other abbreviations.
1.5 Band planning, purposes and advantages.
1.6 The phonetic alphabet. Reasons for its use.
1.7 Safety in the amateur station
  1 precautions recommended by the Radio Society of Great Britain
  2 reasons why equipment to be repaired should be disconnected from the mains supply and capacitors discharged.

2 Electrical theory
2.1 1 The meaning of basic electrical terms; voltage, current, conductor, insulator, resistance.
  2 The relationship between voltage, current and power in a d.c. circuit.
2.2 1 The sine wave, definition of amplitude, frequency and period; peak, peak-to-peak, instantaneous, average and r.m.s. values. Simple explanation of the terms: phase angle, phase difference, phase lag and lead.
  2 Inductance and capacitance; units, inductive and capacitive reactance. Reactance impedance and power in an a.c. circuit.
2.3 Series and parallel tuned circuits, resonance, impedance, dynamic resistance, calculation of resonant frequency; amplification of current and voltage at resonance; Q (magnification) factor.
2.4 Function and uses of the transformer.
2.5 Simple explanation of how the decibel notation is used to express ratios of power and voltage and how it may also be used to define power levels.

3   Solid state devices

3.1   Characteristics of junction diodes, npn pnp and field effect transistors.

3.2   The common transistor circuit configurations, emphasising the bias arrangements and conditions, and input and output impedances.

3.3   Use of solid state devices as
1   audio and radio frequency amplifiers
2   oscillators
3   frequency multipliers
4   mixers
5   demodulators
6   switches

3.4   Rectification, smoothing and voltage stabilisation arrangements in low voltage supplies.

4   Receivers

4.1   The superheterodyne principle of operation. Principles of reception of Morse and telephony (s.s.b. and f.m.) in terms of radio frequency amplification; frequency changing; demodulation or detection; audio amplification.

4.2   Advantages and disadvantages of high and low intermediate frequencies; adjacent channel and image frequency (second channel) interference and their avoidance.

4.3   Typical receivers; use of beat frequency oscillator. Characteristics of a single side-band signal and the purpose of a carrier insertion oscillator. Characteristics of an f.m. signal and the purpose of a ratio detector.

4.4   Reasons for automatic gain control; explanation of simple r.f. derived system.

5   Transmitters

5.1   Oscillators used in transmitters; stability of variable frequency and crystal controlled oscillators; their construction and factors affecting their stability. Synthesisers, advantages and disadvantages: purpose of each stage with block diagram.

5.2   Transmitter stages; function of frequency changers; frequency multipliers, high and low power amplifiers (including linear types).

5.3   Transmitter tuning and adjustment.

5.4   Methods of modulation and types of emission (s.s.b. and f.m.). Adjustment of modulation level. Relative advantages of Morse and telephony (s.s.b. and f.m.).

5.5   Valves and their application as r.f. power amplifiers; advantages and disadvantages.

6   Propagation and antennas

6.1   Explanation of basic terms: ionosphere, troposphere, atmosphere, field strength, polarisation, maximum usable frequency, critical frequency, skip distance, sunspot cycle.

6.2   Generation of electromagnetic waves; relationship between electric and magnetic components.

6.3   Structure of the ionosphere. Refracting and reflecting properties of the ionosphere and troposphere. Effect of sunspot cycle, winter and summer seasons, day and night on the ionisation of the upper atmosphere; effect of variations of ionisation on the propagation of electromagnetic waves.

6.4   Ground wave, ionospheric and tropospheric propagation.

6.5   Fade out and types of fading, including selective fading. Polarisation, absorption and skip.

6.6   Velocity of radio waves in free space; relationship between velocity of propagation, frequency and wavelength; calculation of frequency and wavelength.

6.7   Receiving and transmitting antennas. Operation and construction of typical antennas, including multiband and directional types; end fed, dipole, ground plane, Yagi and quad. Their directional properties. Coupling and matching.

6.8   Transmission lines: balanced and unbalanced feeders; elementary principles of propagation of radio waves along transmission lines; velocity ratio, standing waves.

7   **Measurements**

7.1   Types of instrument used for the measurement of a.c., d.c. and r.f. voltages and currents; errors in measurement; analogue and digital multimeters, oscilloscopes.

7.2   Measurement of
1   d.c. power input to power amplifiers
2   r.f. power output of power amplifiers
3   current at radio frequencies.

7.3   Purposes, operation and use of absorption wavemeters, crystal calibrators and digital frequency meters; relative accuracies.

7.4   Dummy loads, their construction and use in adjusting transmitters.

7.5   Circuit and use of standing wave ratio meters.

7.6.   Setting up and use of an oscilloscope to examine and measure waveforms and monitor the depth of modulation.

Recent change to syllabus. City & Guilds have stated that starting with the May 1996 Radio Amateurs Examination (7650), candidates will be provided with a copy of the schedule to the licence. This lists frequency bands in MHz, the status of allocations in the UK to the amateur service and to the satellite service, the maximum power level, and permitted types of transmission. Consequently, candidates will no longer have to learn these details. Questions on the Schedule will clearly state 'USE THE ATTACHED SCHEDULE TO FIND THE ANSWER'. This will eliminate the problem that can occur when the schedule has been revised after the examination paper has been compiled.

Please note. This syllabus and information is correct at time of publication. A full copy of the current syllabus and examination objectives should be obtained from the City and Guilds of London Institute. Should this book be used as a study aid for similar examinations set by other examining organisations, the syllabus for the appropriate examination should be obtained.

AMATEUR RADIO
and the *RSGB*

RADIO AMATEURS are qualified radio operators who are licensed to talk to other operators, often in distant countries, from their own homes. Amateur radio is a hobby for all ages but it is different from CB radio because a very wide variety of frequencies (wave-lengths) can be used, and contacts can be in different 'modes'; by Morse code or teleprinter, between computers or even television. Many amateurs build all or part of their station equipment.

The **Radio Society of Great Britain** (RSGB) is the national society for all radio amateurs (transmitters and listeners) in this country. It has over 30,000 members, including many in overseas countries.

The Society looks after the interests of radio amateurs throughout the UK. Talks between the RSGB and the Government's Radiocommunications Agency have resulted in the popular amateur radio Novice Licence.

In particular the RSGB is keen to encourage the experimental side of electronics and radio, and the Society's monthly magazine *Radio Communication* is sent free to all members. We're having lots of fun with our hobby, so why not join us?

If you would like more information on the RSGB, amateur radio or the Novice Licence, write for an Information Pack to the address below (enclosing a large stamped self-addressed envelope).

 RSGB, Lambda House, Cranborne Road, Potters Bar, Herts EN6 3JE.

Cellnet operates one of the UK's largest mobile phone networks.
There are currently over 2 million users on the system and this figure is growing daily.

The pictures above show Cellnet engineers making regular maintenance visits to cell sites.
There are over 1000 cell sites throughout the UK, handling in excess of 5 million calls
per day.
All Cellnet engineers are highly trained in radio and electronic engineering and are on
call 24 hours a day.

The picture right shows the Cellnet Network Management Centre (NMC).
It is from here that Cellnet's entire network is continuously monitored - 24 hours a day
and 365 days a year - to ensure the very high standard of service expected by its many
customers.